WITHDRAWN

THE ORDEAL OF MANSART

The Suppression of the African Slave Trade to the United States of America *(Harvard Historical Studies, No. 1, 1896)*

The Philadelphia Negro *(Publication of the University of Pennsylvania Series on Political Economy and Public Law, No. 14, 1899)*

The Souls of Black Folk *(1903)*

John Brown *(1909)*

Quest of the Silver Fleece *(a novel, 1911)*

The Negro *(Home University Library, 1915)*

Darkwater: Voices From Within the Vail *(1920)*

The Gift of Black Folk: The Negro in the Making of America *(1924)*

Dark Princess *(a novel, 1928)*

Black Reconstruction in America, 1860-1880 *(1935)*

Black Folk: Then and Now *(1939)*

Dusk of Dawn: An Autobiography *(1940)*

Color and Democracy: Colonies and Peace *(1945)*

The World and Africa *(1947)*

In Battle for Peace *(1952)*

The Black Flame

A Trilogy

BOOK ONE

The
ORDEAL
of
MANSART

By W. E. B. DU BOIS

MAINSTREAM PUBLISHERS: *New York*

1957

CONTENTS

To Shirley Graham

Chapter I

COLONEL BRECKINRIDGE PROMISES

IT WAS OCTOBER, 1876. On the Battery, the wide plaza which fronts the sea in Charleston, South Carolina, four persons were about to meet; and in a certain way their meeting was critical for a nation and a world. The sea was shining in the evening sun which hovered red above the shadowed city to the west.

On the white-pillared porch of his home, Colonel John Breckinridge was sitting not far from his wife. He was medium in height and spare, almost handsome in countenance, with a sifting of grey in his hair. He was disturbed and unhappy and angry at himself because he was so moved. The reason was simple. He was about to tell a lie. Colonel Breckinridge was not accustomed to say anything which did not seem to him true. Partly this was moral conviction; partly inherited training; and largely the result of economic independence which made reliance on other opinions or prejudices quite unnecessary to his manner of life. Of course, his frank and arrogant expression of opinion was often curbed by natural kindliness and inbred courtesy. It seemed to him quite excusable to tell a devastated beauty that she was still as charming as ever; or to console and assure a sick and elderly friend on his appearance of health.

But today he had been asked to assure a poor white leader that if he would withdraw his voting power from control by the up-state white farmers who were trying to annex and submerge the landed aristocracy of the rich lowlands, that this group would get the political and social recognition to which the poor white farmers now so fiercely aspired. This new group was composed of city artisans and small farmers who had never owned slaves and now hired little or no labor. They resented the piedmont whites only a little less than they hated the Negroes; it had been suggested that by playing on these two motives an alliance might be made which would save the old landed aristocracy of Carolina.

Ordinarily, Colonel Breckinridge would have been the last one to be selected for this delicate negotiation. But the most powerful of

11

the new white labor leaders, Scroggs, had stubbornly insisted on dealing only with Breckinridge, for Breckinridge was a man of his word. He would not consider Orr, Butler, Gary or even Hampton. It was Breckinridge or nobody. This was at once flattering and annoying. Of course, the Breckinridges were gentlemen and therefore men of their word. But quite as obviously, no Breckinridge was going to promise to recognize artisans or laborers as equals on any level. Hampton used all his charm to persuade the Colonel to assent to meeting Scroggs and offering him alliance; but Breckinridge refused to tell a lie. Yet he knew that he was going to lie in spirit if not in actual word. He was within profoundly uneasy as he awaited Scroggs.

He was expecting his visitor but showed no sign of noticing the man already approaching; he glanced at the papers in his lap and smoked. His wife, too, saw the stranger coming and continued to embroider slowly, occasionally glancing off at Fort Sumter burning in the sun, and Fort Moultrie beyond.

Mrs. Breckinridge was a Du Bignon of Louisiana. She was not a beautiful woman; her face was long and her skin sallow, her mouth and ears large, and her frame tall and almost angular. But she was evidently well-bred and even sat with an air of quiet distinction. Her hands were long and exquisite; her hair piled carefully in a black, shining mass with hardly a silver thread; and her clothes, although evidently not new and in part home-made, had been styled in Paris. It had never occurred to Mrs. Breckinridge that aristocracy was an effort or an ambition. It was simply a fact. Her forebears had been nobles under the Roi Soliel in the 17th century; they had met disaster and even poverty in the 18th, but what difference? They were still aristocrats, and when their fortunes were restored in the New World it was but natural, inevitable. She had been educated partly in Paris and used to visit France almost every other year until this war came. But nothing could permanently change the world nor the people in it.

Colonel Breckinridge, on the contrary, was distinctly English by instinct and descent. His clothes came from London and fitted perfectly, even when old and slightly frayed. The Breckinridges had played their part in English history for centuries. He still had titled cousins on the English countryside. One did not boast of this nor drag it into conversation, but it was a well-known fact. Yet the Colonel was troubled; he did not have his wife's complacency of position. The rough experience of war when he was a youngster in his twenties, and the aftermath, had made him realize

that without effort and even desperate effort the old regime might
collapse.

As a boy he had been tutored in the classics by an Oxford Master of Arts and was graduated at Princeton. When the Civil War
broke out, without hesitation he followed his father and uncle into
the field, emerging in 1864 at the age of 36 orphaned, and with his
hereditary fortune sadly impaired. The only reservation in his respect for the English was inability to conceive why the Empire had
not wholeheartedly supported the South in the Civil War. He was
uneasy at the portents of the future and not so sure of his world as
he had been formerly.

With faint surprise, but careful to give no evidence of it as he
relighted his cigar, he now noticed another person approaching; a
Negro was crossing the Battery from the South and apparently coming to his house.

The colored man, Tom Mansart, was walking along the Battery
toward the Breckinridge house. As he neared the imposing white
pillared Breckinridge mansion he began to feel inner panic. He
walked steadily and firmly on, even straightening his broad shoulders a bit. The panic was first a little thing but it grew and grew.
How should he approach the Colonel? He remembered discussing
this small but great point in his union. Aunt Betsy, who had
walked in uninvited, pooh-poohed the whole thing.

"Crawl," she said, "if you have to, only git what you want."

"Worms crawl, but they only git squashed," replied Forbes.

"Right," answered Jones. "Go to Breckinridge's front door;
stand up and talk like a man and not like a slave."

So now he hesitated. Should he walk boldly up the front steps,
or should he enter the gate and knock at the side door? Now, so
far as Mansart himself was concerned, he had no objection in the
world to going around to that side door and going through the
traditional ceremony. Yet he was not a slave, he was a member of
the legislature of South Carolina. He wanted to make a tentative
alliance between the black labor and the white landholders; and
back of him stood 10,000 organized workers and voters.

Now the very first step toward this must be not to surrender a
principle. If he should go to the side door he would go in the status
of a laborer, little better than a slave. On the other hand, if he
could face Colonel Breckinridge as a man and talk to him, the first
and major part of the battle would be not, to be sure, won but laid
out. The principle could not be surrendered out of hand if the
battle was to be won. Yet he realized that by some perhaps needless

insistence on his rights he might lose the battle before it was joined. It was an extraordinarily difficult matter to decide.

Colonel Breckinridge was watching with feigned carelessness. He was puzzled and a little alarmed. He was expecting this Poor White; it had all been finally arranged at the club last night. His was the chosen voice of southern aristocracy to make alliance with a newly organized group of poor whites. He hated the assignment but he could not refuse in the face of unanimity. His was, they had said, the natural voice of his class. Moreover—and this was what irked him—he needed this alliance. Unless his class regained control, lowered ruinous taxation, and forced Negroes to work for nothing beyond the cost of their support, he faced financial ruin. His crops were ungathered, his lands were almost worthless, and cotton a dollar a pound! And he a Breckinridge, who never before this unholy war had ever known the meaning of poverty! Was fear of poverty making him a liar, or was he acting from high principle?

Who, now, was this Negro approaching his house, and what did he want, and at this of all times? He was not a servant, as his clothes and carriage showed. He walked firmly and held his head up. He was probably one of those half-educated darkies who were misleading and befuddling the bewildered Negroes. But where was he going? Not, surely to this house and at this time? He could feel the white man glowering in his retreat. This was the time to unify the whites for an end. True, it was also not the time needlessly to antagonize the Negro nor breed suspicion. Was someone trying to crowd him into lying simultaneously to both sides? Was he being forced to bear a double burden of shame? By God, he would never do it! Let Hampton lie to the Negroes if he must. A Breckinridge would never treat a Negro as a man or even promise to.

As these measured steps of some faint doom approached, the Colonel recalled in a flash the fantastic tale of the last decade. The truth was simply unbelievable. It began in 1865, when black soldiers actually marched into Charleston, down Meeting Street to the Battery singing "John Brown's Body." Beginning with 1868, South Carolina, the leading state of Southern civilization, just beginning to reorganize its lost power after the war, had suddenly been handed over to the former black slaves and a rabble of white scalawags and carpet-baggers. He and his like at first had simply withdrawn in proud refusal to cooperate in any way. The civilized world surely would not let this horror happen. They had simply to wait until this travesty and caricature exploded in its own filth.

A "convention" elected by the illiterate rabble met. A legislature, composed of black ex-slaves, "crackers" and Northern grafters, actually sat in the seats where Calhoun, Rutledge and Pinckney once had thundered. He had lived in amazement to see a poor white governor; Negroes voting; land given away by a Yankee general; a Supreme Court manned by a Negro, a white Southerner and a white Northerner. Free schools had begun, taxes were increasing; one governor, a white Southerner, had sunk to the bottom of graft and chicanery and another, a Northerner, now led "reform." It was nauseating.

Here now in all probability was one of these impossible rulers of Carolina almost at his steps. The astonishing thing that had driven him out of his retreat was that this caricature and pretense of government had actually begun to function; not effectively, of course, but with a reeling rush forward that was, in a way, more frightening than the awaited collapse. The fools had actually started schools and given paupers, black and white, the vote. This was rank bribery of the illiterate mob. They had begun to distribute charity to the war victims and even to divide up some of the big plantations. This was sheer socialism and a blasphemy against the sacred rights of property.

Of course, the Colonel and his people understood the motivation; the black and white rabble was under guidance of conscienceless leaders, mostly from the North but partially envious local nobodies. There was but one remedy and that was for the Southern aristocracy to reassert their power and seize leadership before it was too late. The need became imperative when the wily Chamberlain came to power and began to reform the state. Here lay the deepest danger: a reformed state, honestly conducted but with the aristocracy despoiled of property, with land distributed among peasants, with the rabble making attempts to educate their children, and above all, with Negroes voting and holding office. Unthinkable. Rather begin the war again.

His friends had begun the conspiracy and he had joined. They had reorganized the pre-war secret societies, encouraged mob violence and made alliance with men like Wade Hampton of Mississippi. They proposed at any cost to make him governor in 1876. For this they must get the following and allegiance of the poor whites. The small up-state farmers had to be admitted to the plan at the price of curtailing the political rights of property and sharing some of the power which had formerly been the sole right of the planters. The upstaters were rough, ill-mannered men, yet they had social aspirations and a few had been admitted to clubs and organizations to which they had not dared to aspire before the war. Indeed, they were not simply admitted to the conspiracy but, led by the military, they took direction and charge. All this Colonel Breckinridge had accepted with poor grace but of necessity.

Finally came a further demand at which he gagged. It seemed that a rift began to appear within the ranks of the poor whites. Over against the merchants and farmers and the idle mob which they dominated, the artisans and laborers were organizing. This fellow, Scroggs, represented this new group. Scroggs had demanded to talk with him and the Colonel declined. He had already dirtied his hands as far as he could. But his friends pleaded.

Hampton especially was solicitous. He did not like Hampton too well; Hampton was too theatrical, and all things to all men. He was not quite a gentleman. But his arguments were strong. This new worker group might be so manipulated as to hold in bounds the white farmers who wanted to be the future aristocrats and rule the state. White workers might balance white capitalists with land and trade. Also—and this was important—they might be the best means of holding black labor in bounds simply because they hated Negroes so bitterly. Yet if organized they were less dangerous than the mob of thieves and murderers now forming the new Ku Klux Klan. So here, today, was Colonel Breckinridge awaiting this emissary of the white artisans, to assure him that the new state in making would treat the white worker right and that he, Colonel Breckinridge, would vouch for this.

The Colonel came back smartly to the present and realized that the Negro actually was slowly but purposely mounting his front steps. Sam Scroggs, lurking yonder in the shadows of sunset, was watching. If the Colonel received this Negro at his front door what would the Poor White think? He came to swift conclusion and arose slowly to his feet. He removed his cigar and looked straight at the Negro.

Tom Mansart paused halfway up and lifted his hat. He began: "I beg your pardon, Colonel Breckinridge," he said, "could I have a word with you?"

He could see the Colonel stiffen; his chin lifted itself a bit and then he said with a low, firm voice, "The door is at the side."

Mansart hesitated; he stood straight and looked at the Colonel.

"Colonel Breckinridge," he said, "I am a member of the Legislature of South Carolina . . ."

But the Colonel spoke with cold courtesy. "So far as I am concerned you are a Negro, and no Negro enters my front door."

Tom Mansart turned and again started to speak. "Colonel . . ."
The Colonel interrupted. "Go," he said.

Tom Mansart had tried and failed. He turned and slowly
descended the stairs. It was but twenty feet from the front steps
to the side gate; but it seemed a mile and took a year. Tom thought
rapidly and fiercely. He had been deliberately insulted; his race
had been slapped in the face; his state had spit upon him. What
then? Here was opportunity; perhaps a last chance before disaster.
He could walk quietly and silently away but if he did he lost the
chance which after all was perhaps, indeed probably, no chance
at all. But if he swallowed his pride—his poor, lacerated, lateborn
and almost obliterated pride—and turned in here to plead a lost
cause, perhaps. . . . He turned in at the side gate.

For a while there was complete silence on the porch as the echo-
ing footsteps of the departing Negro became fainter. Colonel
Breckinridge put down the papers he was reading and looked at his
wife. Slowly Mrs. Breckinridge laid aside her embroidery and
looked after Tom Mansart. Silence reigned a few moments. Then
Mrs. Breckinridge took up her embroidery again in her long,
exquisite hands and inserted a needle. The Colonel regarded her
uneasily and said:

"Well?"

She paused until the gate closed and then said: "I wonder if
that was necessary?"

"What? His daring to come here?"

"No, your reception."

"Are you ready to receive Negroes on your front porch?"

"No. But are you unwilling even to talk with a Negro?"

"Yes, I am, unless he remembers that he is a Negro and can
never be anything else."

She stopped her embroidery again and slowly laid it aside. She
turned toward him: "I have no desire to meddle in politics, dear,
and doubtless you know your business best; yet in a sense I have
fought these postwar years by your side. I cannot help seeing and
thinking. The South was right, Negroes should still be slaves. But
the South was beaten and the Negroes legally are free and are
voters. In self-defense you are allying yourself with the Poor Whites.
I wonder—I do not pretend to be sure, but I wonder—if a sounder
alliance could not be made with the Negroes? And if with such
alliance we could not face the North with better arms in our
hands?"

"Do you know what that might cost? Black men on your front porch, if not in your dining room!"

"A revolting price, I admit—but lately planters have entertained some curious guests. . . ."

"Yes, yes, I know, and this Scroggs — well he at least is white —"

"Of course—but this Mansart has manners, and somehow I wanted to hear what he had to say. —But here is your Mr. Scroggs. I am afraid I must go."

From the other stretch of the Battery, beyond the Naval Club, Scroggs had walked slowly toward the Breckinridge mansion, where he saw the Colonel and his wife sitting, until he descried the Negro crossing the street from the opposite direction. He stopped abruptly, and glancing furtively at the porch to see if he had been noticed, stepped back into the shadow of the trees. He was a thin, old-young man of 40, clay-colored and scrawny. He seemed never to have had enough to eat. His clothes were new but fitted ill. His nose was crooked; but his eyes were alive and burning. They seemed to center a fire that was consuming his soul. He was a mass of nerves which shook and tore at him. Yet he held himself in fierce control. Scroggs belonged to the disinherited of the South—the poor, un-educated, neglected whites. The black slaves were valuable property to be protected and preserved. White landholding masters were the people for whom government and civilization existed. Most of the white people of the South fell into neither of these classes.

Scroggs not only belonged to the five million or more Southern-ers who never owned a slave, but also to the lower ranks of this class: landless, half-educated, but with some skills as carpenters, masons and metal workers when cheap slave labor did not deprive them of work. Born in Georgia in 1840, he grew up in bitter competition with slave labor on farm and in town. Emancipation meant to him a chance to be a real white man. White planters had always looked through him; and even black slaves had jeered at him. He had lived most of his life in hunger, cold and dirt until the war.

Then came his chance, as he firmly believed. Between these upstart "niggers" and the haughty planters, and despite the middle class farmers, he was going to find his place as a man. He was going to be equal to anybody. He was going to have skilled work to do, land to till and "niggers" to serve him. He was going to climb out of hell into a heaven like this rich Charleston. Some of his white fellows tried to ride to wealth and power by trampling roughshod over him as over the freed Negroes. He sought to join them and was only allowed to join the Klan and drink, kill, steal and rape. But he soon saw that this was getting him nowhere. But he must be careful — careful.

The darkies had leaders: whites from the North; educated blacks who talked like whites; the Northern army. Even some Southern planters courted them. It made him sick and furious. He had none to turn to for advice. The lower mass of the poor whites were too lazy and ignorant to stick together. Some were stooping to make friends with "niggers" and even marrying them. Others were crawling before the Yankees. The upstate white farmers were going to replace the planters and become aristocrats and lord it over him as well as over the "niggers." But he, Scroggs, was going to make alliance with the real aristocrats. He was going to become one of them and not seek to replace them; his grandchildren would marry theirs. In time they would need him and his folk. He knew it. But he must be careful—careful.

Most of the poor whites seemed to imagine that they were going to become part of the ruling class automatically. He knew better. He knew that the planters would use them to the limit and then kick them around as they did the darkies. They must organize and bargain. They must insist on recognition and equality. His group had grown. While the rabble was killing, drinking and whoring, his group was bargaining. They were willing to join the Ku Klux and kill "niggers" for the planters. They would steal and destroy and wreak vengeance for themselves; but the planters must pay.

It had now come to the showdown. He had demanded the word of an aristocrat like Breckinridge that the poor white workers were to get recognition; but he must be careful. They'd fool him and betray him in a minute. He had asked to talk with Colonel Breckinridge today. He came late on purpose so as not to appear too eager. He planned to swagger and walk boldly up the front steps and greet the high and mighty Mrs. Du Bignon-Breckinridge. By God, he'd show them that he was a man to be reckoned with. Then the "nigger" appeared. Where was he going? Had Breckinridge invited him, too? Did he think he, a white man, was going to sit down and bargain with a "nigger?" Or was he being double-crossed in some way? His suspicion became acute fear. The sweat started on his face as he lurked back of the tree.

Scroggs had seen the Negro finally turn away, and was mollified. He paused a moment, straightened his collar and started forward. He saw Mrs. Breckinridge arise and turn away and he knew she was deliberately avoiding him. He spit elaborately on the hydrangeas which broidered the steps and began to ascend. The Colonel arose as his wife said:

"Perhaps you would like me to find out what our black visitor wanted?"

"It would be kind of you," answered the Colonel as he turned to greet his guest. "Good evening, Scroggs. Shall we go in here where it will be more private?"

They entered the open library door as Mrs. Breckinridge disappeared into the dining room which let upon the sideporch. She walked a bit slowly and was, to her own surprise, a bit perturbed. She knew Negroes. All her life she had been in close contact with them—nurses, maids, servants, laborers. There were even relatives with black blood, passing unobtrusively in the background as favored servants, overseers, or visitors received behind lowered shades. There was a legend, and Mrs. Breckinridge smiled reminiscently, that the current Du Bignons might have a touch of the "Tar-Brush." How Mère Du Bignon had raged when that slur had reached her ears! But Mrs. Breckinridge in her proud young womanhood had merely smiled. After all, what could besmirch a Du Bignon? "Noblesse oblige!" Their blood might ennoble a slave, but they themselves could suffer no taint.

But here was a different matter. She could praise or reprimand a servant regally, she could repel impudence of a presuming worker with a glance, she could command imperiously and with cold calm But here was a New Thing. She had half-expressed it in her shadow of a rebuke to her husband. Law was law, despite fantastic and of course temporary upset. This man came begging a boon of his betters, as was natural. How should he be received? How should he be put and kept in his place? To be sure, he should be reminded definitely of the utter ridiculousness and temporary character of his present position. A Breckinridge must respect law and authority and yet do it somehow without yielding or seeming to yield to any questioning of his God-given superiority.

Tom Mansart was standing by the balustrade, hat in hand, looking out on the beautiful flowers. He turned slowly as she stepped out the door and bowed, facing her fully. She looked at him with a slight, unconscious lift of head, with demeanor quite calm.

"Good evening, boy, what did you wish?"

He talked rapidly and well, not always grammatically but with little dialect. He was a fine figure of a man; forgetting his color and hair she might imagine herself talking to a white man—not, to be sure, a gentleman, and least of all to a gentleman of the South—but to some Northerner or foreigner. Then the thread of what he was saying caught her full attention: his first words disarmed her.

"You remember, Madam," he said, "Aunt Betsy?" Certainly she remembered that black and silent sibyl. Suddenly she glowed with remembrance of days before the war. Aunt Betsy had not been a servant in her family but a servitor in her social clan: a mid-wife, vendor of herbs, and a sort of counselor who had come and gone among the upper class of white families. Starched and immaculate she traded bits of news between family and family, landholders and merchants, the dark world and the white, between white and white. She seemed to know everything. She gave advice and nursed the sick. She brought babies into the world with incredible skill. Also, it was rumored, with equal skill she had gotten rid of uninvited little souls. She had a sort of dignity and wisdom which Mrs. Breckinridge and all her clan acknowledged. With the war she disappeared, silently, without a word. Mrs. Breckinridge feared she was dead. Now here in a curious way was a message from her.

She started to ask after her but Mansart continued. "I am Tom Mansart. I am a Virginian. I marched with Sherman to the sea, farmed in the Sea Islands, worked in the West and came here. Here I meets Aunt Betsy and soon marries her daughter. Aunt Betsy feels strongly about things today. Her trust is fastened, as she tells me time and time again, on the 'quality white folk,' the real aristocrats of the old time. She thinks always of the Breckinridges as standing for that class. She wants me, because I am a member of the Legislature and a sort of leader in the Negro labor movement, to come and offer to Colonel Breckinridge such help as we can give. We has Negro leaders, some of them men of education and honesty, some not. We knows that the whites from the North have tried to lead us—some up, some down. They don't all understand the Negro."

Mansart continued: "What we wants is work and fair pay. We wants freedom and justice. We is willing to work hard but we wants to be sure of enough to live on. Then for our children we wants a chance to learn. That's what we wants and that's all we wants. We don't want no offices exceptin' those we can fill well; we don't want no society. But we don't want no more cheating, lynching and mobs. Now the point is that we been talking over pretty careful how to get these things. We knows we can't do it by force. We can't depend on soldiers from the North. We can't get it just by voting; we knows good and well that our own votes ain't going to force things. We can't get what we wants by strikes; strikes is war. We tried striking on some of the plantations and with the longshoremen right here in Charleston. We gained something but we lost more.

"What we needs is law and order; honesty from employers, and —what can I call it? Kindness, good-will of all people toward each other; not hatred, not murder. Now what we have asked ourselves is where is we going to find all this? And my mother-in-law, Aunt Betsy, has long declared that we can find this only among people of 'quality,' among the old class of aristocrat slave-owners. I don't know, but I want to believe it. My old master back in Virginia was a good man in his limits. After long thought and talk we have picked out Colonel Breckinridge. He is a gentleman, a man of honor; they tell me he will keep his word. Now we offers him an organized labor movement and our political support for the ends we has in mind."

Mrs. Breckinridge listened carefully and thought as she listened: the man is earnest, sincere; his are the manners of the old South, imitated of course, but the imitation is good. It is real. She remembered again more or less vaguely the colored folk of Louisiana who had consorted with her family; some were blood-relatives and so recognized. There was one woman in particular—she wondered what had become of her and the pretty little baby, blue-eyed and blond, whom she had played with. Then she pulled herself back to the present.

She sat down, but did not ask Mansart to sit. He still stood, naturally and easily, and apparently did not notice the slight. She leaned forward with something like excitement in her usually cold demeanor. She said:

"You are right; you are absolutely right. Do not mistake me, I still believe that Negroes should be slaves; that is their natural condition. I believe that in slavery most of them were happier and safer than they will ever be again. Of course, among masters there were exceptions—beasts and tyrants who abused their power—but these are everywhere, especially in so-called free countries. I do not believe that the mass of Negroes will ever rise above their natural status—at least not in our time, perhaps not in hundreds of years. Of course, I realize, too, that among them there may be exceptions, and provision ought to be made for such exceptions. There the South failed.

"Also, I am a law-abiding person. By the edict of this country Negroes are free and they should be treated as free. That does not necessarily mean voting and holding office; it means that they ought to be under benevolent guidance and that, as Aunt Betsy knows so well, can be furnished only by Southern gentlemen. I can promise you Tom, that if you can induce the Negroes to work whole-heartedly along with us we will reform this section and lead it to a new civilization. But of course I shall want to talk to Colonel Breckinridge about this."

Tom Mansart bowed and said: "I'm glad to hear you talk this way. Naturally, I don't wholly agree with you. I reckon, Ma'am, you don't quite understand how it is with us colored folk. We don't want to be other people, we just want to be ourselves. We don't want what belongs to you, but we want what belongs to us—our homes, our wives, our children, our wages. We welcomes your advice and leadership; but if other workers vote, we must vote or we'll be helpless. There are some offices, perhaps most, that we ain't fitted to fill, but a few that we are fit to hold. Wright is a good judge. Cardozo is a gentleman, and honest. Cain wants to do right. We ain't proud nor stubborn, we're humble. But we ain't slaves no more and we never will be again. Things is going bad in the South. It's all coming to a head and something must be done and quick. Thank you, Ma'am, kindly for listening. But—I wonder, could I just have a word with the Colonel? You see my men want a direct word from him."

She hesitated and then said: "I'm afraid not today. He is engaged just now. But I will give him your message and I promise you will hear from him soon." She knew this was not the best time to approach the Colonel, but she believed she could in time persuade him to act. Mansart bowed but did not leave.

"Ma'am," he said, "this matter is urgent. I know we're late making our decision. But I hopes not too late. But time presses. We must have the Colonel's word right from him. I don't mind waiting, but please Ma'am, I must tell my folks that I saw him. Will you tell him? I'll just wait here."

Mrs. Breckinridge bowed and left. As she crossed the dining room she was thinking: "Of course, I could understand all this so easily if Negroes were folks in the sense that I am; but are they? Could they possibly be? Perhaps, partially—a little; but in just that area of lack they must be restrained, guided. And where there is no real lack nor difference, should they not be free? For who could or would drive or compel them?" She paused for a moment, puzzled; then opened the Colonel's study door.

Scroggs had glanced after the disappearing Mrs. Breckinridge and, scowling, walked after the Colonel. He was acutely uncomfortable, sensitive to every slight put upon him. He knew that the aristocratic hostess had deliberately avoided him. He knew that this planter of great and well-known family did not want to shake his hand and did not. He knew that even the "Mr." before his name had been omitted deliberately but with a certain effort concealed with difficulty.

On the other hand, he had a job to do. And he was fiercely determined to do it. These aristocrats needed the total poor white vote and the power of white muscles now if they were going to control Carolina against the arms in the hands of the Northern Yankees; against the white upstate farmers and city merchants; and above all against the impudence of Negroes who thought themselves free.

It was this last matter that festered in Scroggs' mind because it was nearest to him. He hated Negroes with a deep, blind hatred. They typified to him all of his unavailing struggle to be a man. They took the food out of his mouth, they made it impossible for his children to be educated; they sneered at him and his scrawny, ill-clad wife and dirty cabin. For all he had suffered at the hands of the rich white world, he was going to take it out on these Negroes, and this man Breckinridge and Wade Hampton were going to make compact with him and keep it, or "by God!"

One thing that secretly bothered Scroggs and weakened his cause was absence of unified backing. He had a group behind him, but it was still small. As soon as a poor white got up in the world —in money, position or learning—he hastened to become an "aristocrat"; he referred to slaveowning forefathers; he pretended to have had a "black Mammy"; he tried to kick other poor whites around just as he did "niggers." He fawned on and toadied to the real aristocrats. That left a heterogeneous mass of festering ignorance and poverty, bitter and frustrated, but with no centering thought for a leader to take hold of; no class consciousness, plans nor ideals except hate, blood and loot. On these, then, he must concentrate, and this was a shifting, uneasy basis for action. He felt bitterly the need of wise counsel of experienced educated men. He knew few that he could trust—no Northern Missionaries; few Poor Whites who believed in poor whites and had trained themselves as Poor White leaders.

But Scroggs would not give in. He would not budge nor admit his weakness. The inchoate, undisciplined, cruel group behind him would go forward with him against the "niggers" or he'd turn it on the whites themselves and strip them of their last pretense.

He distrusted the riots and rifle clubs of Butler and Gary. They represented the rich planter class, and although they killed Negroes at Colleton, Beaufort, Hamburg and Ellenton, they rode as planters and aristocrats with no recognition for other whites. It was restoration of planter rule that they were seeking, not a new alliance with working men. To be sure, upstate near Augusta lived the Tillmans, and one, a young one-eyed radical, seemed to have ideas. But Scroggs had not yet met him. The Ku Klux Klan was another matter. Here poor whites rode cheek by jowl with great planters. He proposed to increase this common action and kill, rape and rob Negroes so long as the aristocrats stood back of them. In this way the fight would become a struggle of white against black and not of rich against the poor, with "niggers" in both groups.

Although he gave no evidence of it, Colonel Breckinridge was just as uneasy as Mr. Scroggs. It was a horrible duty, not only to accept alliance with upstate climbers, but to sit down with the labor riff-raff on terms of equality and beg them for help. But the alternative of Negro rule was unthinkable, and therefore he steeled himself for this interview. He put a certain tone of geniality, even if of condescension, in his voice and passed Mr. Scroggs cigars to keep him from chewing tobacco. He could not quite bring himself to share his fine brandy with him and he wished he had thought to have gin.

"Scroggs," he said, "we're facing a new world and you and I have got to stand together. While Negroes were slaves, which was their proper place and always will be, the necessity for our alliance with all classes of whites perhaps was not so evident although even then it might have been wiser; but today we have got to put Negroes back in their places."

Scroggs lighted his cigar after some difficulty, leaned back in his chair and eyed the Colonel almost truculently. He said, "We agree about 'niggers.' They've got to be put in their places even if we have to kill a few thousand. But that ain't all. Before the war planters owned nearly all the black labor; whites had some land to work by themselves; we workers, which means most whites, had nothing but our hands.

"Now when all this is changed, what we want to know is where we workers come in? We'll do the work all right, but we won't work with 'niggers' or like 'niggers.' We'll help put the darkies in their place and help kill 'em off; but not just to make little white farmers and merchants into big whites while we be their slaves instead of the 'niggers' or along with 'niggers.' We want to know just what's your thinking on this and we want it straight. Also, we want your word that what's promised will be lived up to." Scroggs slouched back in his chair and lacerated his cigar in a way that showed he'd rather chew it than smoke it.

Breckinridge frankly stared and was for a moment silent. The proposition was to him quite unexpected. He had conceived Carolina as Aristocracy and White Mass. This Mass was ill-bred and lazy, but led today by ambitious farmers and merchants who aspired to be the aristocrats of the future. With these leaders Breckinridge and his class had been compelled to make alliance in order to fight the Yankees and their black dupes. Now it seems that the white mass was divided and their laborers were demanding a share of the spoils. It would have been ludicrous if it were not so dangerous. Suppose for a moment both sets of workers, black and white, should join against Property and Civilization? This would be the End. He saw one ray of light: the hatred, bitter hatred of men like Scroggs for the Negroes. Here and here alone lay salvation. He probed carefully:

"Of course you realize, Scroggs, that we want this state to be white, ruled by whites for whites. But the Negroes are here and we need their work. . . ."

"Sure," broke in Scroggs, "and we can have it. And we'll need it too as we rise. But work—not votes and offices. We won't need no educated 'niggers'; just farmhands, ditch-diggers and servants at 'nigger' wages or none at all which is what most deserve; while we whites do the real important work with good wages. We'll build a new world with 'niggers' at the bottom to do such work as no white man should stoop to; with white labor on top and the way open for all white men who can to rise to the very top."

Colonel Breckinridge thought aloud: "Of course there are some Negro workers—" He remembered the black workers who had built the beautiful homes along the Battery, the tall churches along Meeting Street. He remembered his yellow overseer—but he stopped there.

Scroggs sneered, "Yes, and now instead of working they are sitting yonder in Columbia trying to make laws for white folks and wasting white folks' money on crazy plans. They got to be stopped from voting, killed off or sent back to Africa to eat each other up."

He started to add something about yellow bastards who naturally inherited white ability, but he thought better of that.

Breckinridge groped for areas of understanding. "I agree with you absolutely that Negroes should not vote nor hold office. This is for whites alone. Probably, too, the Negro race in America will eventually disappear, especially if they are free to become lazy and criminal. You are aware that the planters have long tried to encourage Negro migration to Africa. But return to the present.

"We propose to drive the Negroes out of politics by law if possible; by force if necessary. Then the state will be run by the whites. We have agreed that the former political power based on slave property will go and that the vote which the Negroes and Yankees gave to the poor whites, although done too precipitately, nevertheless will stand. Schools for whites must spread. What more can we promise?"

Scroggs was prompt: "We want all the best-paid work kept for white workers, and wages raised to Northern levels. We want white labor to control black labor and to replace it in all well-paid jobs. They must be the machinists in the new industry which will come rapidly to the South when peace is really restored. As machinery replaces muscle we white workers want to replace 'niggers' until 'niggers' disappear."

Breckinridge was aghast. The Colonel bent forward and said: "Insofar as whites want work they must have it and be paid just wages according to white living standards. If and when they can replace Negro labor with better work, they must be allowed to do so. Until then, naturally, it is to your interest as well as ours to keep Negroes at work as contented laborers. As new and higher sorts of skilled labor are introduced, they will naturally go to whites. In time, of course, Negroes will die out. But until then they must live decently for your sake and mine as well as their own."

Scroggs considered: "Sounds right," he said. " 'Course, meantime they don't need schools and colleges and they must be kept out of parks and first class railway and street cars."

"They certainly need no colleges," answered Breckinridge, "but they will be better workers if they read and write and some of them must travel. At any rate, all this will be a matter of law and white folk will make the law!"

He sat back with a sigh. Scroggs rose. "All right," he said. "All right. So then this is the clear understanding, Colonel Breckinridge. We'll help crush and kill the 'niggers'; you take over the state with the help of our votes. We get the best jobs and good wages. We get schools and land and chances to be as big men as we can. 'Niggers' will be kept down."

Breckinridge gulped, took a glass of water and lighted another cigar. He said: "Scroggs, I promise to see to it that white men in this state get employment according to ability at decent wages; that Negro workers are not preferred before them; that we who are the old aristocracy will strive to open every path of progress to all the white people of South Carolina; and that we look forward with confidence to the day when this state will be an entirely white and prosperous community. Meantime we will take from the Negro the vote he is not fit to use and put him in his place as laborer and servant pursuing such skills as he may have. We will protect him in his humble station and assure him a decent life and justice, so long as he is content with the sphere for which God created him."

Scroggs arose smiling. "Done!" he said, extending his hand. Breckinridge, ridding his cigar of its long white ash did not see the hand, but very courteously guided his guest to the door.

"You have," he said, "my word on this understanding, on the honor of a gentleman!"

Chapter II

TOM MANSART

Tom Mansart was tall and broad-shouldered, the color of old mahogany, with crisp hair, straight nose and full lips. He was passing through an extraordinary period of education in the meaning of life. Twenty years ago he was an unlettered Virginian slave boy, destined apparently to grow into a prime field-hand easily worth $1500 at a sale. He was good-tempered, hard-working, and dreamed of no destiny beyond possibly becoming an overseer.

Running away from slavery had never entered his head. Some slaves escaped North, but he heard they had a hard time. His master was a goodhearted man; he had enough to eat and was not overworked. Only the year before the war he had been given permission to marry a comely yellow girl and been assigned a small cabin. Life to Tom seemed good, until suddenly war upset the world. He was dragged from the plantation as soldiers moved over it. He lost sight of his young wife and never heard of her again.

They put a gun in his hand and stood him on guard. He had used old-fashioned shot guns for hunting now and then, but he had never seen anything like this machine. He handled it gingerly, and wondered if he would dare use it, especially against a white man. Then at dusk one day a white man came along. He knew that the man had no business here so near the camp. It was his duty to challenge him, and he called out in an uncertain voice:

"Who goes there?"

The man looked at him insolently, kept walking toward him and ordered him out of his way.

All his life Tom had obeyed white men without question. He was in a grave quandary now. He stared at the man approaching. He was tall and arrogant, well-dressed and confident. It was his duty as a soldier to stop him. But did he have courage to do this? Would the sergeant back him up or beat him, or worse? A moment more he hesitated. He saw the silk braid and shiny buttons on the coat of the trespasser. Then he threw the gun to his shoulder, aimed at a great black button and pulled the trigger. The world exploded. He saw the astonishment and pain on the face of his victim. He saw him pause and shudder, and then the black coat was red—all the front of him became slimy crimson. He swayed, crumpled and dropped to the ground. He lay there still and dead.

Tom turned in panic. He wanted to run. Then he stood his ground and reported to the white sergeant who hurried up. The sergeant looked at him curiously but said nothing. From that day Tom Mansart began to change, became another man; not triumphant nor happy, but a man increasingly grim and determined; a soldier in the United States Army.

With the Union Army Tom moved into Tennessee and then down into Georgia. At night, in the army camps, he slowly learned to read and write. In 1864 he straggled with Sherman's army from Atlanta to the sea, stealing food, ordering scared white folk about until the vast mass of soldiers and refugees reached Savannah in December. He was mustered out and lingered there uncertain and somewhat bewildered until Sherman in January, 1865, opened the Sea Islands to the freedmen. Tom dropped his gun, wandered over the shining land and waters until between Port Royal and Beaufort he staked out a little farm, bought a mule and some tools and built a cabin. He was now a farmer, a landholder. He was more than free; he was earning his own living. Working furiously and alone for a year he raised a fine crop of cotton, beside corn and food.

Then suddenly, almost without warning, the government took his little plantation and gave it back to its former white owner. He never forgot the night when the announcement was made. He could not believe it. His government could not treat him that way! But the Freedmen's Bureau man, General Howard, told them haltingly there in the wide dark cotton field, with tears running down his cheeks. The black folk under the torches wept and sang:

"Nobody knows—nobody knows de trouble I'se seen!"

He tried renting his farm from the white owner, but soon began to grow dissatisfied. His crops were good but he was being cheated in their division; everywhere the plantation owners were pressing harder on the tenants. Slowly, slavery was returning.

He wandered west into the sunset, working desultorily here and there, in the army camps, on farms. Then, without plans or outlook, he came back to the seaboard and went to work as a stevedore in Charleston. It was the largest city he had ever seen. He stared at the proud buildings and wide streets. Carl Schurz and Chief Justice Chase had talked to crowds of Negroes on these streets; Northern merchants were arriving on each boat; and the Black Code which sought to keep Negroes in slavery had been modified.

Now in the summer of 1867 there was to be a registration of Negro voters, and it was rumored that Negroes were going to help govern, to have schools and perhaps to regain the land which they thought they had down on the Sea Islands. Meantime he worked as a stevedore on the docks where trade was beginning to boom. He joined the Stevedore's Union, organized secretly by free Negroes before the war and now flourishing.

It was at this time that he first met Aunt Betsy, a tall, scrawny black woman with burning eyes, who seemed to pick him out as a person to whom she could impart her wisdom. Aunt Betsy was an institution, a black sibyl, chary of speech, grim, with eyes that pierced and gloomed. None seemed to know her background or age; but even before the war she had moved about free and unhampered and there were tales that more than one white man had died disputing her freedom. She was the silent, unsmiling confidante of most of the best planter families, so much so that her refusal to serve a family was a social stigma difficult to ignore. She was nurse and midwife; fortune teller and prophet; confessor and scourge. She knew more of the family secrets of the great clans of Carolina than any other person. She held herself aloof from the slaves but knew them, and among them her word, seldom given, was law. During the war she left her haunts and duties and flitted between armies; carried messages, information and advice; but neither side could be sure which she favored or which betrayed.

After emancipation Aunt Betsy did not return to her vocation as servant and mentor of the rich, but set herself as guide to the freedmen. But her guidance lay in work and land, in family and home. She was continually seeking a foundation of labor and wage to bring independence and rooting to the locality which was wanting to the uprooted slave. She became the influence behind the beneficial societies and trade unions; and by threat and promise, as well as by ancient remnants of African lore and culture pattern, she wheeled church and minister in line.

She early fixed her attention on Tom Mansart and began to guide his career. He went to board in her cabin in one of the alleys near the docks. He was now making a fair income as a stevedore. His union was strong, and he began to think of marriage and a family, or perhaps Aunt Betsy guided his thought. In all his intercourse with Aunt Betsy he had paid but slight attention to her daughter who always stayed in the background and kept the cabin home spotless and well-ordered. She was a slim black girl, as silent and efficient as her mother. Of her father no one had a word to say, but neither had any indication of white blood.

He had come home early one Saturday afternoon, tired but satisfied, with his pocket full of his wages. The cabin was cool, and no one there save the silent girl. Few visitors ever entered this home, and today even Aunt Betsy had not appeared. Tom ate the excellent dinner heartily and lounged back in his chair. The daughter, gliding in, was urging him to have more and he raised his eyes to say no, when his eyes met hers. Usually she avoided his every look, but today their glances clung; her eyes were large, beautiful and black. In them lay a startled desire. He laughingly held out his arms and hesitatingly she glided into them. She lifted her lips to his and then started back, staring over his shoulder.

Aunt Betsy came in slowly and seated herself. The girl began to withdraw from his embrace, but he held her close. The old woman and the young man glared a moment. Then Tom said a bit thickly, "Mirandy and I is thinking of marrying." Aunt Betsy looked at the girl but the girl, shivering, hid her face in Tom's soiled shirt. Aunt Betsy slowly smiled and began deliberately to eat her supper. So Tom was married. He found plenty of work and good pay as a stevedore on the busy docks, when ships were hurrying goods into the empty stores of the South. The wife kept house.

Tom Mansart heard of the Labor Convention called by a Robert Elliott, in 1869, at the state capitol, Columbia. He attended, walking part of the way. Now for the first time he saw an educated Negro leader, a man who looked like a field hand, with black skin and a mat of close-curled hair, but who on the other hand not only was well-dressed but spoke white people's English and had that certain air of confidence which he had always associated with white people. Here was a man who was one of his own race and yet in whose presence he felt uncertain and strange. He did not know whether he could trust this black man or not, but listened to him, and the man spoke what seemed to him excellent sense.

He got no chance to meet Elliott or to talk to him personally for a long time, but he did conceive the idea of trying to work with him and of training himself to be the sort of helper that he knew Elliott needed. The convention demanded a half share of the crop for laborers and a dollar a day wage. But nothing seemed to come of their votes and plans.

In 1871 Tom went to the meeting of the Colored National Labor Union at Columbia. It was presided over by Henry M. Turner of Georgia, a leader who thrilled Mansart. He now began to understand the possibilities of union labor. He worked in his own union until he became president of its 800 members. From then on for three years he tried to improve union methods, strengthened its organization and drew into its influence the carpenters and masons, the teamsters and other skilled laborers.

In 1874 the battle for reform in South Carolina began. Tom did not understand the situation. Panic had swept the North. There were bitter charges of stealing and misgovernment in Carolina. Schools had been opened but there was no money to run them. Land had been purchased for the farmers and 2,000 little farms sold, but there was cheating in the transaction. Taxpayers were meeting and complaining bitterly. Of all this Mansart had little knowledge and no plans. This talk about taxes, railroads, public debt—he did not understand it. He paid no taxes for he owned no property, but the great landholders were not paying even what they were assessed. Stealing, however, Tom understood. If theft, graft, and dishonesty caused the lack of funds for what the state needed to do, this must be stopped. The idea of a wider labor movement to stop dishonesty as well as to increase wages grew in his mind and so when at last Aunt Betsy suddenly broke her usual silence, he listened.

Briefly Aunt Betsy spoke. "The world is going to hell, all business done gone, Freedman's Bank just bust with my $900; Northern carpet-baggers like Patterson is stealing all they can git their hands on. Southern trash like Moses must go. Stop the stealing. Only one refuge: white quality; git into the Legislature and vote the quality back. Them and the black worker can save Carolina."

So Tom ran for the legislature and won, in the same election that made Chamberlain governor, in a struggle for "reform." He would never forget the day he walked into the great hall of the House of Representatives in the capitol of the State of South Carolina. It was in fact a place of decayed grandeur, restored in garish, flamboyant style. But to this Virginia fieldhand it was magnificent to a degree that left him breathless: the great domed roof glinting with gold; the rich panelled walls with paintings of proud and haughty men; the semi-circles of desks; and in them sitting, lounging, sprawling men. But not simply men, but over a hundred men of every color: black, brown, yellow, cream and white. He stared at the unbelievable scene. Of course, he had heard of this but it had not penetrated his consciousness. All these human beings were sitting together as one.

On the platform a black man was nodding permission to a white man to speak. A yellow man interrupted with a question. Black and white boys scurried across the hall with notes and books. Yonder a brown man was asleep, near a white man who was writing. Tom's heart swelled to bursting. This was a new world. Men were men, despite color, despite difference in clothes and accent. What were they doing? How could he help?

Here he saw Robert Elliott again, now Speaker of the House; with his tailored clothes, his clipped English accent; his air of being and knowing. He was black but looked and carried himself like a gentleman. Elliott had just resigned from his seat in Congress and everybody was talking of his debate with Alexander Stephens. Tom listened while Daddy Cain related the occurrence in the cloak room. Cain was a black Virginian with side whiskers who left a Brooklyn church to help South Carolina Negroes. He entered Congress as Elliott left. He said:

"There sat Alexander Stephens, once Vice-President of the Confederacy; wizened, slight, cloaked, looking like a skeleton and yet representing that mighty South which had challenged the nation for four fearful years. For years he had been kept out of Congress, but now at last he had won his admittance and took his seat with all his old defiance of the North and contempt for Negroes. Yet today he must listen to a black congressman.

"A hush fell on the chamber. Elliott was a fine figure of a man, polished in manner and clear in word. The Galleries bent forward. Stephens sat motionless as Elliott levelled his finger at him and said:

" 'Sir, it is scarcely twelve years since that gentleman shocked the civilized world by announcing the birth of a government which rested on human slavery as its cornerstone. The progress of events has swept away that pseudo-government which rested on greed, pride and tyranny; and the race whom he then ruthlessly spurned and trampled on are here to meet him in debate, and to demand that the rights which are enjoyed by their former oppressors— who vainly sought to overthrow a government which they could not prostitute to the base uses of slavery—shall be accorded to those who even in the darkness of slavery kept their allegiance true to freedom and the Union. . . .' "

Tom began to believe in his black leaders and feel that they could unite in a successful group. He came to recognize Beverly

Nash, once a slave: blunt, ungrammatical, honest; Wright of Pennsylvania he saw, now black justice of the State Supreme Court; Cardozo, handsome, free-born and educated at the University of Glasgow; Ransier, dignified and alert, President of the Senate; Smalls, self-taught, crude and popular; Richard Cain, preacher and editor.

The real world as Tom had always seen it was of course that of the big plantation owners. They were to Tom Mansart a curious group of people. In common they had manners, poise and a certain kind of education; but more, they had particularly an awareness of the greater world. They had travelled; some had visited Europe; all of them were familiar with Washington, Philadelphia and New York. What intrigued Mansart most was their self-control, the calm way in which they looked at the world and ordered it about. He was not sure whether this was mannerism or a real sense of power; he suspected something of both. At any rate, they had a custom of command, they expected obedience of everybody, of their families, of the poor whites about, and of course of their slaves.

Here in this hall were fieldhands like himself; there were also white gentlemen and poor whites, and there were Negroes—some of whom presented the same wall of cool courtesy that Mansart found between himself and the white planter class. In fact, he supposed it was the same sort of thing—the result of training and contact, of travel and knowledge, and reading. It rather intrigued him to wonder if these manners of the aristocrats were after all not a matter of race but the result of training; perhaps that was true. He had not had experience enough to know, but he wanted to talk with these black men. The point was, after all, that these Negroes of all kinds and types, these white men representing all sorts and grades, were governing South Carolina; they were building a new world. He ached to work with them, but how? What could he do?

Then, after days, he got more used to the scene. He saw uproar cut the quiet; he saw frayed tempers. But business got done. He followed the talk eagerly. But he wanted to grasp the whole idea. He soon sensed by the debates, by the newspapers, by the talk on the streets, that things were not going as they should.

It was a long, hard job. He voted, of course, for dividing the land among the poor whites and Negroes; for public schools; for pensions and relief and for better work and higher wages. But these things were side-issues to most of his fellow-lawmakers who were immersed in taxes, debts, borrowing capital from the North and electing men to office. Of these matters Tom knew little, but he saw poverty increasing, cheating in land sales, and little money for schools. He resented the open bargaining and bribery, and saw a number of shifty persons, Negroes and whites, who evidently were getting paid for their votes or some illegitimate service. Mansart said to a brown man beside him:

"There's dishonesty there!"

The man was a small merchant and looked at Mansart coldly. "Where are you from?" Tom told him. The man hesitated and at last said as he rose to leave: "Men with $10,000 a year don't have to steal. They can be honest. But men who only earn $100 a year either steal or starve. I happen to know that yonder sneaking darky cleared $97 from his crop last year!"

He left Tom thinking. He walked far out into the country along the inlets of the sea. Rounding a mass of shrubbery he suddenly came across a Negro sitting in the shade eating a recently roasted chicken. The man was black, ragged and relaxed. He was sitting on a log and looked Tom over speculatively. He had a pleasant face and laughing eyes.

"Where did I git dis meat? Well, I tells you honest, Bud, I stole it. Ah took it right from ole man Breck'ridge's home place. Wrong? Nawsah, ah don' tink it's wrong. Hit's risky, but hit ain't wrong. White folks been stealin' me all my life. Now I'se takin' some of it back. Jus takin' it back. Work? Ah done done all the work I aims to do de balance of mah life. I's gwine to rest wid a little stealin' on the side. I'se through wid work. I'se free, ain't I? What's freedom but not doin' what you don't want to? Never did like work, never will! Workin' for mah people? Ain't got no people; nevah had none. Nobody evah cared for me; now ah ain't caring for nobody but me. May git jailed? Sure. Sit still and let white folks feed me. Beat up? No, oh no. Ain't no white man evah gwine to beat dis nigger again. Git kilt and go to Hell? Could be. But see heah, Bud, when I gits up there, know what ah aims to do?

"Gwine to stan' up and talk to God straight as man to man. Gwine to say, 'Massa God, maybe you knows yo' business bettern I. But as ah sees it you ain't doin' so well. Looks like to me you done messed up dis world something awful. Starved de good and fed de bad; made scoundrels happy and made saints sad. Turible mess. Look at me: born wid nothing, always hungry, beat up and drove to work. Then you frees me and ah thanks you, jumps

an prays an hollers! Den you tells me ah ain't free but gotta
work. Hell, no! I jest ain't gwine to work! Ef you wants to burn
me forevah—well, go ahead. Ah still ain't workin'! Reckon ah'll
last as long as the fire.' "

Tom smiled wryly and then turned silently away. The man
with his mouth half-full of succulent chicken, threw back his mas-
sive head and guffawed.

"Plumb disgusted, ain't you, Buddy? You goin' right on savin'
the worl' an' worryin' yo' fool head crazy. An' wen yo' done, ole
worl' wus off dan evah. But go 'head. Yo' caint hep yosef! Go
'long." Then he straightened up, bent forward and a cruel scowl
leapt across his face. "Only don't git no ideas 'bout de police!"

"I won't," answered Tom and walked on.

In May, 1876 Tom ordered his agricultural union in Colleton
County to strike for higher wages. The workers threatened crops
and property. They had some success but not great. In August,
just at the time of gathering the crop, his union in Beaufort
County, where once Tom had a farm, struck for a fifty per cent
increase in wages. They were miserably paid and systematically
cheated. They imprisoned the scabs who swarmed to replace them;
overpowered the sheriff and his posse. But at last the ringleaders
were arrested and jailed.

Mansart paused here. His union plan with strikes was not
working. They could not keep from violence for without violence
scabs would break the strike. Scabs were plentiful because of poverty; while the planters and merchants stood ready at the slightest excuse to arrest his leaders.

Meanwhile, Mansart followed the routine work of the legislature, without seeming to accomplish much. He stood back of
Governor Chamberlain and his reforms. But when Elliott opposed Chamberlain and the white City Chamber of Commerce
praised him, Tom paused. The black leaders were divided. Some
began to feel that they were being used by a group of bond-
selling bankers and business men, North and South, with little real
care for the working Negro. He faced the election of 1876 completely bewildered.

What Tom wanted to understand was how income was determined; why good, hard-working men were poor and others who did
little or no work were rich. He did not question inheritance; that
seemed to him, if not altogether fair, at least logical. But these
new-rich, these idle upstarts whose contribution to production and

service was so hidden, how did they get rich so quick, while black and white laborers worked so hard and remained poor? Ignorance explained much but not all. He pressed for better schools. But more money was needed. He voted for asylums but there was no money. He wanted big plantations bought up and divided among poor farmers, but if money could be found there certainly wasn't enough honesty and good will available for these purposes.

Tom was still inclined to follow Chamberlain, especially since Elliott finally gave up his opposition and was running for Attorney-General on the Chamberlain ticket. Elliott had once been a labor leader. Where now did Chamberlain himself stand? Against theft and graft, sure; but that was not the complete answer. He must talk to Chamberlain who seemed like a reasonable man. It took some time to get a chance, but it came one afternoon on the Capitol steps. Tom lifted his hat and apologized.

The tall, bald-headed and well-dressed governor paused with cordial courtesy, not being sure at the moment which of his black followers this man was. He sensed Tom's honest groping for information.

"Governor, I'm all with you for driving out dishonesty and graft. I'm glad you hit Moses, that low white Southerner, and Whipper, the colored thief. But what I wants to know is this: after we stop this stealing, is that going to do away with poverty?"

The governor smiled. "You know what the Good Book says: 'the Poor ye have always with you.' "

"Yes, Sir, I'se read that. It say we got 'em, but it didn't say we got to keep 'em. And I'm wondering if we Negroes always got to be as poor, ignorant and sick?"

"Oh no, no; they'll gradually improve. But we'll aways have the lazy and criminal."

"Yes, Sir, and there's a lot of both among us. But that's what bothers me. Take us colored folk, by and large. Do you really think our condition is mostly because of laziness and stealing or more because of injustice of landowners and police?"

The governor was silent and Tom went on: "And if injustice is the real cause, what are we going to do about it? We must do something. Now what I've been busy on is organizing the blacks to work good and steady and then get together to ask better pay and more regular——"

"Oh, yes, now I remember. You're the labor union man. Now see here, Mansart, you're on the wrong track. There's a lot of that stuff in the North among the foreigners, and it's going to be put down. You can't force people to give you their own property. If you are not satisfied with what you get, leave and go elsewhere——"

"But Sir, I'm talking about wages we earn and don't get; of property they take when it ain't theirs; and after all we can't leave here for there ain't no place to go."

"Exactly. Then why complain? And say, have you by any chance been reading about the Socialism these foreigners are talking?"

"Socialism? No, Sir: never heard of it. I'm talking about farm laborers trying to live decent on 50c a day and that sometimes not paid, and them thrown in jail for complaining. Why, Sir——"

But the governor, glancing at his large silver watch, started to walk away. "Sorry, Mansart, but I've got an appointment. Been nice to meet you. But drop that trade union business—this is a free country. Goodbye!"

Tom stared after him. Chamberlain right there had lost a sincere follower. There Tom decided to listen to Aunt Betsy and appeal to the Democrats; or at least to their best leaders.

He remembered Elliott's labor convention of 1869 and his speech in Congress. Tom determined to consult him on a scheme forming in his own mind. It was not so much his own scheme as Aunt Betsy's. In her slow, cool, unhurried way she kept track of Tom and his efforts in the county and in the legislature. Continually she recurred to one theme. He must talk with Colonel Breckinridge. He and his wife were "quality." They talked straight even if harsh, and they kept their word. She distrusted Elliott; she did not believe in any of these educated Northern "niggers." The "quality" Southern aristocracy could and would lead black folk if appealed to right. She hated Gary and Butler after the Hamburg riot. They stood for the white upstate farmers and violence. And Hampton?—well, only if Breckinridge vouched for him. He was no South Carolinian. He was from Mississippi, and Black Belt slaveholders were bad.

Tom's chance to talk with colored leaders came when he was appointed to the important Committee on Land and Labor. After several routine meetings he found himself with Elliott, Cain, DeLarge and a number of the very leaders with whom he wanted to talk. They did not pay much attention to him, which was not surprising for he was young, diffident, and had never made a speech. But just before the committee arose, he ventured a word and was listened to courteously:

"Gentlemen," he said hestitatingly, "will you let me say a word? Like most of you, I'se been trying to support Chamberlain. He's got Northern business in his pocket; he thought he had us, and he almost got the planters. If he had, I'se afeared we'd a been finished. But the Devil stepped in and the Democrats, instead of supporting Chamberlain or not fighting him, followed the 'Straight-Outs' and named Hampton. We know what happened. Mobs, and murder, and armed whites everywhere. But ain't there a card here that we can play? After all, it ain't railroads and taxes so much as work and wages that's the main thing today. Why not organize black labor far beyond what we have done, and offer to join the planters? Not the new strivers but the old quality? My mother-in-law, Aunt Betsy, is always hammering on this, and specially she names Colonel Breckinridge."

A silence ensued and the members looked speculatively at Tom. The idea was not new. It was one of the first suggestions offered after the revolution of Abolition; Northern missionaries suggested it; Northern businessmen emphasized it. But few realized its difficulties: who could get the ear of the planters, and who now were the planters? The Negro political leaders, whether educated Northerners or intelligent freedmen, were anathema to the former slave owners. Freed slaves who had taken no prominent part in politics might approach their former masters, but only as suppliants too ready to yield anything which the masters demanded.

Now here came a new sort of man: a minor politician to be sure, but a worker—a labor organizer, at a time when efficient labor spelled the difference between bankruptcy and wealth for most landholders. Not only that, but this man had an unusual path of approach to one of the most influential planters. Elliott had heard of Aunt Betsy, and Cain knew her.

Elliott, however, was skeptical. He was sure that it was already too late. Already the coalition between planters, merchants and upstate white farmers had, he was sure, been consummated, and with the acquiescence of the North, the Negro was doomed. Little of all this, of course, was voiced. The committee merely paused; then the chairman thought that the matter "was of interest but hardly in order just here and now. . . ." They adjourned, and the members filtered slowly out, leaving Mansart disappointed and affronted, until he realized that several of the members of the Committee were gathering about him for further talks.

There was Elliott, Cain and Delany. They walked apart, stopped, and finally sat down together on the Capitol steps, at a point where listening in by outsiders was impossible. They questioned Tom as to his life and experience and seemed especially interested in Aunt

Betsy. They knew of the Breckinridge family. They were among
the great landholders of Carolina and represented the slaveholding
planter aristocracy. They were a proud, incorruptible clan. They
would not see eye to eye with Butler and Gary and the "Straight-
Outs." But on the other hand, they would face bankruptcy unless
change came, and soon.

"I am afraid," said Elliott, looking at Mansart thoughtfully,
"that probably it is too late to accomplish much. If the old aristocracy is not already compromised it soon will be. But one thing you
say, Mansart, interests me. And that is your labor organization.
The weak link in the program of the white bourbons is labor. They
can and probably will disfranchise Negroes unless the North inter-
venes, which as matters stand now is unlikely. But the South needs
labor: black, willing hands to reap the harvest for high post-war
prices; the planters are keen for this. Suppose now—and it's improbable—but suppose that through men like Breckinridge we
could somehow unite black union labor and the old land-holding
aristocracy? Of course it is impossible, but—by God! It's worth a
trial. Mansart, why don't you talk to Breckinridge?"

Cain interrupted: "It will be useless. I tell you I know it has
all been settled; the Democrats are putting on a campaign this
month which is race war. Murder at Hamburg in July; here and in
Ellenton in September. Chamberlain can't talk at his own campaign meetings, and the whites are arming and parading. Hampton
is going to put the 'Mississippi plan' through in South Carolina.
The white merchant and upstate farmers are with him, and with a
Democratic president in Washington we'll be beaten."

"But is Breckinridge with him? Can Hampton swing the planters? At any rate, will it hurt to ask?" Elliott turned to Mansart. "It's
a last chance, but try it, boy, try it." He shook Mansart's hand.

"When?" asked Tom.

"Now," said Delany.

Tom arose immediately; but Delany detained him. Delany was
a black man, a former major in the Union army. He was intelligent
and far-seeing. He looked Tom straight in the eye and said, "I'm
voting for Hampton."

"Why?" asked Tom.

"Because his followers are set to disfranchise and crush my
people; but if they get into office through Negro votes they won't
dare carry out their program. So you see your plan is right along
the line of my thinking. If we fail there is only one path left—
migration out of this accursed land." He put his hand on Tom's

shoulder, and looking at him quizzically: "Talk for yourself," he said, "and do not mention us. I have a feeling that the Colonel will not appreciate advice from Northern 'niggers'!"

So it was that Tom Mansart had approached Colonel Breckinridge and been repulsed. He had gone to the side porch and there had talked to Mrs. Breckinridge. He was now awaiting the Colonel.

Colonel Breckinridge watched Scroggs descend the porch steps and shuffle off. Then he turned wearily and sat down. It was just here that Mrs. Breckinridge entered. The Colonel leaned back with a sigh, but she did not sit as he indicated.

She said, "I am sorry, my dear, but the colored man is still waiting. No! Listen—" as he made a gesture of impatience, "—just say a word to him. He really is interesting."

She was about to explain further, but the Colonel did not wait. Without a word he arose, bowed slightly and walked to the side porch. He had his mind made up as to just what he was going to say to this black man. He had already been pushed too far today. He would say a few clear words. But before he could speak the black man rose, faced him and spoke clearly and directly:

"Colonel Breckinridge, we black folk needs help and you can give it to us if you will. We never asked to come to this land and it was little use for us to ask for freedom after we got here. We'se helped make this nation rich and powerful. Suddenly we'se set free. We can't refuse freedom even if we wanted to, and we don't. We wants to be men; not white men but men. We want work and decent wages. We want to rise in the world as far as we deserve and no further. If other working men don't need to vote then we don't. But if white workers vote we got to, or starve. Most of us ain't got no business holding public office because we don't know enough. But some of us has made good, honest officials. There ain't no reason in keeping a man from holding office just because he's black. But even that is no matter just now. Today, 999 Negroes out of every 1000 want work, not office; want victuals more than votes.

"Now, Colonel, will you and your folks promise us this much justice? Others promise us, but they lie and we know it. All they want is to put the black worker back in slavery, and that we won't stand for. We don't want everything at once. We'se willing to be judged by what we does. Now, Sir, the 'Straight-Out' Democrats want our votes and promises that if they win they'll treat the Negro worker right. You support them and Hampton. Can you tell us he

is honest and will do what he says? It don't seem so just now.
He's play-acting and his followers are killing our folks. On the
other hand, we know Chamberlain. He's talking reform and honest
government. But he's long been working with Northern and Southern money-makers. If he wins with white votes what will we do?
What can we do?

"Colonel, we'se in trouble and know it. We'se having a last rally
tomorrow night in Emmanuel Church. It will be a closed union
meeting but it will represent 50,000 votes in city and state. Will
you come and tell us plain just what you stand for and what you
think we should do? We ain't promising to do everything you say.
But we is promising to listen and trust the word of a Breckinridge."

The Colonel sat down and stared out into the yard. This was
about the last line of talk he had expected. He started to speak
and then hesitated.

"When is this meeting?"

"Tomorrow night. We'll expect you at nine."

The Colonel arose and said, "I will come. I will come and I
will tell you honestly what I think you Negroes should do for your
own good, and what we whites will do to see that you get justice.
I promise that on the word of a gentleman."

Then he turned, and without further word or gesture walked
slowly back to the front porch. His wife had left. As had been his
wont for twenty years he stood at sunset and stared out to sea.
Out to that ocean whence the drama of fearful history had rolled in
on this fated land, this Carolina named after that stiff-necked king
who lost his head to Cromwell; an empire larger than the king's
own England. De Ayllon had seen it three hundred and fifty years
ago, and by black fate his own Negroes had driven him away. De
Soto followed, with that grotesque Negro who later opened up the
unknown Southwest. Then followed Spain. But in 1580 Sir Walter
Raleigh, that blood-stained pirate, swept his plumed hat over these
sands and made them English until his settlers were murdered by
Indians or starved to death. It was fifty years later that the first
proprietors wangled from that gay dog, the second Charles, a grant
of this realm where the first Earl of Shaftsbury settled with Locke's
slave constitution in his pocket.

The Colonel knew that from that day the Black race had
haunted Carolina and its ghost remained today. Virginia tried to
become a land of gentry and lordly estates, with trained black
service. But from the first, South Carolina was gripped by commercial slavery, with hordes of driven slaves whose value was in

the crops they raised—first rice and then King Cotton. They poured in after that war called "Spanish Succession," but really fought by English merchants to gain control of the trade in African slaves. They came at a rate that frightened the white settlers whom they soon outnumbered two and three to one.

From the first, slave revolts began: Sebastian in 1711; Goose Creek in 1715; all around Charleston from 1720 to 1730; in 1739 with Jemmie and Cato at Stono, down to that fearful nightmare of 1822 with Denmark Vesey. The Colonel never forgot this horror of his cradle, and the sinister figure of the leader defying the gallows: "Die silent as I do!" The Colonel turned away. Was this land, this beautiful land of his fathers, always to be cursed by black men?

It was a mad and perverse fate that had made Carolina, created to be a land of beauty, art and culture, become instead the foundation stone of the Cotton Kingdom. From South Carolina cotton fields and led by Carolinians this kingdom had spread west to Georgia, Alabama and Mississippi until it met decadent French and Spanish empire in Louisiana, and dreamt of a slave empire from the Mississippi to the Amazon and the Atlantic to the Pacific. And, too, rolling eastward, this cotton culture had built industrial revolution in western Europe and colonial imperialism over the world. To support this fearsome superstructure had come the philosophy of labor as slavery, and in support of this war and counter-revolution. Where next, asked the Colonel, whither next?

Chapter III

THE COLONEL BREAKS HIS WORD

Colonel Breckinridge, about to dress for dinner, stood stock-still before his mirror with his black cravat untied and his hands hanging. He somehow just realized that he had given his word to two different men and that both promises could not possibly be fulfilled. He knew this before, but just now the enormity of it really struck him. He had promised the poor white leader that the planters would stand with him to take political power from the Negroes, place it in the hands of the whites and give white labor preference over black. A moment later he had promised Tom Mansart to advise Negroes how best to secure justice for themselves.

Of course, in neither case did he say all that he meant. He knew this at the time, and the reservations did not then seem unfair nor unreasonable. After all, the poor whites knew perfectly well that they were not the equals of the aristocrats in ability, education or desert. If some did become equal, they must be so treated, but of course few would or could. And in the case of white laborers the portion of ability and desert was very small—little beyond that of Negroes, less than some Negroes. That was clear in his own mind and must have been even in Scroggs' dull brain. And also to Mansart—a really good fellow, with respect for his betters. He had intended to say, and of course Mansart knew it, that Colonel Breckinridge and his comrades stood ready to give the Negro every right and opportunity they deserved, if they stopped trying to be what God never intended and followed their natural white leaders.

Yet now the Colonel realized that not only was this not exactly what he had said or implied; it certainly was not what either Scroggs or Mansart understood. He had let them go with a false interpretation. With neither interpretation could he himself agree, and most certainly not with both, for they were contradictory.

The Colonel was puzzled as never before. He could not remember ever having faced such a moral quandary. Telling the truth, even the harsh and unpleasant truth, had hitherto cost him nothing important; indeed it had added to his reputation and self-esteem. The blunt fact was: "I want a world ruled by those born to rule; that natural supremacy I will share, indeed can share with no one; not with low-class whites, certainly not with inferior breeds of half-men. Moreover, if asked, I will tell them both so—openly and bluntly."

Yet he had not done this. He had told Scroggs—or at least he had let Scroggs understand—that henceforth the Scroggses would be allowed to share power with him and his class and be recognized as equals. He had not said this plainly and simply, but he had implied it; he had let Scroggs believe it, "on his honor as a gentleman!" He had promised Mansart to advise Negroes how to attain such goals as they were able to reach. He had not added, as he fervently believed, that the most Negroes could hope for was to be obedient servants under kind masters, and that was what he would help to make them and nothing more. But that was not what Mansart understood, and the Colonel knew it.

Why, why in God's name had he done this? He knew why; he knew perfectly well. He had lied to Scroggs because the awful— the unthinkable alternative—was to surrender political power to men like Gary and Tillman or share it with a Scroggs; if not that, then to rule with the help of higher apes.

On the heels of this came the monstrous demand that he repeat this shameless performance and promise Negroes their "rights," and for the identical reason: these Negroes and the white scalawags had at present the power if united to out-vote the planters and merchants and rule the State. So someone must lie to them. But not he, not a Breckinridge; let others do it. And he winced to realize that he had already done this. To what depths of double-dealing he had sunk! What a mess life was!

How had he ever come to such a pass? What had induced him to assent to such promises, unless it was the breaking of his rule never to argue with an inferior on matters which of necessity they could not understand? And then deep down within himself he knew he had another motive, long concealed but growing in pressing importance: It was the wraith of poverty. Not perhaps actual hunger but loss of loved luxuries, wearing shabby clothes, keeping few servants or even none—gradually sinking to penury and want. He had felt it creeping on him.

There was the case of the new saddle-horse. His loved friend, the mare Maggy, was undoubtedly getting old. She had served nobly and well for long years. But the Colonel postponed replacing her until one day he caught sight of a beautiful young gelding ridden by a Northern horse-trader. He tried him and was more than satisfied. Carelessly he ordered the horse sent to his home, as was his wont, not deigning to haggle over the price. But the horse did not arrive and his mulatto overseer told him why.

"He wants his money cash—and a lot of it."

"Then pay him," retorted the Colonel impatiently.

Sanford, the overseer, was a tall, thin, slow man with an expressionless face. His skin was warm yellow and his hair grey. During the war as a young slave he had been sent to the Colonel from his uncle's plantation as his body-servant. He had remained with the Colonel ever since. The Colonel knew that this man was his own blood cousin, but the fact was never admitted, not even alluded to. He looked like the Breckinridges and had been called "Breckinridge." But after the war he had taken his mother's name, Sanford. Sanford was thorough, absolutely honest and methodical. He never wasted words. He answered now briefly:

"No money."

The Colonel froze. "Why not?"

"No crops, no labor."

"Hire labor!"

"What with?"

"Sell land!"

"All right, Sir, but this can't go on much further."

Sanford left. The Colonel knew he was right.

The Colonel's uncle had invested in railroads before the war, sums he could ill afford. He himself had inherited from him and his father bundles of miscellaneous railway stocks which he had eventually converted into the widely touted Texas and Pacific. All these he had eventually turned over to his steward and forgotten them. His whole outlook for future income was now apparently only his land. The income from his land was slowly decreasing. He had sold much of his former large acreage and there was no market for what was left, where the proud home of his youth was beginning to moulder and fall. His few ventures in investment were futile. Either the past must be restored with faithful black labor and complacent whites or the landed aristocracy was doomed. This was the unacknowledged reason, he realized, that he was dickering with poor whites and Negroes. He was ashamed. But what else could he do?

He would talk the situation over at the club. But here again, he mentally paused. Many of his fellow-members were well-bred gentlemen of the old school. But not all; there were lately increasing numbers of politicians, military men and shop-keepers. Few of these would have any scruples at what he had done. Many would laugh and count it good politics. No, he could not bring it up for general discussion. He was not good at doubletalk and frankness now would spoil everything.

He went down at last to his own beautiful, oak-panelled dining room, dressed for the meal. The linen was smooth and white, the lovely old silver perfectly polished. Of course they missed the old butler, but Mollie, the maid, really was learning fast. Mrs. Breckinridge looked regal in her white lace. The Colonel asked his usual question:

"Betty Lou is not with us?"

"She may come in later."

Betty Lou was their only child, and as she grew seemed to fit less and less into the family pattern. She was twenty-four, having grown to womanhood in a torn and distracted world. Nothing was normal nor ever would be so far as she could see. Offers for her hand, few as they were, had not suited her parents in the least, and indeed she had no inclination for marriage. She was bored with conventional life and craved excitement. She wanted something to "happen," but just what, beyond more and gayer parties which again did not satisfy her, she did not know. She was born too late to be a Southern lady of the old regime, and too early for real education and a career. The men she met were drab or wild. She despised or feared them. She wondered what would become of her, and so did her mother.

So Betty carved out a desultory, indefinite life, which her father was too distracted to follow and with which her mother was unwilling to interfere. She had herself seen too much of straightjackets for "jeunes filles," to fashion one for her daughter. After all, her daughter was both a Du Bignon and a Breckinridge, and could do no wrong. She therefore waited patiently to be taken into Betty's confidence. She was at the moment not progressing.

She and the Colonel lingered over their excellent dinner with appreciation. The dry Sherry and gumbo soup were excellent. There were shrimps, fried chicken and rice, of which they never tired. Aunt Jane's hot beaten biscuit could never go untasted, and today there was ice cream, flavored with mangoes. After the maid was dismissed the Colonel turned to his fine old port with relish.

"I do wish you'd see that Betty joined us more often," he said, turning his glass to the light. Mrs. Breckinridge over her coffee did not answer. Neither mentioned Scroggs. Mrs. Breckinridge sensed it was a matter of which the Colonel did not like to think. It occurred to her that the conversation with Mansart might be both relief and solution.

"The Negro was interesting," she began. The Colonel did not encourage her. He simply nodded and crumbled his bread. "And by the way, he is a son-in-law of Aunt Betsy."

He looked up. "Is she still alive?"

"So it seems, and she sent him to us."

"Indeed."

"I really think, dear, that the Negroes, or some of them, are beginning to see the light."

"Possibly."

"It appears that Aunt Betsy still believes in white folk and especially in us. This Negro who married her daughter is a stevedore and wants to lead black labor into our camp."

"So he said—but will he give up voting and trying to hold office?"

"No, not entirely. But they offer to be guided by us if we—and by that he means especially folk like the Breckinridges—will guarantee justice and good treatment."

"I wonder if any number of Negro leaders are ready to surrender their impossible ambitions and return to their places?"

"No, not quite that, but something almost as rational. Mansart sees clearly that Negroes need leadership and advice; there are not enough educated and experienced Negroes; he distrusts the Northerners, black and white. He and his followers want Southern leadership—but not the Ku Klux. They want the guidance of Southern aristocracy, and they want your word to bind the bargain."

"What bargain? Do they expect me to promise to let them vote and hold office? Well, I will never do it. I've promised him advice. That is all. I've lied to the limit to appease poor white trash. I'll go no further."

"Others have gone further."

"If Hampton, Gary and Butler want to lie that is their burden. Perhaps a promise of votes to Negroes is a justifiable deception which some can bring themselves to mouth. I can't and I won't. My conception of the word of a gentleman differs from theirs." He was all the more vehement because again he was not telling the exact truth.

"But my dear, is the difference so great as you assume? Mansart and his folk ask only such political power as is absolutely necessary for just relations between employer and employee. We know that all employers are not just."

"Nor are all Northern employers or English factory owners. Who is to judge between servants and owners? The owners, or a committee of slaves?"

"What Mansart asks is that men like you guarantee them just rights. He wants to consult you and he asks that the intelligent blacks have some voice in decisions."

"There are no Negroes intelligent enough to have voice in government; or such as are intelligent are not honest."

"Oh, my dear, that is not fair; there are some Negroes both intelligent and honest. There might be more if they had a chance," she added, musing.

The Colonel made no reply. He could not share this line of thinking with his wife. He saw between them a certain difference of attitude. He had sensed it before, but it was clearer now. She believed in Negroes more than he did, and less in whites as such. If alliance must come, she leaned toward Negroes rather than poor whites. It was natural; she had been brought up in Louisiana nearer to blacks; she had lived close to them in childhood and youth. In fact—and he started as he remembered—there were even rumors of Du Bignons whose blood was not untainted.

Then he pulled his thought sharply back. It was only that because of knowing Negroes more intimately and poor whites hardly at all, that his wife conceived alliance with Negroes possible —at least with some Negroes, having no idea of the horrible and unavoidable results. Or had she? He remembered suddenly that dark, hawk-nosed harridan, old Mère Du Bignon, head of the rich and haughty clan. She had drawn him apart during his last visit in 1856.

"Damn it," she growled. "John, look yonder."

He saw a beautiful brunette with flashing eyes and strong limbs go swiftly by.

"See that bitch? She's determined to go 'nigger,' when I could easily pass her for white. She's got our blood—plenty of it. What can I do?"

The outraged young Breckinridge had stammered and withdrawn awkwardly. The blasphemy had cut his visit to New Orleans short. He hurried back with his bride to Carolina. Of course this contamination was far from her and the incident had passed from his mind. Now he remembered. The thought, the tolerance, had lingered unconsciously in her mind. She would forget it in time; now he must not affront her. He must agree with the necessity of placating as many Negroes as possible, especially of the Mansart type of worker. But he would not—he could not stoop to another and more revolting lie.

He spoke slowly: "This is interesting—very interesting. I will lay it before the committee and we will act upon it."

"Only remember, dear, these men want your assurance—none other. It is in a way a great honor."

"Too great, I fear. But do not worry; I will do my duty."

She glanced at him quickly and uncertainly, but at this point Betty Lou entered and the subject was dropped. Later, as they were getting ready for bed, he spoke slowly and earnestly:

"This is, of course, an important overture. It may forestall any union of white and black labor with Northern radicals. It may help checkmate the grafting whites; it may bring into alliance the landed aristocracy and the backbone of black labor. We must grasp this extended hand; but we must act with care and thought or everything will be spoiled. We must not affront the whites. We must not raise too high any hopes of Negro equality."

"I am sure there'll be no danger of that. I stressed it in my talk to Mansart. I told him frankly that I did not believe in Negro equality with whites."

"How did he answer you?"

"He repudiated any desire for equality. He wanted a chance to work at decent wages; education for his children and—oh yes, he said workers must have the right to vote as a matter of self-defense!"

"Nonsense! But after all, what is voting? A gesture and a futile one in most so-called democracies. Power is the real question—power and control. But of course I'm in honor bound to consult with the Committee. We will work it out, I'm sure."

The next morning, as she helped him into his light overcoat she said: "Because of the meeting will you be late to dinner or dine at the club?"

"At the club. Do not wait for me."

She said, half hesitating, "I'd half hoped you'd come home—and let me go with you."

He stared at her in astonishment. "To a Negro political meeting? Certainly not! I shall go from the club. And my dear, let me warn you about keeping off the streets at night, even here in this neighborhood. These are—uncertain times."

He kissed her and hurried away. He walked slowly. He did not want to go to that meeting. The whole sordid mess revolted him. Why not fight all this in the open? No, there was the law; there was still the ache of defeat in war. Very well, then cajole, cheat, but don't lie. Gentlemen don't lie. And where in God's name are the gentlemen these days? And—very well, he wouldn't go!

Quite instinctively Colonel Breckinridge dropped in for tea with his old friend, Dr. Baldwin, who was visiting in town and stopping at the boarding house where he usually stayed.

Sophocles Thrasymachus Baldwin had always seemed old, even when men first became aware of him and he was forty. He had seemed too old and frail for war duty, having been born in 1820. He was not unwilling to seem old, because he was opposed to war. He was a teacher and philosopher, the son of an overseer, trained at a "private academy" in Georgia—little more than a poor high school. He had come to the old city of Augusta just before the Civil War to teach. When the war broke out he continued with his difficult teaching. After the war he kept on teaching. His own education had been the so-called classical training. He knew a great deal about Greece and Rome; less about Egypt and practically nothing about Asia. He had a stereotyped conception of England and New England. He deliberately forgot France.

He was, however, interested in matters of the mind. He believed in the training of the mind as the only worthwhile salvation. In Augusta he developed the local "Academy" into a growing institution. He became a center and an institution in himself. He was an optimistic man. He believed in Progress. There were interruptions to be sure, and setbacks, but the world was going forward. That much he knew. He believed in democracy among the chosen few; a democracy like the Athenian, which included slaves and foreigners, but neither as voters nor rulers.

He was eager for the discovery of talent, for freedom of self-expression among those who had something to express. There were plenty who had not. He was not sure about the mass of poor whites, but some of them had talent as was proven by the fact, he twinkled, that he himself was born one and that many very aristocratic planters were descended from them. He had many questions about women. Certainly a well-ordered world should primarily put their women to the fine business of recreating the species.

As to Negroes, he was quite certain that the place for the great mass of them was in a benevolent servitude, and despite the current experiment in emancipation, that would turn out to be the status to which they would eventually return or die out. For years he had been close friend of Colonel Breckinridge who was some five years his senior but who had been associated with him in thought and action. They did not altogether agree. Old Dr. Baldwin was against force but strong on evolution and the "survival of the fittest." He advocated thrift, saving and property. Colonel Breckinridge was also against unnecessary force, but was not so certain about evolution, and thought too often he saw the survival of the worst. Thrift and saving had never been necessary for him, but he strongly believed in Property.

They sat and talked. Dr. Baldwin asked after Betty Lou, who was sort of a protégé of his, almost a god-child but not quite because of Mrs. Breckinridge's Catholicism. Betty Lou, from a baby, had always regarded him as a friend and playmate, and as she grew up she had a sort of half-contemptuous affection for him because, of course, he was not quite a gentleman, being the son of a mere overseer. But he was a very learned man and for this Betty Lou had respect.

From this they drifted to the subject of Tom Mansart, and Dr. Baldwin was disposed to regard his overture as an important symptom. It would perhaps forestall, he said, threatened mob rule in the South. The South was not ready for democracy. It had a working class split by race, and ignorant. It had the leadership of white demagogues. It needed long tutelage. Its greatest threat and danger was a false unity between these demagogues and the ignorant working class. Breckinridge had a chance to split the workers and forge an alliance of great political significance between Negroes and white aristocrats.

Reluctantly the Colonel remembered that this was not what he had promised Scroggs. What could he honestly say to the Negroes? He wandered down to the Club, to which Dr. Baldwin did not belong. He sat there lost in thought. From 1876 the South had been in revolution—a revolution succeeding war. Most of Breckinridge's fellow clubmen remembered all this, but remembered from different points of view and angles, with many variations and blind-spots. Like all revolutions, this was no matter of mass action directed miraculously toward conscious ends. It was a complicated, contradictory mingling of human motives, directed by individuals but without common cause or vision. The actual deeds were individual; often the directing thought was individual. But the coherency which made the vast social movement was more often mere coincidence or plain accident. The mass moved; the mass acted; but they acted through those men who represented at the moment the thought and desire of most of them. Conversely individual thought and desire influenced and directed the trends of the mass.

It was all complicated and difficult to explain, but none the less it was true, and fifteen million Southern people, white and black, reeled drunkenly on toward goals which they tried desperately to envision with clarity but failed. First of all, the white aristocrats wanted restoration of the former social organization; and the social situations to which they were used seemed absolutely essential to any life at all. Those who thought this impossible lay down and died, or went North and joined the Copperheads, or left for other lands like South America.

To most, such uprooting was unthinkable. Work must go on as before; the giving of services, homes and help. Land must be cultivated, crops raised and sold, goods brought in for sale. Men must live as men had lived in the South for centuries; nothing else was conceivable. Therefore slavery must be restored in all but name, with perhaps disappearance of human sale, which after all had nothing to do with the essence of the system. So thought the sons of Southern planters almost to a man.

But nine-tenths of the white Southerners were not planters or landholders and neither they nor their fathers ever had been. The world did not understand this. The United States did not realize it. They pictured the old South as slaveholders and slaves. It was poor whites and Negroes to an overwhelming degree. Emancipation opened doors to the whites long before the slave lost his chains. The whites lurched forward—the gifted, the lucky, the unscrupulous. They became traders, shop-keepers; they seized cheap land; they formed alliance with the Northern government and commerce. They began to rule the South and the more successful and unscrupulous rode roughshod over white and black workers.

But the South saw in the Negroes an uprooted, ignorant, poverty-stricken and sick mass of workers, with crazy ideas of possible change. This nonsense must be stopped and stopped peremptorily in sheer self-defense, to protect civilization. Negroes must think of themselves always as workers and never as thinkers or owners;

nor as men in the sense that whites were men.

Shot across this obvious fact came a system of Negro schools, lugged in by the white Northern Carpet-baggers, who ignorantly insisted that Negroes were men. They should have seen, said the Southerners, that their own popular education in the North was leading only to crime, poverty and a travesty on democracy. This might work out in time, since the laborers were, after all, white. But it was worse than stupid to think the African could be educated. It was criminal misleading of a simple people born to be servants of men. The first effort, then, of the South for reconstruction of agriculture and normal life, was to stop the ruin of the working class. This was the well-nigh universal public opinion of those who had hitherto always expressed the opinion of the South.

But there was another class who must be counted now, the mass of the poorer whites, laborers owning none or little land and having few skills. Hitherto poor whites had hung on the fringe of the slave system as peasants living drably on marginal land; a few became overseers; some had got education or capital and escaped into the ruling aristocracy. More now wanted to, and they pictured progress as sharing rule and wealth with planters, at just the time when the planters themselves were bankrupt and deprived of rule.

Colonel Breckinridge reported his interview with Scroggs to a few men in the smoking-room. It was six o'clock and there was general satisfaction. The price demanded was high, but thanks to Colonel Breckinridge this need not be as high as they had feared. There must be legal caste for the blacks, and preferential status for white labor.

Then at last Colonel Breckinridge mentioned the unexpected visit and offer of Mansart. Excitement increased.

"Why, that Mansart is the best labor leader in the state. His stevedores have 10,000 members, welded like a rock. They are reaching into the carpenters and masons. This is marvellous. If we can get control of this union labor we can build a dual, mutually self-effacing labor class, which will eliminate strikes, keep down wages and set the South on the road to an unrivaled prosperity. Breckinridge, follow this up, you must! Talk to them, promise them anything—everything—"

"No," answered the Colonel, "I won't."

There was silence, and then some of the members, realizing they had gone too far for the stomach of this straight-laced aristocrat, began to take a milder line. Their argument was strong; no omelet without broken eggs. We have stooped low in the last 30 years; another handful of grime and we may be free.

"Moreover," argued the father-in-law of a banker with Northern affiliation, "perhaps this is our chance to do for the Negroes what we long have promised: give them an opportunity; make them a real working class, with skill and decent life and broad guidance to real progress without the mirage of mob rule."

"But will they give up the ballot? Will any Negro leader dare to promise that?"

"Perhaps—sometime; but now can't we skirt that issue and promise good wages, justice in the courts and even schools suited to their capacities?"

"We can sure promise, but will the white labor vote allow fulfillment even of this?"

"Maybe not immediately or ever; but now at least we can promise. . . ."

"That, gentlemen, is a lie I cannot tell," rejoined the Colonel. "We all know that Scroggs and his gang with whom we have made alliance hate Negroes worse than starvation. If I talk to the Negroes tonight I will tell them to vote for Hampton; that naturally Hampton must promise lip-service to the law, but that nevertheless his object, like ours, is to take the vote away from Negroes. They can have schools for such as can learn to read and write, but no office-holding, no social equality. On the other hand, we'll protect them in the right to work at fair wages, justice in the courts and no mob violence."

Then suddenly the Colonel burst out with something he had never before said but which had long festered in his soul. "And too, gentlemen, I'll tell them that I'll do all in my power to stop turning our courts into tools to restore slavery and machinery for manufacturing crime for money-grabbers to fatten on."

Most of his fellow-members listened in consternation.

"This will drive the most intelligent and best organized Negro workers out of our party and it will convince the Scroggs gang that we have double-crossed them. It might unite black and white workers against white property."

Breckinridge knew this was logic. "What would you have me say?" he asked. There was an awkward pause, but the inevitable mal-a-prop blurted out:

"Stall them. Lead them along. Promise them. . . ."

"I am not skilled in lying," answered Colonel Breckinridge

coldly as he arose and started out. It was seven o'clock. Hampton
followed and they went to the dining room. Hampton saw that it
would be a calamity for Breckinridge not to keep his word to Mansart, and he hoped during dinner to effect some sort of compromise. He ordered carefully, carrying on a light conversation in
his most charming manner. It was eight o'clock. They finished, and
before any compromise was in sight. The Colonel was nervous
and wretched. Others joined them in the coffee room. It was past
nine o'clock.

Wade Hampton insisted: "This is important, very important.
We are going to carry this election at any cost. But afterward we
are going to need satisfied Negro labor. Colonel, you must go and
promise everything—you must!"

"Pardon me," someone interrupted, "but Colonel Breckinridge
is not the man; he is too straight-forward and forthright; in fact,
too much of a gentleman." Breckinridge writhed within to think
that anyone could be blamed for being "too much of a gentleman!"

Hampton continued: "It must be Breckinridge. These men
picked him. They trust him. Breckinridge, what you have got to
do is to keep their faith. Remember, this is war—race war. Post-
pone action as late as possible but offer them something now; not
everything. Use your influence, try to offer them enough to keep
them under our control. Meanwhile things are going to happen
which will alarm them; but reassure them and in the end promise
them anything—anything. Then after I am governor we will act!"

It was eleven o'clock. Just as the clock struck, a white man
hurriedly entered the Club and was finally ushered to the room
where Colonel Breckinridge was in conference. He came around
and whispered in the Colonel's ear.

"Pardon, Sir, but they say that the Negroes have seized your wife
and ridden out toward the Isles. We called at your home to check.
Your daughter said she was not there but had left on foot some
two hours ago."

The Colonel went grey and staggered to his feet. All the fears
of all the years of slavery fell suddenly upon him. That had happened which every Southern white man always secretly dreaded
but never believed could happen to his own family. He whispered
to Hampton and others and they talked low in turn. Then to a
man they arose, grim-faced and silent and hurried out of the room
and building. Just as they reached the door, a masked and foaming
horseman rode up.

"We caught him trying to escape," he gasped. "We've driven him back this way—come!" A dozen horses were offered and mounting, the Colonel and his friends dashed toward King Street just as a buggy, lurching crazily, wheeled into view pursued by masked riders.

Mrs. Breckinridge, sitting beside a colored man, descried her husband in front on a great black gelding. She leaped up and cried:

"John! John!" Suddenly she fainted without a word. All that the riders saw was a dishevelled white woman screaming in the grasp of a Negro. The Colonel gathered her in his arms and rode madly home.

Chapter IV

MANUEL MANSART IS BORN

In a close-curtained room in the basement of the Emmanuel A.M.E. Church, Mansart and his friends sat waiting. An open meeting might have brought down on them the Democratic riders who were breaking up the Chamberlain campaign. Breckinridge had not come and it was well past the hour. They had received warning that trouble was brewing in the streets and strangers from outside the city were gradually increasing. They shook their heads doubtfully. Nevertheless they all agreed that it was worthwhile to wait and listen to Breckinridge and then act accordingly. There was nothing to lose and perhaps something to gain.

Of course the chances were that it would come to nothing. Reluctantly Tom realized that there could be no doubt that the planters, the small farmers and the merchants, the people who had for generations ruled and those who planned to rule in the future, had been in close consultation. Secret organizations had been flourishing; no one knew this better than Mansart. He knew even some of the things they talked about and decided, and he was pretty sure that they had come to a definite decision as to the Negroes. The decision could hardly be final; for after all, did they understand what the Negroes were thinking about? Were they not taking their reports from stoolpigeons and wishful thinkers?

But not Mansart nor Breckinridge, Scroggs nor Hampton, understood the enormous significance of the drama in which they were called to act. Right and wrong were terms that scarcely could be applied to this situation. A mass of men and women, varying from conventional aristocrats to ignorant slaves, through masses of stolid farmers, narrow artisans and crafty tradesmen, were asked to have and act on opinions of the deepest human interest, which it was physically difficult and psychologically impossible for them to do intelligently and honestly. First came the aftermath of war with hate between Confederate and Yankee, with most Negroes ranged with the Yankees and the mass of white workers with no allegiance but bitter race prejudice.

Then hurriedly followed the contrast of property and poverty

59

which follows all war. Property was faced with poverty and Poverty was looking at starvation. The first charge against the Reconstruction legislatures was that they were filled with poor men, when before the War they represented the Rich. This seemed against nature. But the poor must have land and relief, and increasingly conscious of their ignorance, wanted schools.

Property complained of over-taxation, refused to pay the taxes assessed, and tax-payers' conventions spread. But they got nowhere because the poor and needy were untaxed and yet must insist that there was wealth and whosoever owned it must share it for the common need. This was Socialism. It frightened North as well as South, and it alarmed such poor whites and Negroes as knew no path to become rich except by exploitation of the poor. Thereupon arose a new, strong, and only too true cry of waste and theft in the conduct of the state. It rose and spread. Chamberlain eventually led it. Honest and intelligent Negroes joined, and whites joined. There was a prospect of clean government with wide social objects for Negroes and whites, conducted by whites and Negroes for the benefit of all who were strong enough to reap the profit.

When the Democrats, led by Hampton, Gary and Butler and later by Tillman, saw this, they realized that from such a state Negroes could not be excluded. Men like Elliott, Cardozo and Cain could only be eliminated by force. They suddenly whirled in 1876 and made the rift along the Color Line. They determined to split Carolina into races regardless of ability or character, and in defiance of American democracy and the Christian religion. They used work rivalry, social hates and finally Hampton dramatized Sex. The die was cast and, with murder, lynching and legal caste, division by race and color gripped the South for a century and spread to the wide world.

Mansart saw the grim drama beginning in October, 1876. White supremacy, naked and unashamed, started. Three hundred rifle clubs of armed whites covered the state. Chamberlain's campaign was practically stopped by armed men invading his meetings and taking charge. Riot and even murder followed refusal.

Hampton's campaign became a crusade. He was a Southern gentleman, born and bred; a veteran of the war and personally a big and powerful figure weighing over 200 pounds, handsome and suave, beautifully whiskered, with flowery speech and fulsome compliments for "the Ladies, God bless them," who thronged to his rallies. Colonel Breckinridge and his wife had attended the

Fort Moultrie centennial. Thousands of mounted and armed Confederate veterans marched in a procession a mile long. Troops crossed over from Georgia, insulting and spitting in the faces of the Negro policemen.

The Hampton campaign became a triumphal procession, greeted by increasing crowds. People came scores of miles, marching amid music and roar of cannon. There were torchlight processions and all the memories of the past were aroused to pray for the redemption of the "Grand Old State." Women had special seats; Hampton rode in a flower-bedecked chariot and the crowds became hysterical as here on a stand a young white woman sat bowed, draped in black and chained. Hampton approached with acclaim and martial music. The woman arose, young, white and beautiful, and throwing aside her black mourning, stood radiant and free!

Back of this theatre came grimmer coercion. The white state was armed, the colored militia disarmed. Prominent Republicans, white and black were spotted and followed, quarrels were picked and "duels" arranged. White Republicans were subjected to intolerable pressure, social and economic, until scores of them hurried to newspapers to insert cards professing conversion to Democracy.

Tom Mansart soon saw attacks on his workers' unions. Despite his efforts they were being infiltrated and undermined. In a newspaper advertisement, "The Workingmen's Democratic Association" offered to furnish 100 to 200 able-bodied men for any kind of work. A Broad Street merchant was prepared to furnish "Democratic" labor at reasonable cost to any extent at a moment's notice. On the plantations, laborers who declared for Hampton got better contracts, higher wages and debts wiped away; Republicans were driven off. Mansart worked continuously and held the mass of city artisans firm within the unions, but his country following began to dwindle.

Then prominent Negroes began to come out for Hampton; some honestly convinced of his sincerity toward Negroes; some still distrusting Chamberlain; some bribed and intimidated. Hampton made public overtures:

"Talk about putting the colored man back into slavery or qualifying their suffrages. . . . It is against our interest to do either of these things, if we could. In the first place, the labor of the colored man is more valuable to us as he is than if he were a slave, because he was then perishable property and as soon as he passed away, it was so much loss to the general wealth of the country."

It was an extraordinary argument for unlimited and irresponsible exploitation of free labor; but it came at an extraordinary time and fell on itching ears far from South Carolina. It was followed by a statement that sent a wave of fear into the hearts of even thinking Negroes:

"If . . . the white people of South Carolina were to give you the State, and give you everything, land, houses, churches, banks—you could not live without whites. The only way to bring about prosperity in this State is to bring the two races in friendly relation together."

"True," replied Mansart and his workers. "True," cried Elliott and Cardozo and Cain, "but who will arrange these relations and just what will the relations be?" Chamberlain, the Governor, thought he had the answer. He was relying on the North to back a fair election by military force if necessary. He issued a proclamation and told the nation:

"Upon my full official and personal responsibility, lawlessness, terrorism and violence far exceed in extent and atrocity any statements yet made public."

Grant responded with a proclamation ordering the disbandment of the rifle clubs within three days. All available federal military force was ordered to Columbia. But the Democrats responded quickly. The rifle clubs became "baseball clubs," "church sewing circles," "mother's little helpers" or "Hampton and Tilden Musical clubs"; military display and exercises stopped but the organizations remained. Sixteen companies of federal troops appeared and the whites received them and overwhelmed them with ovations. They thanked them for coming to protect them from corrupt Negro rule which they were striving to overthrow. They set aside October 26 as a "Day of Prayer."

Against these tactics the Negroes and the dwindling number of their white friends had no adequate means of reply. The social ties which subtly drew the army officers and the Southern whites into sympathetic contact were missing in the case of the Negroes. The nation to which Chamberlain tried to appeal was hopelessly torn in two; on the one hand the eyes which saw "the coming of the Lord" were closed by the "orgy of theft and graft" which was sweeping the whole nation. On the other hand high tariffs, low wages and rich profit were the goal of industry in politics.

Graft and political control burst up from the swarming immigrants at Ellis Island under Boss Tweed, out to the thieving landgrabbers of the Pacific railroads. The liquor trade, increasing from 30 to 300 millions a year, was caught bribing the President's cabinet. A flamboyant centennial celebration of 100 years of vain attempt at democracy which could not pass the color line, saw an Emperor talking into the first telephone while far to the west an Indian, bitter and deceived, was eating General Custer's heart.

Depression had fallen on the nation like a blight, with crime, hunger and unemployment. Blind revolt spread among farmers in the new Grange; among workers in the demand for cheaper money. A Liberal Republican revolt sweeping from the West had for the first time since the war put the Democrats in control of the House of Representatives; 23 of the 35 states, led by Tilden in New York, had gone Democratic. President Grant, discredited, did not dare run for a third term.

Here was the chance of the white South, if they played their cards with care. They must reorganize their strategy: the Negroes must not be fought as ex-slaves but as grafters like Tweed and the Whiskey Ring. The alliance of Chamberlain with Northern business must be disrupted and the white South must enter as the new business partner of the North, with cheap Negro labor as the bait. Only disfranchisement could keep labor cheap—this the North must be led to see.

So now Mansart was waiting, and the group was watching him doubtfully. It was getting late, not only in the day but in the year and in the culmination of the Campaign of 1876. The meeting began to get turbulent and out of hand.

"Where is Breckinridge?" they growled, louder and louder. The door opened softly and a man glided in. He spoke to Mansart low and long and then went out. Mansart sat in startled silence and then arose heavily.

"Gentlemen," he said, "we have been ignored—or betrayed. Breckinridge is sitting at his club. He has not started here; perhaps he never planned to come. The Klan is riding the countryside; they are gathering here quietly in the streets. We must. . . ."

There was a slight movement at the door. It opened slowly and framed in it against the night was the figure of Mrs. Du Bignon Breckinridge, tall and slim, with the carriage and simply gowned grace of a born aristocrat. She was a white woman in a world of black men. Silence was complete.

It had come about quite by accident. Colonel Breckinridge, she was sure, had gone to address the Mansart meeting. She was, of course, disappointed because she had hoped he would let her accompany him. Yet she half-expected that he would not think this proper; and even if he did he was advising with Southern gentlemen like Wade Hampton—darling old man that he was, with his courtly bow and smile and his facile "The Ladies, God Bless them"—and keep them out of politics and business. No, she would not be expected; and she wandered out into the never palling beauty of night on the Battery, when a little black figure slipped up the front steps, handed her a note and was gone. She smiled. Negroes so loved secrecy!

The note was from Mansart. He said the Colonel had not yet arrived; could she say if he was coming to the meeting and when? She glanced back at the clock in surprise. The meeting had been set for nine. It was well past ten. What could have happened? What could have delayed him? Many things, of course, but Mansart must be reassured, the Colonel was sure to come. He was doubtless already on the way. Then she turned quickly—of course that was the thing to do—she herself would take the message. She would meet the Colonel there—he might not like it, but he would understand. She threw a mantilla over her black dinner gown.

Betty Lou came out on the porch: "You're not going out, Mother?"

"Just a moment."

"The Streets didn't look quite safe as I came in."

"Nonsense. I'm not going far." And she went out. The Battery was beautiful; always she had loved to saunter along it at night, revelling in the beauty of the harbor beyond. She walked slowly since she might meet the Colonel on his way to the meeting or even possibly already returning; but perhaps it had been easier to approach the Negro church from the club by way of other streets. She paused to recall that labyrinth of alleys that branched east from the docks. She used to know the nearer ones well in the days of Aunt Betsy, when she went to call on her or fetch her. Of course she could find that house, and the church was not far. Anyone would tell her. It was now quite dark, and she hastened her step.

As she started to turn into an alley which she recognized, suddenly a white man loomed in front of her.

"Where do you think you're going?" he asked unsteadily.

She realized with quick revulsion that he was quite drunk. Disgusted, she made no reply but walked on without quickening her step. Never before had she even thought of insult on these streets, despite war and evil. But as she stepped into the darker

alley she heard behind her men snarl and curse, and without looking back she knew they were white men.

She walked calmly on toward the flickering gas light on the
next corner and descried a crowd of Negroes. The crowd had something unusual in its aspect. It made no effort to shuffle out of her
way but remained stolid, silent, except for another voice beside
her which said, "Better go back where you belong, lady."

She stepped off the sidewalk. Suddenly she was startled; suddenly she realized that she had blundered into something of which
she had not dreamed: hate, fear, hurt and revenge swirled silently
round about her.

But she only knew a part of what was happening. The whole
situation in the state was coming to a head, with attempts at final
and fatal understanding. Everyone was suspicious; the hoodlum who
accosted her at the head of the alley suspected the worst. He
lurched to find Scroggs. Scroggs, who not far away in conference,
was telling doubtful men what Breckinridge had proposed to him,
was startled. Was he being double-crossed as he always suspected
he might be? Perhaps the aristocrats were playing a shrewd game.
This mysterious white woman at night in the Negro district might
be a messenger or spy; might be a lady or a bitch. In any case
she was up to no good and must be caught. Or better, killed and
her death laid to the "niggers." What would quicker unite the
whites and seal the bargain? He sent armed spies gliding silently
under the cover of night in the unlit alleys of the Negro quarter. In
bitter rage he brooded.

The crowd of Negroes gathering in the alley and seeing a white
woman approaching, began to wonder if some Negro was not selling out to the whites and that here was evidence of negotiations
through which their freedom and rights were to be sold away.
When they saw the whites moving at the head of the alley they let
out a growl of distaste and hate. Mrs. Breckinridge paused and
looked either way. Something hard and cruel was afoot and she
did not quite know what to do. Then she saw a man approaching.
He was well-dressed and walked erect. Instinctively she turned
quickly toward him, assuming that he was white, and started to
speak, when she saw to her surprise that he was black. She hesitated
but a second however, and then said:

"I beg your pardon, but could you direct me to Emmanuel
Church?"

He started to brush past unceremoniously. Then he stopped, peered into her face, hesitated and without a word turned abruptly.

"This way," he said and hurriedly led her across the alley, around a corner into a wider thoroughfare and toward a large dark building. She was surprised, thinking to see a crowded, lighted edifice. She turned to ask but her guide had gone. There was a shadowed basement door before her. She groped her way to it and knocked. The door opened and a lantern was thrust into her face. There was a gasp and hurried whispering. An inner door opened and she stood before five hundred colored men, with Tom Mansart on the rostrum.

It was by no means the first time Mrs. Breckinridge had faced a colored audience. She had talked to Sunday schools and churches; to picnics and gatherings of servants. She knew their giggling, fidgeting and soft laughter; their hearty "Yaas ma'am" and "Thank you!" But this was different. Here was silence—cold, exploring silence. There was no laughter, no expectancy; rather she sensed surprise, doubt, antagonism, distrust. The silence became oppressive. She looked at Mansart uncertainly and stepped toward him. She spoke low and clear.

"I represent Colonel Breckinridge," she began; "he has been detained, but I expect him any minute. He has, meantime, authorized me to say—"

She got no further. From without two shots in quick succession rang out. Suddenly the lights of the room went out. She was unceremoniously seized and propelled along to a dark closet-like room. She turned on her captor in outraged repulsion. He was Tom Mansart.

Lighting a small candle he looked at her. "Why did you come here?" he asked. He was in deadly earnest and the sweat poured from his face.

She choked back her indignation and answered: "Colonel Breckinridge was coming to this meeting tonight, to give you his word of honor to guard your rights if you will give us your cooperation and support. I cannot imagine why he has not come—or perhaps he has come and. . . ." She paused and stared at Mansart in sudden fear—had they kidnapped her husband—or killed him?

Mansart looked at her long and hard. Then he answered slowly: "Madam, you acted very wrong. Colonel Breckinridge ain't been here. Why, I don't know. But I do know that unbeknownst you have put yourself unprotected into the middle of a race riot—

perhaps of a long death struggle. You have put a terrible weight on us. If anything should happen to you here in the Negro quarter tonight my whole race and all its friends would be held guilty. We must get you home to your friends—quick, if we can!"

"What difficulty will there be—" she began. But Mansart interrupted brusquely: "Plenty."

She bridled: "I will be judge of that."

"You will not. You'll do as I say or I'll gag, bind and carry you. Listen," he said, speaking roughly but still low-voiced, "what I'm doing is not for you, I am acting for my people. If you get hurt here tonight we would get the blame no matter who was guilty. I am going to try to save you. I don't know whether I can or not; it's a risk, a great risk. I wonder your husband didn't tell you to stay home! Hell will be loose in this city tonight. Come, and for God's sake don't act like a damned fool!"

She stared at him a long moment and then bowed her head. "I will do as you say," she said. His dead earnestness impressed and frightened her. With a body guard of two or three persons staying close, they went out into the darkness and sneaked along the alleys, turning here and there. They walked far and fast and at last in a little narrow alley came to a house, neat and alone; and after knocking and low whispers they entered the door.

Immediately she remembered the room. It was the home of Aunt Betsy which she had often visited years ago. Little had changed; there was the wide fireplace with its crimson and yellow flame; there was the old carved table and the black framed picture of Christ above. Opposite was the cavernous four-poster bed. On it lay a moaning woman and beside—yes, beside it stood the grim, silent figure of Aunt Betsy. She started toward her but the woman, giving her a grave curtsy which was both greeting and warning, waved her back. She drew back and saw Mansart and his companions listening at the door. Save the low moans of the woman, the house and street were very still. Then there came a loud and peremptory knocking at the door.

Everyone stood still and held his breath. Even the woman in the bed sighed after a paroxysm and lay exhausted as Aunt Betsy fanned her. Again the knocking, and finally Tom Mansart threw wide the door. Two white men stood there, armed with rifles. One looked straight at Mrs. Breckinridge and bowed.

"Colonel Breckinridge sent us to bring you home, Madam; he was afeared the streets might be rough."

Mrs. Breckinridge stepped forward and then stopped. "Why didn't the Colonel come himself?" she asked.

The man shifted his gun—. "He's mighty busy, Ma'am. . . ."

"That's a lie!" The heavy voice of Aunt Betsy came from the shadows. The men swore and both started to raise their guns. Tom Mansart struck one full in the face, and black arms from behind throttled the other. There was a scuffle, a rush, and three shots rang out. One man fell groaning, the other disappeared.

Mrs. Breckinridge found herself lifted, almost carried, rapidly in the darkness out through the back door, until they came to a shadowy barnlike building, and Mansart's voice whispered in her ear: "Madam, that was a trick. You must trust me. I must get you away from here and safe back to your husband. That may prove our faith in him."

He opened the door of the stable and went quickly about harnessing a horse to a light buggy. She waited, feeling soiled and disarranged. Mansart helped her into the vehicle and began driving slowly through the alleys until they approached the harbor. He paused and pointed to the left. Yonder ran the river, and beyond was her home. She started but he held her back, still pointing: "The Klan," he whispered. She saw the shadowy bedecked horsemen moving in groups and mustering in columns.

Without another word, he wheeled the horse out into the street and lashed him. They turned north instead of south toward her home, and involuntarily she gave a low cry. He drove even more swiftly, whispering, "If we went to your home we'd meet the mob. My life would be as worthless as your honor!"

She stared at him. Was this the truth or was this black man taking her out to the massed Negroes of the islands, to prison or worse? She went stiff and cold as she heard him still whispering, "I am trying to reach Race Street and then come in through King to the full-lighted center of the city. Likely there'll be no riders there and I may be able to drop you near the Court House. That's our best chance."

The horse dashed through the night. She sat back in the seat and began to recover from her panic. She said slowly but distinctly: "You must believe me when I say that the Colonel fully intended to meet you and give you the assurances you asked; neither he nor I pretend that we regard Negroes as men fit to take part in government; but we do want you to have justice, a chance to earn a decent living; and an opportunity for your children, especially for the gifted and deft."

Peering anxiously ahead and guiding the horse carefully by railroad tracks and unpaved roads he replied: "Slavery was worse, much worse than you think. I knows; I was a slave, with a master called 'good.' Negroes has more brains and can learn more easily than you think. I'm a Negro; I knows. If you and I had our way freedom would have come not by blood but by prayer. We wasn't asked. Now freedom is come; it's going to stay. What now can we do to see this happen in peace? I thought out a way and tried to get you and the Colonel to back me. He failed me. He sits tonight with the Klan."

"I do not believe it," she cried, "he meant to come; he believes as I believe!"

They had reached Race Street. He turned left cautiously and drove west more slowly. They were out in the country now and the roads were rough but they met few travellers. At long last they turned South into King Street and began to approach the city.

"There is still time," she argued, "what proof have you that all is lost?"

"The whites are set to steal the election and drive the blacks back to slavery. The blacks could fight but they got few arms, and are divided up in leadership. But they'll fight if they must. The poor whites, who ought to be with us, hate us worse than they hate the planters. And we are just as stupid and hate them. The North, torn up with panic and graft is turning back to the planter. Everything then, rests with the planters or with their leaders—the quality. If they could see straight they could meet the money-grabbers in the North with a mass of good labor, black and white. But no! They are massing the poor whites to kill the 'niggers'!"

She started to speak, then paused in perplexity. He slowed the horse to a walk. Finally, nearing the sidewalk he stopped, glanced about. No one was visible on foot and only now and then a carriage and horse passed.

"You are safe here," he said finally. "Yonder is the junction, beyond you can see the Court House. Your husband will be two blocks further."

"You want me to walk?" she asked, astonished.

"Certainly not; I wants you to take the horse and buggy and drive on. I will send for the rig tomorrow."

She stared at him. "You mean to say that you are sending me home alone in this dangerous night?"

"A white woman is safer alone than with a Negro."

She spoke angrily. "And he himself is certainly safer; but don't come if you are afraid." She reached for the reins.

He hesitated. "Naturally I am afraid," he said slowly, but he was thinking fast. The woman was without doubt straight-forward and trustworthy. If he got her safely to her husband she might yet persuade him and the planters to balk the plans of the extremists. If he deserted her she would turn against him and his plans and her husband would certainly be his enemy. She might even be killed deliberately—even here in the city,—and her murder placed at his door. On the other hand, it was dangerous to drive openly into the very center of the city tonight with a planter's wife, and into the very midst of a gathering of the Klan. Everything depended on how far he could penetrate before discovery, and how much time would elapse between discovery and actually meeting with Colonel Breckinridge.

If without mishap he could deliver Mrs. Breckinridge safe into her husband's keeping, he might even become a hero to the whites. But if his plan was intercepted and made to look like a frustrated kidnapping, he would be a corpse before his child was born; and the South would be lost to democracy. He silently took the reins again, glanced about, listened, and began to drive. Mrs. Breckinridge smiled grimly and settled back in the seat. Her panic now had fled and she was thinking clearly. It had all been a mistake. She would get Tom Mansart and her husband together and talk it all out; but she must not let Mansart leave her; it would not be safe for him.

They drove silently and at a not too rapid rate until they were opposite Market Street. Suddenly without warning two masked horsemen, with white gowns and pointed hoods, came out of the street at full gallop. They swept up, one at either side, and stared at the couple. Mansart slowed down a bit but said nothing, and Mrs. Breckinridge, lifting her chin, stared back calmly. Without a word both horsemen turned, one racing back northward, the other galloping full-tilt south. Mansart saw his one chance.

"Hold on tight," he cried, and bending forward he whipped the mare. She leaped forward and they lurched, swaying, toward St. David's Church. The horseman in front far outdistanced them and soon they were aware of the pounding hoofs of a cavalcade in the rear.

Tom lashed the horse into a gallop. Mrs. Breckinridge was

frightened, but had gained complete control. She knew just what she would do. She would find her husband at the Hall or drive home. She would explain about Mansart and his bravery. He would be protected and rewarded. Then conference with his followers would start. She thought it all out clearly.

They reached Broad Street, but a swift riding cavalcade of unmasked horsemen faced them and reined their horses to a halt so quickly that Mansart was upon them before he could halt his foaming mare. Mrs. Breckinridge saw her husband coming on a great black gelding. She called to him and fainted. She was lifted to his horse and they rode wildly home.

His fellows and the masked cavalcade did not follow Colonel Breckinridge. They turned toward the dark and heavy waters, dragging the unhitched buggy. The wind from off the bay rose and shrieked in their faces as they swept back into the sinister alleys. They dragged Tom Mansart from his buggy and threw him against his own door. He fell against it with out-stretched arms and blood-shot, staring eyes. A hundred guns thundered and lightened as a wind of lead shattered the house where his body leaned, and left it a jelly of mangled flesh, blood and bone. Three cries rent the cold night; a howl of death, the scream of birthpain, and the wail of a new-born babe.

Within, the tall black woman, looking incredibly old, never raised her head from the laboring woman who writhed on the bed. Slowly she soothed the mother, and lifted the child. She held it to her, approaching the door, and silently anointed its forehead with its father's blood. Then, stepping in the blood and entrails, she bore it wailing softly into the night.

All the long night mad men rode in darkness and darkness rode to dawn. The world began weeping and its tears blinded the stars. In the white city. homes were dark and close-shuttered. Women cowered and men fingered their guns. In the black alleys dark forms scurried north until the mass merged and a thousand Negroes hid in the wide new sanctuary of Emmanuel Church. Bishop Cain welcomed them quietly—Bishop Cain, once Congressman and editor, dark leader of the unled. A song started deep in the bowels of the men—

> *O Brethren, my way — my way's cloudy!*
> *My way — O send them angels down —*

The Bishop started to speak but another voice pealed and hearts stood still. The old woman came in, naked from neck to loin, marching with one thin arm aloft. In her vast hand lay a blood-stained child. Slowly she swayed and danced through the church. The Bishop, standing still behind the altar, saw a thousand years of the African Dance of Death gliding out of the past. Snake-wise, the throng followed the dancer, moaning to her cries:

"Curse God! Ride, Devils of Hell, with the blood-bought baby! Burn! Kill! Burn! Crawl with the Snake! Creep and Crawl! Behold the Black Flame!"

Shriek rose on shriek, with tossing hands and spitting mouths. Slower the sibyl moved, almost whispering: "His name is Manuel," she cried. "He is Called!" She disappeared into the night.

The throng sat, stood and lay prone, exhausted. The Bishop stepped before the Altar, sank slowly to his knees and said,

"Let us pray."

Chapter V

THE WORLD AND MRS. BRECKINRIDGE

For weeks Mrs. Breckinridge was severely ill. She lay almost motionless and the physician gave but faint hope. Then gradually she rallied. She began to recognize the Colonel as he came in, and to press his hand faintly. She was pleased to have Betty Lou come now and then and sit beside her. Now as the bright winter sun poured through the windows she began to be more fully aware of herself and the world. She was weak, but her mind was clearing. She was beginning to be able to separate fact and dream, to remember something of the fancies and something of the scenes that had occurred.

Today she lay quite at peace, watching the great white clouds with their mauve edges hover in the sky. The Colonel would be in soon to talk with her; and then the nurse and her daughter. With a certain reluctance she turned her mind resolutely back again toward that night—that terrible night. She was not sure just how she had gotten home, and yet she dimly remembered the wild ride on horseback. It took her back to those rides that she and the Colonel used to have in Louisiana and out toward Lake Pontchartrain, in the beautiful days of the past. Resolutely she brought her mind back and tried for some time to recall just when it was she had told the Colonel the story of Tom Mansart, and how much she had told. She must say more about it to him and be sure that he knew the whole tale.

Then her mind wandered to that old woman bringing a baby to birth—ushering him into a new world. How many babies had she brought into the world? And again she began to think of her own daughter, brought by those same black hands—of her daughter's cool and careless demeanor and her own continual wonder at just what the girl was thinking and what she was going to do. Betty Lou was 24; singular it was that she had grown so fast.

Mrs. Breckinridge's mind wandered again. She liked Mansart— that curious, tall black man who had shared with her a frightful incident in her life. In a way, and she almost smiled as she thought it, he was a great gentleman, so simple and direct, and so utterly self-sacrificing. She had been mad to drive him on in her panic and confidence. Yes, and his people were hers; they were nearer, much nearer, than most of the whites of Carolina.

She thought again of her old Louisiana home and the great family of the Du Bignons: of the legend—at which she could smile —of their Negro blood—which of course was ridiculous. And yet— it might be. She remembered that dark, angular woman who was often about her home, and her beautiful, imperious little baby, evidently a white man's child whom she brought with her. Yes, the colored people were near to her; the slaves were part of the South and could never be separated. Arrangements must be made, now that they were free. She would talk to the Colonel. And just then he came in.

He came in quietly and looked at her and was pleased when he saw the calm light of full consciousness in her eyes. She did not start to talk as she had planned but said, as she held his hands:

"Have I lain here long?"

"Six weeks," he answered.

"And the election?"

"Is over—now, now, no politics; all will be well."

"Was the General elected?"

"Yes," he said slowly. He patted her hand soothingly. "Wade Hampton is Governor of South Carolina," he asserted almost dog-matically. Then he spoke of the weather and crops, and after a few minutes started to rise. A vague unrest came into her face. She stirred a bit on the bed and gripped his hand, saying,

"Dear, I can't quite remember how much I told you that night."

He glanced at her quickly. "There, there, dear, don't talk about that."

"I know, but I must—I am sure I told you what a splendid thing, what a noble act Mansart did for me."

The Colonel arose, turned to the window and looked at his watch but he did not answer. She pulled herself a bit straighter in the bed and talked to his half-turned shoulder.

"I had no business to walk down there that night. I was upset and thought that you had been detained. I wanted to reassure the men. Then I found myself between mobs; and this black man at the risk of his own life took me through the alleys and through his own house and around—I taunted him to drive on until we came into that racing mass of men. I told you about it and gave

Mansart into your protection—I did tell you about it, didn't I? You did take him into your care?"

But just then the nurse entered with the daintily prepared lunch, and the Colonel without a further word kissed her and left the room. It was then that Clarice Breckinridge suddenly felt the shadow of so great a tragedy that she lay back upon her bed and closed her eyes.

Next morning the Colonel came in hurriedly and looked at her with searching eyes. Was it imagination that she thought she saw through her half-closed lids the ghost of fear and almost consternation in those eyes? Perhaps not; but she did not say anything. If there was anything to be said he would say it. He did talk, rapidly; unconsciously he was seeking sympathy and justification. He had not realized how much he had missed talking with her. As he talked on he almost forgot how ill she had been and still was. It was as though he were the one returning from a far country to tell her of the strange and baffling things which had happened and which had left his soul in curious indecision.

"We are in revolution," he said as he walked to and fro nervously. She was glad of his perturbation for it gave him no time to notice the despair on her face. "There are two governments in Carolina and two legislatures. No president of the United States has been elected. The election here was a nightmare; a farce; all elections are farces but this outranked them all. Charleston County never cast more than 20,000 votes; yet although three or four thousand black voters had been scared by the whites into refusing to vote and another thousand bribed to vote for Hampton, the total vote was 24,000 and the county went Republican by unprecedented majority.

"In the white counties the whites voted time and time again, and hundreds of North Carolinians and Georgians crossed the border and voted with them. In Edgefield County where there were 7,000 voters and a large black population, 9,000 votes were cast and the Democrats won by 3,000! When the returns were in, the State went Democratic because of fraud, and the electoral vote went Republican because of the Republican majority on the State Board of Canvassers. The Board was put in jail. The Republicans organized one House of Representatives, the Democrats another, and the two bodies began a wild fight for control until the United States army interfered.

"Chamberlain was inaugurated Governor December 4th, but ten days later the Supreme Court of the State, with one black justice, recognized the Democratic legislature as legal. Hampton was declared Governor; he demanded the Great Seal of the State from Chamberlain and enjoined the mulatto State Treasurer, Cardozo. The whole mess was referred to Washington and now I am urged by Hampton to go to the hearing before Congress."

He paused. She knew he half expected her to speak. She did not. She could not. There was one matter on which both knew neither could speak; both waited nervously. He began again. He wanted to tell her how the Mansart incident had changed his whole attitude and led him to acquiesce in murder and cheating without protest, but he could not do this because if what she had said about Mansart was true (and it could not, it must not be true), then he had no excuse and had been doubly wrong. He must get away—he must think. He found himself saying:

"I do not know why Hampton is so set on my going. I am no diplomat. I am disgusted at the present situation. It amazes me. Just because, as Hampton insists, I am a —" he gulped, "gentleman of the Old South, — yet I cannot see — I cannot see —"

She managed to keep the tremor out of her voice and said, as she knew he longed for her to say, "You must go; of course you must go." She knew they were both fighting for time and adjustment. Both wanted time for thought. Neither could think nor act normally now. Perhaps in time—but not now. In her heart she said *hurry, hurry, go now!* With her voice she asked:

"When will you go?"

He glanced at her and was stricken by her pallor and thinness. "But you —?"

"I shall be quite all right. I shall sit here and grow strong. When you return and all is well, we'll talk it all out." She was very, very sorry for him. He was both glad to go and reluctant. All his natural impulses were at war with each other within. He looked old, drawn, and distraught. *But he must go and go now.* She wanted to say this and scream it. But she only stroked his hand and closed her eyes.

The Colonel left next day, after solicitous arrangements for his wife's care. She lay a long week, husbanding her strength, dozing and fighting back her urge to think. She walked a little each day; first staggering from bed to chaise-longue; then crossing the room, then standing by the window and staring at the unseen sea.

Today she turned and went back and lay on her chaise-longue, facing and seeing the sea. Then resolutely she put her mind to the past. What had she told her husband that night? Had she told him anything? She remembered seeing him there as she rose and screamed, and then—nothing more. Suppose — and it was possible — that she had told him nothing; that she had had no time to talk before she fainted? In that case, how would he and the others know what her situation had been; what had happened? She and her husband had flown home in the night, where lying senseless she had known nothing. What had become of Tom Mansart? Why was her husband silent? Because of accomplishment or tragedy?

Two more long days she waited, getting stronger in body and weaker and more utterly despairing in spirit. She asked nothing of anyone, but gradually without information she knew. She knew that some way in that night of disaster she had not said to her husband what she had meant to say; she had not told him or anyone just what had occurred. She did not dare to think what had happened; yet she must know. Today as she heard the door opening she composed herself and lay back quietly with her eyes closed.

Betty Lou came in, tip-toed toward her, humming a little tune. As her mother's eyes were closed, she sampled the cosmetics on the bureau. Mrs. Breckinridge gripped herself and spoke:

"Oh, Betty Lou," she said casually. "You remember that man, Mansart, you know, the black man?"

Betty glanced at her with surprise, but went on with her puttering. "Yes?" she answered.

"What became of him?" asked Mrs. Breckinridge.

Betty Lou whirled and looked at her in surprise. "Why mother!" she said. "What could have become of him?—they lynched him on his own doorstep, of course!"

Mrs. Breckinridge said nothing; she closed her eyes and fainted. But she did it so quietly that Betty Lou thought she had dropped to sleep again, and tip-toed out of the door.

As that great black wave of faintness engulfed Mrs. Breckinridge, she hoped it might be death itself. She welcomed it. She felt that she could not just faint and wake again. So she lay half-dead, with fluttering heart. When she opened her eyes the nurse was standing over her with a puzzled look on her face.

"Are you feeling badly?" she asked.

"A little faint," Mrs. Breckinridge gasped. "No, no lunch — let me rest a while longer." And the nurse went out.

Colonel Breckinridge, riding north on the ramshackle train, brooded long. He had not wanted to go to Washington and had told Wade Hampton so repeatedly. But Hampton continued to plead:

"We are going to rule the South. Mississippi, Georgia and Alabama are safe. Louisiana and Florida will follow. Nothing can keep South Carolina out of our hands. Then our problem will be how to handle the poor whites and the Negroes. We'll bribe the poor whites with votes, a few offices and as much social equality as we must. The Negroes we'll disfranchise, and draw a legal color line which will keep them in their places. This will take some time and more killing and cheating, but finally, with the help of the North, we can settle down to civilized life again.

"If the North keeps alliance with the Negroes as it did in the war and since, we will be crushed. But we have good reason to know that already this has been stopped. The real North never liked Negroes and was not willing to attack slavery. Now that it is gone they are glad and so are we; but they no more than we want to make Negroes their equals. They want good, cheap, profitable labor and so do we.

"Our first job is to secure control of this state. I want you to go to Washington. I want the Northerners to meet and talk to a Southern gentleman. Show them that we have already regained the state. Show them how the Negroes stole and raised taxes. Get the sympathy of the reformers. Rejoice that slavery is gone forever. We propose to govern justly and within the law. We will stop high taxes and stealing. We will encourage business and agriculture. We will put the Negroes to work."

Colonel Breckinridge felt vividly his distaste for Hampton's talk. He was disgusted with the campaign. They had gained victory by lying, cheating and murder. What excuse was it that their slaves had cheated and killed in turn? What race superiority of white over black did that show? And stealing—my God, who had stolen more or gotten as much as white men whom they both knew? No! He wanted nothing more of it. He was going back to his plantation to hide and think. This had cost too much in blood and violence. It had cost much more in the honor of gentlemen.

He had left abruptly and gone home. He had gone to his wife's bedside and received the crushing blow of her story of Mansart. He was struck dumb with astonishment and horror. He had always shrunk from that grim lynching, but had never questioned its inevitability, its absolute justice. What else in God's name could he have thought?

He had wanted to come to some understanding with Mansart, but what could he think when in the night there came rushing to him a reeling wagon, his torn and disheveled wife screaming, and a Negro holding on to her in the buggy? He did not kill the Negro but he let him be killed. He thought it final justice. Now he was desperately sorry, desperately sorry and ashamed. Had he known all the circumstances he would have rescued Mansart from the mob, but at what cost? Was he in his heart glad that he had not known? What would Scroggs and his group have thought if he had kept Mansart from death? And now this white rabble which Scroggs led was and must be his allies. They must be pacified and led.

But about Mansart, there must have been some mistake; he was unconvinced. Clarice, of course, believed absolutely in Mansart's innocence, even bravery; but how was that possible? Where did Mansart find her and how? How did Scroggs and his emissaries find out? There must have been deviltry afoot of which Clarice did not dream. But he could not talk to her about it; he had to have time to think. She must have time to get strong. He had warned the household to say nothing while he—he had determined to go to Washington as Hampton urged. Who was he to have qualms and shrink from reality, if he had in truth murdered an innocent man? He had taken hurried and embarrassed leave of his wife, sure that in her weakness she noticed nothing. He had warned the nurse and maid. He had not time to find Betty Lou, but had stalked into Hampton's office and said brusquely: "I'll go."

If Hampton had been surprised he had not betrayed it. He was profuse in his thanks, prepared letters and credentials, and Colonel Breckinridge was soon on his way. His first stop was Richmond and his heart cramped at the sight of the stricken city. He had seen it last in 1850 when it was gay and proud, and he at 25 was on the way to Mardi Gras in New Orleans. There he met and married Clarice Du Bignon — brave and beautiful days.

There were on the train today several members of the Congressional committees who had been investigating conditions in the South. Some approached him and a few almost fawned on this aristocratic planter. He rebuffed them as coldly as possible without positive rudeness, but not before several had expressed their sympathy with the white South and contempt for the blacks. There was one man whom he could not shake off. They met at the stops for meals and finally on the way from Richmond to Washington sat in the same seat. The man introduced himself as a business man from Pennsylvania, now Democratic member of Congress. He persisted in talking.

"The problem of the South is not Southern, it is national. Since the war I have travelled all over the country. I think I am familiar with what most Americans think. Nobody in this country, except a few fanatics, likes Negroes or regards them as equals. Nobody wants them to vote except as a step to compel reunion. After that they expect them to be disfranchised under some form of law. What Americans want is a great united country organized so as to make this people rich and comfortable and give it leisure to broaden and cultivate the graces of higher social life."

"Indeed," retorted the Colonel, "I am glad; but they have very successfully concealed their wishes in the last twenty years."

"I do not think so. We made the mistake of war and war kills reason. But war was a mistake and we all know it. Now we are sane again and ready anew to start on a greater and wider path."

"I hope so," answered the Colonel shortly. They continued the conversation until they reached Washington and, alighting at the dirty Sixth Street station, sought their hotel. The Colonel's distaste for Washington was greater than his disappointment at Richmond. He had known it when it was a Southern City. He came back to a Northern camp filled with Yankees and Negroes. He reflected that since he was here 17 Negroes had actually sat in the halls of Congress which Jefferson Davis, John C. Calhoun and Daniel Webster had once graced. What possibly could be rebuilt upon this mire of civilization? There had been stealing in South Carolina and misrule; but here in this Den of Thieves graft, plunder and barefaced robbery had climbed up to the very presidential chair.

As the Colonel sat in the Senate gallery and saw John B. Gordon of Georgia champion the case of Wade Hampton on December 29th, and from then to January 16 when Patterson of Pennsylvania defended Chamberlain, the Colonel began to sense in the attitude of the Senate and the talk of his neighbors the change which had come to the nation. The panic of 1873, which in the South seemed but part of the war, had loomed as a revolution in the North. Here money was Power. A Democratic majority had replaced the Republican rule of Reconstruction. Twenty-three states out of thirty-five, led by New York and Tilden, now had gone Democratic. Reform was in the saddle. Grant did not dare run for a third term. Everyone said that Hayes was ready to placate the South.

Breckinridge began to see hope for the South and the nation. He wrote his wife daily and the nightmare of Mansart began to recede in importance. It was unfortunate, but it was part of world disaster. Perhaps he could make it up some way. If Mansart left children he would see that they got training as good laborers. Meantime, the greater world and a Southern future beckoned. Congress refused to interfere, and it became certain that Hayes, assured of the presidency, had given his word to recognize Hampton and withdraw troops from the South. The Colonel wrote the news to his wife and told her the day of his return. Then he went to his hotel to pack.

As he entered his private hotel suite he was surprised to find sitting there a stranger, tall and broad-shouldered, white-haired and handsome.

"Colonel," the stranger said, rising and bowing, "I humbly beg your pardon. I had to be sure of seeing you in private before you returned South. I therefore prevailed on the hotel manager to let me await you here. Permit me to introduce myself: I am Aurelius Beauregard, from the Louisiana family which you know. I have the honor of bearing a letter of introduction from your mother-in-law, Mère Du Bignon."

The Colonel, taken aback and ruffled at this intrusion on his privacy, motioned the gentleman to a seat, read the letter, and a bit stiffly shook hands. This gentleman would seem to be a person of high birth, vouched for by no less authority than Mère Du Bignon, head of the Du Bignon clan. He remembered her vividly: hook-nosed, white-haired, with an inbred air of domination. She was an aristocrat to her finger tips and a born ruler of men.

But Mr. Beauregard was speaking: "And now, Sir, may I explain the reason for this unpardonable intrusion. I am a Mason"—and he gave the Colonel the grip of one of the highest Degrees—"but more to the point now, Sir, I have the honor to be General President of the Knights of the Golden Circle." He disclosed a maltese cross surmounted by a star on the reverse of his lapel.

The Colonel stared. He remembered joining this order a decade before the war, when the "Southern Rights Club" of Charleston, to which he belonged, joined in a body. "But—" he started to say, "I thought—"

"I know, Sir, what you are thinking: that the organization had been discredited and disbanded. Discredited, it is true, by Bickley and border state folk who meant well but were common people with no idea of our high mission. Vallandingham disgraced us and made us look like a conspiracy formed to encourage deserters and saboteurs."

The Colonel said, "The organization which I joined planned to extend the South and its culture and institutions south of the

Rio Grande into Mexico and Central America and throughout the Caribbean, perhaps even to South America; and to face the traders and shopkeepers of the United States with a great civilized nation of real culture based on black slavery."

"Exactly, Sir. Our efforts, save in Texas and California, failed; we lost our forays into Central America, Cuba and San Domingo. We lost a war in this land. But we still survive, re-organized and set toward a wider, more glorious destiny than was ever dreamed of in 1855."

"But surely you do not plan to revive the mummery of secrecy and tinsel which cloaked our aims then? Slavery is gone. What is left of it to be restored, even if we had the power?"

"Sir, the deathless duty of leading to survival and power those high-born elements in the white race whose domination of world culture is the hope, and only hope, of civilization! This, Sir, is worth even a bit of ancient ceremony and — mummery, as you call it, is it not?"

"I presume so — but in my state the Ku Klux Klan and other efforts at 'white supremacy' have not impressed me. Rather the contrary."

"Precisely. That represents a degradation of our aims, or at most a passing expediency for handling ignorant and debased allies against Negroes and carpet-baggers. Believe me, all that is past or at worst will linger only as long as it takes to restore law and order and white supremacy. After that, our principles will rule the world. — But Sir, I argue too much. I am authorized to show the rescript to you for the new World Grand Castle, summoned by the Knights' Marshall, to meet beginning tomorrow and to invite and urge you to sit with us. I am humbly to ask your pardon for the unavoidable lateness of this invitation."

He unrolled and handed Colonel Breckinridge a great sheet of thick parchment, engrossed, heavy with gold and color, and adorned with seals and ribbons. The Colonel began to read, at first with doubt and suspicion, then interest and at last with amazement. If this document was genuine and its signature authentic it marked an epoch-making movement. He stared at Beauregard. "But this is unbelievable — it is astounding. How —"

"Certain gentlemen, most of whom you know personally or by reputation, will call on you today or tomorrow morning to confirm what I have said. If finally you are convinced, a carriage will be sent for you at this hotel tomorrow night. I have the honor, Sir, to be your obliged and obedient servant. Good day."

So it happened that the next day in the late afternoon Colonel Breckinridge, after telegraphing his wife, was whisked down the sweep of Pennsylvania Avenue, from the grey unfinished dome of the capitol toward the tall, thin monument of Washington; past the White House where the conqueror of Appomattox was preparing to leave the Potomac. They crossed into Virginia. It was clear and cold and a light veil of snow lay across the hills. At twilight they were at the docks of Alexandria. Silently they transferred to a dispatch boat which, making hurried departure, rushed them a hundred winding miles to the broad waters of Chesapeake Bay. They swept up beside a stately yacht in the darkness and climbed aboard.

It was a beautifully designed and lavishly furnished vessel which started on its voyage soon after the Colonel and his companions stepped aboard. They were received with quiet courtesy and the perfect punctilio that satisfied the Colonel's best traditions. A late, simple and well-appointed supper was served in his cabin with an exquisite bottle of Sauterne and hot black coffee. He slept heavily in the cold night and noted, as breakfast was brought to his bunk, that the servants were not Negroes, as he was used to, but white foreigners speaking English with an accent but perfectly trained to service.

On ascending to the salon he saw a few gentlemen, none of whom he recognized. Having his overcoat proffered by a ready servant, he went out on deck and fell in with a tall gentleman, evidently from his manner and speech an Englishman. It occurred to him that this gathering must be international, which gave him food for thought. This invitation, although couched in secrecy and all the paraphernalia of oath and grip, had attracted him because he was assured of the deep purpose and planning back of this front of pageantry and theater. They fell in step and walked in the fresh air.

"I am glad you came, Colonel Breckinridge," said the stranger, to the Colonel's surprise.

"I am afraid I do not recall—" he began, hesitating and then extending his hand.

"Of course not, Sir; we have not met. But you are well-known. My name is —" He paused a moment, — "Leicester," and then added diffidently, "Lord Leicester, if you will forgive the anachronism of a title in your free America."

The Colonel concealed his astonishment, but said courteously, "I'm afraid, my lord, that we have just had an overdose of freedom."

"Much of the world is suffering from the same malady," answered the nobleman drily. "If I mistake not, Sir, there is some kinship between our families."

The Colonel almost flushed beneath his tan, and bowed gravely. "I have heard some such legend."

"Well, Sir," continued the Englishman as they fell in step and sauntered along looking at the dark, heaving waters of the Atlantic, "I presume you agree that in this crisis of the world we need to prolong this parade and mumbo-jumbo to keep and maintain leadership. We have not yet named this culminating secret organization, but we maintain its ancient appeal as you will see. I often revolt, but when I saw Little Victoria—God save her—and the Parliament which just named her Empress of India with crown, robe and orb, — well by Jove, I said, there's something to ceremony as an arm of government. And, Sir, it is World Government that we begin to erect this week."

The Colonel was silent a moment and then spoke slowly. "I was not fully cognizant of your plans," he said, "before I came. But certainly if ever there was a time for the leadership of the forces of blood and breeding, it is now. This world is on the road to hell!"

The nobleman smiled and said, "There is no reason to despair; we are entering a new world." And he excused himself.

The Colonel looked about and saw a number of friends, persons of breeding from the old days. He talked with one who said:

"I don't understand the Yankees. I never believed before the war that the better part of them really opposed Negro slavery, and I don't believe it now. I believe they were caught in a current of fanaticism and greed they could not stem. But if once they would be sure of firm alliance with Southern gentlemen and the aristocracy of Europe, they would be as happy as we to chain the darkies to the soil like the European peasants, and erect a laboring class of whites held in the hand of a firmly rooted aristocracy like England's."

The Colonel looked up with interest. "But that would take money and power," he said.

"Good," was the answer. "They have the money and we can

have the power. We can vote the black millions even when they are free, if the North consents, and we have climate and resources."

"Yes, but which North? The small nucleus of gentlemen or the mill-owners and railway owners, the bankers? And what about the masses of white laboring riff-raff who fought and won this war?"

"This about them: They fought slavery, but they despise darkies and are as eager as we are to disfranchise them. If while they and the Southern whites are fighting 'niggers,' we are consolidating our power in the world so as to hold all labor in its tracks, we can own the world!"

A Northern merchant got into the conversation next and pointed out that the Southern poor whites would probably exact heavy toll for any alliance with the planters. The Northern whites had the whip hand, but after all they were men, and white men. So too, the poor whites had been the real victims of slavery. Give them a chance, give them education; they could be raised.

Colonel Breckinridge made no answer to this argument, but he did not believe it. On the whole it was his opinion that no persons with fantastic beliefs concerning the uplift of the lower classes, even if they were white, could be gentlemen born. There were differences, and radical differences, even among white men. Granted that alliance must come between classes so far removed as the planters and poor whites, the differences would remain.

One man, whom he could not quite place, (he sounded like a Northerner)—spoke to him vehemently and half secretly:

"I tell you, Colonel, this world is on the brink of vast change. England is going to try to be another Rome and is making America play along. If we are not careful we will all be submerged and in the end find ourselves facing Asia in the East, under Japan and China, and Africa right here in our bosom. There is no use estranging these Africans; we are going to need them."

Another broke in: "Nonsense. 'Niggers' can never amount to much."

But the first man insisted: "Don't be a fool. Darkies with education and leadership can do anything. Diamonds have been discovered in South Africa, and gold. Black fanatics are holding England today in the Sudan. Nightmares? All right. But our task is plain: treat these 'niggers' well, build up leaders among them who are our allies and will join exploiting all labor, white, yellow and black!"

Colonel Breckinridge turned away in disgust and sat down beside a calm, clean-cut New York banker, who began conversation first about his railway investments and then rather suddenly pointed out the path to follow in the North to bring Anglo-Saxon rulership of the world in the Americas, in Europe, Asia and Africa. The laborers in the United States must be controlled; the power of the corporations must be expanded.

"Disfranchisement must be enforced in the South with regard to the Negroes, but we must not try to keep them in ignorance. No such mass determination to know can be permanently dammed. But the course ought not to be Greek and Latin but guidance to intelligent workmanship. In time they may die out or they may become a good, profitable laboring class.

"But above all we must keep our eyes set on the white workers. They are uneasy, and coming under the leadership of demagogues and fanatics, might join the Negroes. There are the Irish, the Italians, the riff-raff from East Europe whom we crazily called in to do our work after the war. Naturally our democracy is not working in the North. It can't work. Our industry is in the hands of freebooters and Europe is on the edge of revolution. We have had one depression, we are going to have others. It's time for real leadership to take hold, and that leadership ought to come out of the South."

The Colonel listened, when another objected that this disfranchisement of the Negroes was not going to be so easy with the War Amendments in force. A man from New Orleans answered.

"The Supreme Court will attend to that."

"But," said the Colonel, "surely the Supreme Court is unbribable?"

"Of course," was the answer, "but all men have their price. Already we know the court stands 5 to 4 against the radical interpretation of the war amendments. Of the four, one has an ambitious son; one is a Southerner who is willing to listen; and the third would like to be president of the United States.

"Right down in New Orleans we have already rigged up cases by which, with proper decisions, the fourteenth amendment can become a bulwark of property, permitting disfranchising the Negroes and reducing them to a caste. Difficult? Of course it will be. It calls for patience, finesse, money; but it can be done. Once done and the United States will be the most powerful nation on earth. And England? Well, England will be our handmaiden—or we hers."

The morning passed in conversations like these. The Colonel

examined the participants rather carefully and at his leisure. They came from all parts of the world—from England, France, Germany, Italy and Belgium; Russia and America—North and South—Yankees and Southerners. They were, so far as his sharp eyes and sharper senses could descry, nearly all of them gentlemen, men of breeding and education, used to society, broadly schooled in modern knowledge. He could not imagine how such a body could have been assembled and where they were meeting. It argued extraordinary planning, wealth and unusual secrecy.

There came an excellent lunch out of doors, with an afternoon of equally fascinating conversation. Then followed a dinner of unexampled magnificence without vulgarity; and finally in the late afternoon they swept in sight of one of those exquisitely beautiful little islands which dot the Caribbean. Its beach was beaten gold. Immense and somber trees guarded the shores, and far above, behind, rose great, shining peaks of mountains reflecting the sun. Between the beach and the heights one descried the gleaming towers of an old castle, with battlements and waving banners. Notes from silver trumpets greeted the docking of the yacht. The Colonel was used to stately splendor. He knew something of England, France, Spain and Italy. But he had never seen anything more perfect in richness, elegance and taste than this elaborate estate.

They were welcomed to beautiful gardens bursting with flaming color, green coolness and subtle scent. An army of silent, deft white servants guided them to restful quarters, wide salons, billiard rooms and shaded seats; and served every sort of iced titillating and subtly flavored drink.

About nine at night all were asked to dress for formal dinner and the Colonel, a little nervous as he thought of his frayed dress suit, found laid out for him a new Confederate uniform, perfect in fit, with an embossed sword and a beautiful embroidered cape which he recognized as a replica of his old Golden Circle regalia. On it he saw his family's ancient coat of arms, entwined with the quarterings of the Du Bignons. He felt again that old stab of disappointment that he had no son. He wondered what Betty Lou was doing and if Clarice had received his hastily scrawled letters and his telegram. Of course it would be days before he could hear from her. But what news he would have when once again they were in touch!

At midnight they ascended a staircase that might well be compared to the Paris Grand Opera and entered a hall whose magnificence surpassed anything the Colonel had ever seen. There was marble and gold, silk and velvet. The persons present were resplendent in uniform and order. The Colonel was sure he recognized not only the insignia of the British Garter and the French Grand Cross of the Legion, but the Spanish Golden Fleece, the German Black Eagle and a score of other orders and decorations. His own grey colonel's uniform was duplicated by a half dozen other Confederate officers' and at least two Generals' uniforms in blue. Many were in civilian evening dress.

There was opening ceremony and fanfare of trumpets, and then almost suddenly a cold, business simplicity took charge and a conference began which Colonel Breckinridge never forgot to his dying day. He did not remember nor try to remember speakers nor sequence, but the clear thread of argument, fact and conclusion he never forgot:

We face a world crisis. Unexpectedly in the Southern United States there has come the violent overthrow of a social system and half-barbarous blacks are being put in control of white civilization. Property has been destroyed and confiscated and re-distributed. If this succeeds the world is upside down. In England the half-educated laboring class led by demagogues is getting votes and seeking control of government. This gang stopped England from saving the South, and if uncurbed will break up the British Empire.

In France, a second peasant parvenu has run amok, but has been overthrown by Germany, leaving France facing social revolution. In Germany, a strong hereditary aristocracy has arisen to rule but faces socialism, disguised as democracy. Open and underground anarchy threatens ancient Imperial Russia, while new Italian monarchy reels and staggers before radicalism and religious feud.

Yet at just this time a mighty Europe, under guidance of its inborn superior talent, is arming itself for world conquest; it has unparalleled technique for manufacture and commerce. It has conquered and held the hundred millions of Asia. It had just bared and marked for division the undreamed of riches of Africa.

The critical year was 1870. France was defeated at Sedan; the Suez Canal was near-completed. Europe was looking toward the tropics for raw materials for her factories. International finance was beginning and the corporation had begun its fateful role. Gold and diamonds had been discovered in South Africa. Paul Kruger was 45.

Europe had been depending on the Southern states of America to complete the conquest of the Caribbean, where half-free and bloody-minded Negroes had ruined the Sugar Empire; and South America where Latins, Indians and Negroes were trying to imitate European civilization. Here it was that the Northern United States, misled by fanatics, overthrew Southern economy, freed the contented slaves and started Hell on earth. What to do? To your Tents, O Israel! The battle is not lost. It cannot be lost as long as white Nordics live.

This is our Program:
1. Show Northern leaders the truth about the world.
2. Beat the Negroes back to their kennels.
3. Cajole and control white labor.
4. Consolidate capital into imperial control of the world; guide world trade and monopolize gold and credit.

At the closing session a youngish man, blonde, slim and straight, in a uniform resplendent with orders, arose to nominate a World Commander of the new international order. All bent forward to hear some exalted name, perhaps even that of the German Emperor who had just risen amid the smoke of Sedan to triumph over France. Or his mighty Chancellor, Prince Bismarck. But the name presented was unknown to the Colonel: Cecil Rhodes.

Others too, were mystified and a wave of whispers circled. But the Prussian major spoke impressively in his clipped Oxford English:

"Gentlemen! My cousin, the Princess Radziwill, has just arrived in America bearing the consent of Cecil Rhodes to accept for him the honor which I trust we are about to confer. My cousin, perhaps the most beautiful woman in Europe, certainly the wisest, has known this man some time. To some of you his name is still strange. He is a young Englishman of but twenty-three years of age but already a millionaire and coming master of Africa. I met him first at Oxford three years ago. Together we heard Ruskin point out the destiny of England. I can see the high gothic curving of that ancient hall, aspiring upward, and the figure of the Prophet, austere and inspired:

" 'You youth of England can make your country again a royal throne of kings; a sceptered isle for all the world, a source of light, a center of peace.'

"Rhodes was tremendously moved as were all of us, even a foreign visitor like myself. We talked much thereafter. Rhodes wants a giant super-government under England and America, with a federal parliament, recruited from the elite of the world; a managerial revolution guided by a giant secret society of financiers. He thinks of Loyola's jesuits as a type to follow. His consent to head us is of tremendous significance. We must make the offer!

"If only he lives to realize his dream! You know he has been tuberculous for years—that was the reason which sent him to the high plateau of South Africa; but my cousin will nurse him back to health once they are married. England is behind him. Her control of Egypt approaches completion. We Germans have entrusted little Belgium with the vast valley of the Congo to hold for us in trust for a season. Gentlemen! The Star of the White Race rises, never to set!"

The election of Rhodes was rushed forward almost too precipitously for Colonel Breckinridge and many others. It smacked of deliberate prearrangement. But of course the Colonel knew that all this had to be planned ahead. So the vote went through.

All these matters had taken long hours of debate, fact-finding, comparison and decision. But the meeting was admirably organized. Experts were there. Colonel Breckinridge especially remembered that dark, keen-faced explorer just back from a death-facing trip across Africa—his picture of resources, methods and plans already afoot. The calm, cool grip of British aristocracy on the world was succinctly shown; and methods of combating socialism and anarchism and the communism of Marx; and ways of appeasing Italy in Africa and Germany in South America. General Hampton himself had sent a written outline of how the Negroes had been put in their places in the southern South.

Thus Cecil Rhodes became Grand Commander, although many, like the Colonel, were in doubt over the choice. But most of his confreres seemed wildly delighted. One young officer, evidently a little intoxicated with champagne, took the Colonel's arm as they ascended to bed.

"You should see him, Sir! Just picture him—'high on a throne of royal state, which far outshines the wealth of Ormus or of India —or where the gorgeous East with richest hand showers on her kings barbaric pearl and gold—.'" He hiccoughed and paused. The Colonel added thoughtfully: "Satan, exalted sat!"

The young man straightened, scowled and smiled. "Ha, ha," he laughed, "so Kruger says. What matter, God or Devil! We are no longer children; we're done with fairy tales. All is well so long as the White Man rules." Curiously, the Colonel did not wholly agree.

After three days they all sailed away at night so that none or few knew where they had been. Colonel Breckinridge could almost have persuaded himself that he had passed through some fantastic dream, had not the clear program and results been burned so vividly on his mind. He telegraphed his wife again, naming the day of his arrival. He hurried South by every means of conveyance, missing much of his mail on the way. He landed in Charleston late at night and rushed home by rickety, rolling cab.

Clarice Breckinridge had read his letters in mounting consternation. By now, through old newspapers and chance words, she knew the whole story of Manuel Mansart. She was still weak, but better in body and sicker in soul. After long, long days of brooding she had taken to pacing her room more and more restlessly. She kept whispering to herself—"There is blood upon my hands. I am guilty of murder of a good man who gave his life for me." She could not bear it. She did not for a moment blame her husband. "He did what he did for me; he was a Knight of derring-do for his lady, the greatest deed a man can perform for his woman. Yet I cannot face him again."

At last came the letter announcing his home-coming, then the telegram like a reprieve; finally the last telegram setting day and hour. She drew her cloak of silk and fur about her and stepped quietly into the hall. A moment she listened, moving slowly to the balcony and looking down on the carriages and prancing horses amid the foliage. The whole house was sunk in the stillness of mid-afternoon siesta. She began climbing slowly to the third story, above the great carved pillars of the porch with their white Doric capitals. She rested a moment and then climbed more slowly for she was desperately weak, until at last she stood upon the topmost balcony and the city lay before her.

Yonder was King Street, the beginning of her world, her lost world. They who had much to lose had nearly lost all; but what of them who had nothing to lose—of a man like Mansart? A man who owned scarcely himself and then lost all he hoped to have; how can one measure such emptiness, such death of all hope; and then Death itself—cruel, terrible, bloody? She could almost see yonder the old slave mart in Chalmers Street, off Meeting-House, hiding like a foul wraith. Everywhere the ghosts of Africa greeted her. Yonder behind, the cupola of St. Michaels reared defiantly its pale and four-tiered head. She remembered how the buggy swerved on two wheels to fly by it and never succeeded.

She repeated: "And the slave that saved St. Michaels. . . ." Slowly she turned and faced the eternal sea, the old and ever-lasting sea. In front, frowning over the bay, gloomed the long, low bastion of Fort Sumter with its ten holes of death. It seemed now ages ago that she had prayed and sobbed, bowed in grief, before this dark symbol of the beginning of war. Out beyond Fort Sumter lay Moultrie; and then there to the right lay Nothing, not even the hill which Fort Wagner once crowned. But ghosts still paraded above it, and beneath the ghosts lay a pale young Yankee, "buried beneath his 'niggers.' "

She lifted her hands and saluted heaven and all its forts. She threw aside her costly cloak and leaned far out over the balustrade. There was level ground about the basement, covered with hard Belgian blocks and embroidered with foliage and flowers. The early lilies leaned pale faces toward her; the brilliance of the azaleas floated up like a veil. The great black earth, like a waiting mother lifted its loving arms. And Clarice Du Bignon leaned far out and dropped into the areaway sixty feet below.

Chapter VI

THE MARRIAGE OF BETTY LOU

Colonel Breckinridge was playing solitaire, sitting in the parlor of his dilapidated plantation home on the banks of the Savannah, half-way between Augusta and the sea. The plantation whither he had fled was old and neglected although there were still remains of a sturdy and even beautiful Big House. But it was run down; its floors sagged, some windows were broken, there was no furnace and the plumbing was all out of gear. He huddled there and thought of the world. With his hands he was leading the cards slowly; but with his mind he was laying his life before him and trying to scrutinize its trends and meaning. The two activities merged queerly.

He played the king of clubs and stared at it. Clubs—force, power, murder! That was it; that was the way he and his friends had tried to right the world. What had they gained or lost? He laid the six other cards face down and then turned the ten of hearts. Yes—that was it—hearts, love, had been reddened by war and were gone— dead.

He had failed in almost everything, but how and why? What had been wrong with him? Surely he had meant well, he had tried to hold high the ideals of his nation and his clan. The world said, and he was silent, that his wife had accidentally fallen from that roof. But he knew better; she had left him a letter and told him simply and lovingly why she had taken her own life. She laid no blame upon him. She put it all upon herself. But he knew that that was not true.

Their life together as man and wife had not been romantic and exciting, but in some way it had been more than that. There was no great sexual attraction for either of them. There was little of embracing and kissing, but there was friendship: a calm, thorough, basic friendship and understanding which had seldom been disturbed. She knew what he was thinking and what his fundamental principles of life were. She knew, indeed, often better than he did. And he understood her, her passive enjoyment of life, her love of flowers, her friendships and reticences.

Perhaps their greatest lack of understanding was in the case of Betty Lou. Of course, he had wanted a son, and perhaps she, too. But in the case of this daughter he, without conscious thought, simply abandoned her whole training to her mother and at times almost forgot her existence. The mother, on the other hand, was timid in the presence of her daughter. She realized vividly that this was another soul, another personage; she did not want to command and rule her, she wanted gradually to gain her friendship. Perhaps, if everything had gone normally, this would have happened, but in the upturn and revolution of war and Reconstruction, mother and daughter seemed to fare even further apart than before.

He fingered his cards and turned the queen of diamonds; he thought of his impending bankruptcy lurking in the ruins of Reconstruction; he must look into his planting and see what he could retrieve. Then came the ace of spades, and he shrank from the thought of black folk digging, toiling, loafing and laughing, crying and dying. Was it really his fault that Mansart was murdered horribly? How could he have acted differently, knowing what little he did? What sort of world was this that sends its puppets blind and groping for a light which does not exist? What was the place of Negroes in the world and what was his relation to them?

Clubs again—a nine, and hearts—the little deuce, fading away; and the king of diamonds. His mind moved superstitiously. Suppose by some miracle he became rich in the phantasmagoria of national revolution—what good, what end? He laid the queen on the king, the nine on the ten; he drew three cards and placed a knave, as was always true in this mad world; and then the black ace loomed alone above the whole array. He scattered the cards angrily. That was it—that was the Fate.

All this Colonel Breckinridge was thinking out as he sat in the old plantation home. He had abandoned the town house to a couple of servants and expected that Betty Lou would return there from New Orleans. They had both gone to New Orleans to the funeral. It was, to the Colonel, a terrible ordeal. Many people liked New Orleans, but he hated it. It was to his mind dirty and coarse. Naturally, back of the iron grilled homes were interesting and well-bred people; there was delicious cooking, there was a certain fineness to life, together with meanness and vulgarity.

But this trip to his wife's funeral tore his entrails—there were long Catholic services for his wife, who had never given up her religion although it did not fill much of her life. They buried her in the great family mausoleum. standing high above the swampy grounds of the cemetery alone, superb and terrible. He had turned immediately toward the home trip.

Mère Du Bignon had of course talked to him on every occasion about property, a subject about which he never knew anything. Then she brought up again the matter which seemed to him indelicate, of certain black Du Bignons, branches of the family with colored blood, whom he would have certainly preferred to forget. Colonel Breckinridge said flatly that he was not interested. This brought coolness between them, and after a last ceremonious dinner he slipped away with a promise to visit New Orleans again soon, a promise which purposely he never kept. Betty Lou wanted to stay on, and indifferently he consented.

Week after week, month after month, he sat and brooded until Winter burst into Spring and Spring bloomed into mid-Summer. He received no visitors. He read no papers. He did not even open his mail. Only briefly and brusquely he spoke to Sanford, his colored foreman, and signed now and then checks and papers; but he allowed no explanations and answered few questions. When his bankers called and almost peremptorily demanded audience, he would not receive them. It was, he knew, the old question of debt. Well then, let them foreclose, what did he care!

He knew where, tripping through the woods in mud, rain or shine, followed by his two dogs, there could be found a great bluff above the brown river where someday, when he had courage, he was going to drop into nothingness. Meantime he shuffled, again and again, the cards of his life. He remembered the astonishing meeting in the Atlantic Ocean, but he began to question it. Was it so certain that the white world was going to rule everything? Might it not happen that they would meet increasingly bitter opposition? Or was it not possible that falling out among themselves, (for after all, what did they have in common but greed and delusions of grandeur?)—suppose that falling out among themselves they should commit suicide and leave the world to black, yellow and brown? He did not know! He did not care.

It all seemed curiously petty, but he could not drag himself away from this thought of the colored people, of Mansart, of the fight in South Carolina. What was going to be the end? Was he so sure as he used to be that Negroes were all fools and apes? There again, perhaps they were the real men of the world. Perhaps they had grasped something that he in his aristocratic assumptions had missed. And too, how far was there anything real to all this pretense at aristocracy?

There was a curious old uncle, usually drunk, whom his father
hated with perfect hatred because he represented the family as well
as anybody else. His foreman was this man's son, as everybody
knew and nobody mentioned. What was all this pretense of descent
from English nobility except payment to impudent Northern
shysters who manufactured coats of arms? And so far as that was
concerned, might there not be mulattoes in Carolina descended as
directly from Charlemagne as any Breckinridge? Of course, he repeated to himself, this was all nonsense, this was all mixed up.
But the point was, was there any chance of straightening the thing
out? Was there any line of thought and action that was going to
lead somewhere?

He could not forget what a generation of lying, stealing and
cheating had done to the gentlemen of South Carolina; had done
to him. It had left an ineffaceable scar. He saw it; he felt it. And
more: out of the state had been driven by death and migration
thousands of Negroes and mulattoes. Had this been gain or irrep-
arable loss? How much had black blood and black ways and black
music contributed to this state and its civilization? Perhaps only
a little, perhaps the major part of all that made the state. At
any rate this source of human development had left in immense
numbers, and behind its going lay a void. He knew it. He could
not forget it.

At first he could not sleep; he tossed and worried and muttered
all night. He was sure he was going insane. And then at last, in the
dull deep quiet of the woods of the plantation, with the voice of
birds and the talking of his dogs, at last he began to sleep—long,
heavy, dreamless drafts of perfect unconsciousness. He ate regularly, probably because the simple meals with plenty of good meat
and fresh vegetables were regularly prepared by his quiet housekeeper. He began gradually to feel himself alive again, his brain
functioning and stronger; and one day coming downstairs he turned
toward the library, dusted off the papers and looked at the mail.

It was by sheer accident that he took up that letter first. That
astonishing letter dated ten days ago from old Dr. Baldwin. He
opened it and read it; sat down and stared for a long space un-
comprehendingly. He had forgotten, he had completely forgotten
his daughter. It was not unnatural. He was not used to seeing her
around. His wife had always attended to her and her wants. Even
at home he saw her comparatively seldom. She did not come regularly to meals,—never to breakfast, and only now and then to dinner. He paid her bills without question and her mother gave her

such money as she needed. There was really no nexus between father and daughter. And after leaving her there in New Orleans, it was true that in the overwhelming impact of his grief and despair he had completely forgotten that she existed.

Against this background the letter before him came like a thunderclap, announcing simply that old Dr. Baldwin had married Betty Lou. He wanted to come and explain about it and have announcements sent out. The Colonel was first astounded and then furious. He had never thought that Baldwin knew there were such things as women in the world; he had never evidenced interest in them; naturally there were none in his school.

As for Betty Lou, her father knew nothing about her. He let her go the usual way—that of well-bred young white women of the pre-war South. She ought to have been presented to society some time ago; it had been delayed by post-war turmoil. He remembered with a start that Betty Lou was nearly 25. She should have been married long before this. He should have thought of it. His wife had probably thought of it. But she had not mentioned it, —or had she? He had assumed that Betty Lou was back in Charleston and that her short and sketchy letters lay in his unread mail. Money she could always get from Sanford. How on earth did she make up her mind to marry this old man, who was at least twice her age, had no property, and did not really belong in aristocratic society? What had happened?

As a matter of fact, old Dr. Baldwin was as surprised at his marriage as Colonel Breckinridge. He was sitting rather late one rainy night, considering a proposal that he should head the University of Georgia, which he had once attended and where for a time he had taught. It was not in itself a very attractive offer; the school was old but not popular, and poorly supported by the state. Its buildings were falling down; the salary offered was hardly enough to live on. And yet Dr. Baldwin was convinced that a new era was coming to the South and the nation. Here might be the place, then, for his leadership toward a New South. And then the doorbell rang.

His housekeeper had gone for the night to her cottage at the rear. He went to the door himself and there stood Betty Lou Breckinridge—bedraggled, drawn, ill. He had not seen her for a long time; they used to be rather pals in the past when he visited her father's house. He always had a joke for her as a child, and a book. He told her stories, and their friendship, although a bit superficial, was real. She always had great respect for his learning but never forgot that he did not belong to her class. He ushered her hurriedly into the house and had her remove her coat, dress and shoes. He covered her with blankets and made her sit before the blazing fireplace. Then she told her extraordinary story.

She spoke dully, without animation or apparent interest. She was exhausted and hopeless. The stay in New Orleans had not been pleasant; there was the horrible funeral, the gloom and black clothes, and the mother lying stiff, still, and as her daughter suspected, happy. And then that terrible old woman, Mère Du Bignon —vast, tall and domineering, with her white hair, dark skin and black moustache; with her frightful eyes and heavy voice.

Betty Lou avoided her as much as possible; but she hated the thought of returning to Charleston and began to go out with the crowd of young people that swarmed about the big house. There were people of her class together with others such as she had never met before: bold men from whom she shrank; and haughty women who ignored her. But they did all seem to be having a good time. They threw themselves into life with terrible zest. They danced and drank and went about without chaperons. It was on one of these excursions that she met Him.

She did not know his age; she never did. He might have been young, he might have been middle-aged. His face was dead white and strongly carven. His hair was dead black and flowed down like a mane. He loved to toss it here and there. He was thin, not tall, but all grace and rhythm; at the same time arrogant with absolute self-possession. His every movement was poetry. From the time he first saw her he simply took possession of her. It seemed to her as though he were always looking right through her; that she was naked, without clothes and with no privacy even for her soul.

He danced with her and held her more closely than any man ever dared to; and yet she did not try to extricate herself from his physical strength or from the fiery spiritual lure which he exercised over her. He seemed to assume always that he knew her every secret thought, and pretty soon they were inseparable. Mère Du Bignon looked at him with a certain distaste when she saw him at all, and once threw a word of warning at Betty Lou, but Betty Lou could not hear it.

After her father had gone back to Charleston and characteristically forgotten to leave her any money, although of course she could have had it from her grandmother or from a letter—suddenly this man made the proposal:

"Honey child, let's take the boat for St. Louis," he said, "I have cabins for tonight."

She stared at him, but knew immediately that she would go. She could not resist. After all, this was a break in the boredom, the utter monotony of life. She was going to see the world, she was going to know, perhaps, what this thing called Love meant. And so with faint hesitation and almost no baggage, she tossed her old life lightly away and found herself on that great boat filled with crowding, crying, laughing people, on the broad waters of what seemed a little ocean, "Old Man River," called the Mississippi.

He was to marry her, of course, but he didn't. He didn't even mention it once they were aboard; he simply possessed her. Sometimes he made romantic love, but mostly he raped her in drunken frenzy. He disarranged her clothes at any hour, laughed and sneered at her modesty, and told her dirty stories. He read nothing, did nothing, and thought of nothing but women, horses and gambling.

Gambling was his life's real occupation. He loved it with perfect fascination. It began every night after dinner and lasted until early morning. Sometimes he came down to the cabin and threw thousands of dollars on the floor, the bed and the table. Sometimes he came, drawn and angry, apparently without a single cent. They disembarked in St. Louis and went to a flamboyant hotel, occupying a regal suite. There his luck at the gaming table seemed to flourish. He bought her jewels and dressed her in magnificent but gaudy clothes.

On the one hand he exhibited her; and on the other hand he guarded her like an ogre, as though he was suspicious of her every glance and movement. She waited, in proud fury and hesitation, for him to mention again the marriage ceremony. She even felt the first stirring of a baby within her, and then it happened. He came home one night with a knife hole in his breast; he lingered white and still, gasped at last and whispered:

"Bring a priest. We must be married; I am going."

The priest came, but before he entered the door the man was dead. What else should she do? She was in panic. She searched his pockets and found nothing. She went out and sold her jewels. She did not stop to pay her hotel bill or get her clothes, but boarded a train to Memphis; changed trains, and without sleep or bath hurried on toward Charleston. Then she became frightened, stopped at Augusta and took refuge with old Dr. Baldwin. She looked to the old man like a scared, sick and bewildered child.

"I came to you. I did not know what else to do, I did not know where to go. I could not return to New Orleans and that awful grandmother. She would have blasted me with disdainful words. I could not go to my father; I do not know how to talk to him, he was always a stranger to me. I could not bear the thought of his utter inability to comprehend what I had done; that a Breckinridge, and a Southern lady, should have stooped and for a moment been tempted by so sordid a situation. I came to you, then, to ask advice, to tell me where I can hide; and how in some way—any way,—I can work and make a living for myself and for—anyone else that I may have to support."

Dr. Baldwin had been thinking far ahead while she was talking. The problem before him was pretty difficult, but nevertheless he never hesitated. He said, with an air as near lightness as he could assume:

"I am afraid there is only one thing for you to do, my dear, and that is to marry me."

She stared at him in utter astonishment. Such an idea had never entered her head. She could not for a moment comprehend it. Marry this old man, this companion of her father's! How could he even think of such a thing? Then—there darted into her head the hard logic of the thought. With him she would be safe; she would be at peace. Then her fears started again: But the child—Good Heavens!—the child! The same thought was in his mind: How could he hold his position if he married a girl half of his age and became father of a child a few months later? They would send him packing from Augusta with a sneer and a growl.

And how could he after that make a living? If he accepted the call to the University of Georgia he might outrun and outlive evil gossip and start again. Well, he must try it. He could teach, he might write; he was physically strong and if compelled, could farm. After all, there was no question, he had to do this. It was the kind of call that a gentleman responded to. He thought of the words rather cynically. He had never called himself a "gentleman," and certainly no one had regarded him as belonging to the upper class. His people had been poor and insignificant so far as he knew anything about them, and he knew very little. But he had certain ideas of life and obligation and here was a case where he must be Knight-Errant.

"We will get married," he said. "That settles it. Of course I must let your father know, but not everything; only as much as is necessary. We will say nothing about a child. We will meet that bridge when we come to it."

Betty Lou said nothing more. There was nothing to be said. She simply accepted what was offered, and after the short private marriage ceremony, occupied her room upstairs where she lay and slept and slept. It seemed to her as though she would never get enough sleep. And one afternoon in early Fall Dr. Baldwin got into his buggy and rode 40 miles away. He crossed the broad river, turned north and slowly came to the plantation of his life-long friend, Colonel Breckinridge. He hated to meet him; it was a hard job. He climbed rather clumsily down from the buggy and rang the doorbell.

Distraught and bewildered, Colonel Breckinridge had mechanically laid aside this astonishing letter and began to open the rest of his mail. There were a number of letters from his bankers. He might as well face the truth—ruin was probably staring at him from all sides. He opened letter after letter, and read with mounting astonishment. His plantations, save this home place which he had not allowed to be touched, were unusually successful. His crops had been selling at high prices. Instead of debt and deficit he had a large cash balance in the bank. In addition to that, his railway investments which he had long since written off as absolute loss, had become of great and increasing value. Sanford, his colored foreman, with the written consent which the Colonel had not realized he was giving nor paid any attention to, had sold most of the stock at a high price, and as a result Colonel Breckinridge was a rich man, worth at least a hundred thousand dollars.

He stared at the letters in utter astonishment, and read only half comprehendingly the strong advice of his bankers that he get rid of his colored foreman and stop placing so much confidence and discretion in his hands. The mulatto was bound to steal at last, and more than that, it made a bad example to have this fellow with so much power over so great a fortune. Colonel Breckinridge threw this letter on the floor and snapped:

"I'll be damned if I'll dismiss him. He'll stay as long as he wants to."

Just here the doorbell rang, and looking out he descried old Dr. Baldwin climbing heavily out of his buggy. He felt affronted. Then he remembered that all of ten days had passed since Baldwin had written, and he had not read his letter until today, much less answered it. After all, courtesy among gentlemen demanded something. He arose and, waving the maid aside, opened the door.

Old Dr. Baldwin stood there. They looked at each other with

embarrassment, concealed with courteous bows. Neither knew just how to begin; both the weather and the crops as topics were not available. The Colonel thought he was looking upon a lecherous old man who in his age had succumbed to the temptation of sex and deserved a thrashing if not worse. He simply could not realize how it was possible that a scholar and a philospher could act in such a manner. Nevertheless he fell back into his armor of meticulous courtesy. He waved his guest in and to a seat. He should at least be heard.

Dr. Baldwin looked upon a man who had been through the fires of hell; who had lost a wife by suicide and a daughter by abduction; although this latter he did not yet know and Dr. Baldwin could not tell him. He could not explain what had happened. He must let the Colonel go on believing what he evidently was believing, that in his old age Dr. Baldwin had become a fool or something worse. In the end, common sense prevailed. They were old friends and shared a mutual cultural pattern.

The meeting and explanation proved easier than either anticipated. First of all, the Colonel was acutely conscious that he was rich and Betty Lou need not suffer from want or live on Baldwin's meager income. Crazy as the situation seemed, perhaps after all she would be safer with this solid old scoundrel than with some harum-scarum youngster. How the liaison came about he was not interested in asking, and Dr. Baldwin was not telling the whole story. The old man was so relieved at being even admitted that he had to repress a feeling almost of exultation at the way in which this tragedy was dissolving into the possibility of something like understandnig.

Then the thought of the child dropped on him like a thud. If it were born in the next few months the Colonel would know that Dr. Baldwin could not be its father. How in God's name could this be explained to the Colonel? The Colonel knew perfectly well that Betty Lou and Dr. Baldwin had never been closely associated. His suspicions would be aroused and the whole sordid story would have to be told bluntly or the matter left as a festering sore. Or worse, the Colonel might suspect him of planned seduction. But, thought Dr. Baldwin philosophically, "Sufficient unto the day is the evil thereof!"

He leaned back and began to talk. They talked at length on various topics and then on what the world was doing and whither it was going. Dr. Baldwin was astonished at what the Colonel did not know, and the Colonel began to open his eyes on the world again. They parted in recovered, even if slightly stilted friendship. The Colonel would send out wedding announcement cards.

Then, to Dr. Baldwin's utter surprise, his housekeeper announced on his arrival home that she was leaving. The woman had been with him now about a year and given unprecedented satisfaction. He noticed little about her personally. Her name was Mirandy—he never asked her last name. She brought with her a little baby, probably, he complacently assumed, a stray brat, after the fashion of Negroes. She occupied the little cabin in his back yard.

Tom Mansart's wife had left Charleston after the lynching and had come to Augusta, where she found work as housekeeper for old Dr. Baldwin. She proved a very excellent housekeeper, quiet and methodical. At first he had objected to the baby, but it was either the baby or another housekeeper; so the baby was installed and to his satisfaction proved quiet and well-behaved.

The important fact was that the house took on new efficiency. It was clean and quiet; the food was, so far as the Doctor noticed, excellent and well-cooked, and his favorite dishes appeared in perfect flavor. The woman moved about the house like a quiet ghost. The few callers and guests were so well served and attended to that they noticed nothing at first and then later inquired whence he had obtained this paragon, and tried to hire her themselves. She seldom spoke, never gossiped. The baby was black, beautiful and shy. He cried very little and was never in the way.

It was a perfect household for a teacher, and Dr. Baldwin sighed with relief as he remembered the slatternly, dirty cooks and maids of the past, some of whom he had "owned." Now, transient washerwomen never intruded. The white, clean clothes emerged magically out of that cabin in the yard. Men cut and raked the lawn when it was needed; even white tradesmen acquired new promptness and care.

But when his new wife appeared Dr. Baldwin was immediately aware that his housekeeper did not like Betty Lou. She stared at her and said nothing. Later she announced that she was leaving "next month." Dr. Baldwin was aghast. He offered her more money. She refused flatly. He begged her to stay. She simply walked to her cabin.

Then Betty Lou, aroused from her resting and her listless indifference at the mere thought of taking charge of a house and of having someone new in her rooms to stare at her, hurried to the cabin and faced the woman with tears in her eyes.

"Why?" she began, and then the woman faced her and told her. "Because your father killed my husband!"

Betty Lou sat down heavily and stared. This was Tom Mansart's widow. Yonder played his child, and in Charleston lived Aunt Betsy who knew all about babies. This woman must stay; that mystical midwife and nurse must come, no matter what the cost. She crouched on the floor and opened her heart to the dark maid in utter abasement, so that the child left his play, crept to the door and stared. Yet this would all have been in vain but for one thing, and that was that for months Mirandy had been trying to get in touch with her mother and bring her to Augusta. If she came now on the plea of this wretched girl, they could all soon leave for Atlanta where Manuel must be educated.

Next day, despite the pleas of Dr. Baldwin, and with all the money she could find in her pocket, Betty Lou went to Charleston. What was said and done on that trip no one ever knew. But the next week Aunt Betsy appeared in the cabin behind Dr. Baldwin's house. Tall, black, spotless and imperturbable, she presented herself to the old man and briefly announced that she would nurse Miss Betty Lou, who was far from well, and that her daughter would stay until the mistress was recovered.

A month passed. Then suddenly, overnight, Betty Lou fell severely ill. Mirandy was called. She looked at Betty and without a word went and fetched her mother. Dr. Baldwin started up to bring a white physician, but Aunt Betsy looked at him and said briefly,

"Better not!"

So Betty Lou had a miscarriage, which passed among Dr. Baldwin's friends as a severe attack of malaria, always so widespread about the Savannah valley. The old woman waited on her with unflinching care and perfect method. Thus the greatest fear that had beset this queer marriage passed; and for a time no further word was said concerning the leaving of the housekeeper. There was no show of affection between Betty and the black women. They kept severely to their places, and after some ineffective efforts to show her thanks and appreciation, which elicited not the slightest response but no apparent resentment, the household resumed its quiet, efficient way with the new wife who had no wish to interfere with its running. Yet Dr. Baldwin felt the truce was armed. There was some element here that he did not understand and soon ceased trying.

When in the Spring of 1880 he finally accepted the call to the

University of Georgia at Athens, he half feared another revolt of his housekeeper. But after careful inquiry about the colored schools near there, and especially about the school in nearby Atlanta impudently called "Atlanta University," she quietly consented to go, and Dr. Baldwin realized that she was thinking of the education of that black child, which struck him as funny. How much better the lower classes would be if they were educated for their place in life!

Atlanta, too, was in Dr. Baldwin's mind when he consented to go to the University of Georgia at Athens. The university was in a bad way; its buildings were old and falling to pieces; its students were dwindling in number; the alumni were indifferent, and many of them insisted that the institution should be moved to the young, growing city of Atlanta where it might get from private sources money which the state did not and insisted it could not furnish.

Dr. Baldwin was not at all convinced that Atlanta was the place for a real university. He loved the old exclusiveness of Athens and was intrigued by a vision of scholarship and culture hidden away among old trees and green fields, without the money-grubbing of Atlanta. Nevertheless he promised the alumni to look into a move to Atlanta, to get acquainted with some of its influential people, and in fact carefully to give consideration to an eventual removal. Then, too—although he naturally dropped no hint of this—he wanted to see at first hand one of these Negro colleges of which he had heard, and judge how far they were real institutions of learning, with pupils capable of even the beginnings of scholarship. In his own mind much depended on the answer to this question as to whether he would consent to remove his college to this field.

Under other circumstances Colonel Breckinridge would have resented the removal of his daughter from Augusta. Athens and Atlanta looked toward the Wild West; Atlanta was on that ridge of hills that separated the culture of the Coast from the western wilderness of the Mississippi. But finally he concluded that under the circumstances it was just as well. It removed his daughter from the gossip of Charleston, and perhaps near this crude, new, bustling town she would find some comfort and even satisfaction.

He had planned to go and see her in Augusta, but put it off because of reluctance at facing her and also because of new plans for himself. He had not yet got used to his new wealth and the freedom of no longer having to worry about debts or expenses.

He sent his daughter and old Dr. Baldwin a check for ten thousand dollars and drew his will so as to make them secure. It would have been so different if Betty Lou had married a young man and he could have expected grandchildren!

He thought of rebuilding the plantation mansion to something like his old and stately home. But he was continually worried by the attitude of the people in Charleston and round about. They not only gossiped about Betty Lou but they more and more resented his colored steward. They kept advising that a white man be put in general control. They began to visit him and tried to make him suspicious of the colored man's honesty; and they went even further to threaten Sanford! They seemed to forget or never to have known that before the war colored stewards often ran estates. The Colonel declared that he would choose his own servants! But at last there came a note from the steward himself which could not be ignored.

"Tell Sanford to come here," he ordered.

Sanford came. He was a tall, thin, slow man with an expressionless face. His skin was warm yellow and his hair grey. The Colonel looked at him curiously, as though seeing him for the first time, which was not far from true. Here was an honest man. Had he wished he could have stolen thousands and disappeared. The bankers had been frantic with fear and voluble with warning. Sanford had said nothing. Yet he must have suffered in many ways. Whites must have tempted, threatened, cajoled him. Blacks must have laughed at him and jeered. To the Colonel he had said little. Every week he had appeared with reports, bank statements and such cash as the Colonel asked. Briefly he had asked for signatures on checks and receipts. Now and then he had drawled a bit of advice: "Better sell off the cotton quick; prices are still high." "Better plant wheat instead of corn on them plantations." "We need mules; several have died." "That railroad stock is too high to keep."

Yesterday came a note: "Sir, I have decided to quit work here and go north." Today came Sanford. The Colonel stared at him. Why had he served him well? There was no friendship between them. They hardly knew each other. What did this man think? What did he want? Why did he live?

Then Sanford spoke. "I'm thinking of going north."

"What?" almost snarled the Colonel. "You'll do nothing of the sort! You'll stay here. If you want more pay, take it!"

"I don't want more pay. I get enough. I want to live like a man

—and I don't want to have to kill nobody."

At this point Colonel Breckinridge, in an old dressing gown, unshaven and hair long unshorn, turned impatiently to say his accustomed "No" to the housekeeper announcing, "Gentlemen to see you, Sir!" But he was too late. Three men entered: two bankers and a well-known physician. The Colonel straightened and grew red.

"How dare you," he began. But his steward interrupted.

"Colonel Breckinridge, these bankers have insulted me and refused to honor your last draft which I drew, transferring the bulk of your funds to Atlanta. They have brought a doctor to begin efforts to have you committed for incompetency."

The president of the bank, choleric and insulted, tried to speak but Colonel Breckinridge drew his steward aside and, turning his back on the white men, talked with him a few minutes. Then deliberately, he signed another draft and gave it to his steward and accompanied him to the door. Turning, he held the door open and said to the white men: "Go!"

The president of the bank protested. "Colonel Breckinridge, this sudden withdrawal of so large a sum may ruin us. I wanted to be sure this was your signature and that you were well—"

"Go!" repeated the Colonel.

Sanford returned late in the day. His face was deeply seamed and he no longer held his usual impassive control. He stood flushed, and his eyes wide and angry. His resemblance to Colonel Breckinridge was the more plain and startling. He did not wait to be addressed but burst into speech.

"Here, Colonel, is the draft on Atlanta. Outside are all the books covering the ten years of my service. I'm leaving you tonight. That bank president called me a yellow bastard. I knocked him down and smashed his nose with my heel. Soon a mob will be after me, but I'll cross the river within the hour and they'll never find me."

The Colonel looked his steward in the eye for the first time in his life and started to protest, but the man drew back to the door, stood straight against it and continued.

"John Breckinridge, I'm your first cousin by blood, as you know damned well. I promised my father, your uncle, to look after you as long as you needed me. He said it was my duty as a Breckinridge. I have been honest, hard-working and faithful to my trust as your records will prove. You've treated me like you treated your horses. You took no notice of me as a man and your closest living relative.

You pretended to forget my existence because you knew well how close I was to you and how like you I looked. All Charleston knew it and laughed. My job is done now. My daughters are educated and are now both safe in the North, married, and have good homes. You are rich. I am going to leave now this hell on earth, this South Carolina which strutted and boasted and led this nation to the devil.

"When the whole country was fawning on this state and the South, fearing to oppose your disgraceful arrogance, you could have had anything in reason. You chose war and destruction. Then your 'niggers' came to your rescue. Never in history has an humble peasantry furnished such faithful service to rescue fools. They toiled for you, they gave you schools and votes; they divided your land, they tried to make you human and decent. In return you mobbed and murdered them, stole from their poverty, lied about them over earth and time, and then fronted them, helpless and unarmed, with armed hoodlums masked as leaders of civilization.

"You won. You crucified their leaders. Gone is Elliott, ruined is Cardozo, disgraced is poor Beverly Nash. You have swept all knowledge of these great leaders of American democracy from the record so that today, unled, the masses of my people crawl in abject servitude while you bow to the circus performing of Wade Hampton and the coarse brutality of a Tillman.

"But, John Breckinridge, you have not won. You'll never win. The black leadership of the South has not been killed. It is not lost. It has spread to the nation, and the nation is heir to what this blind state has lost. They still live and lead in the West and North —in Illinois and Ohio, in New York and Pennsylvania; in Massachusetts. White Carolina has nothing left; not a statesman, not a poet, not an artist, not a writer."

Sanford closed his eyes and swayed a bit. Seldom if ever in all his life had he so let loose his deepest, most passionate feelings. His seething brain searched the dark future. Perhaps he saw, perhaps he dreamed how the granddaughter of Cardozo, treasurer of the state, married Paul Robeson; perhaps he saw that young black teacher who escaped from Charleston slavery to become the greatest bishop of the greatest black church in the world. The first Negro graduate of Harvard was professor at the University of South Carolina in 1876 and, driven out by Hampton, became builder of Grant's Tomb in New York. The law partner of Elliott was professor in this same university and left to become federal judge in Hawaii. The Grimke brothers, blood relatives of a great

Carolina family, escaped north to become leaders of democracy
and give birth to a poet. Kelly Miller, black fugitive of Reconstruction, became one of America's keenest minds. When, after
fifty years, white Carolina began to write literature their subjects
came from the alley where Aunt Betsy lived.

Sanford opened his eyes and glared at the silent Colonel. Then
he turned and disappeared into the night.

The Colonel felt curiously alone. He had lost his last real friend.
He had long since lost touch with his former associates. He increasingly hated what was going on about him. He prepared to sell this
plantation and the home on the Battery. It hurt him to do this,
but what point was there in keeping them? He gathered courage
at last for the long delayed visit to his daughter.

He wrote Dr. Baldwin telling of his proposed visit, and as he
wrote outlined a plan for travel abroad to see again after long
years the Europe of his dreams and hopes. But even as he wrote he
knew that he was not a well man; that the toll of strain and disappointment was beginning to show. Still he would not consult a
physician, partly from fear, partly because in fact he did not greatly
care to live.

CHAPTER VII

THE EDUCATION OF MANUEL MANSART

For the Negroes, as physical resistance became impractical without aid of the Northern troops and as the power of the Ku Klux Klan and caste legislation increased, one recourse remained: migration, the Free Negro's version of the slave's escape to the North and freedom. Despite the efforts of Negro farmers and laborers to adjust themselves to the rural economy, the farm ceased to be attractive. The return of ex-Confederates to power, intermittent agricultural depressions, unfair and often cruel treatment by landlords and merchants, and rumors of rich opportunities in the cities and in other parts of the country, stimulated an exodus of Negroes from the rural South that began as early as 1879. Thousands of Negroes left Mississippi, Louisiana, Alabama, and Georgia.

The movement chiefly was west, to free soil and money wage. This escape lay unconsciously in the minds of Manuel's mother and grandmother: west to the hills of Atlanta; first for education such as the low-lying slave-East did not offer; then later—who knows? Further west or north to real emancipation? The logic was plain and often expressed by Negroes and their white friends. This was at last a Free Country. If a worker did not like his work or his pay he could and would seek better work and higher pay.

The Negroes stood awhile bewildered by the new "freedom" conferred upon them. Most of them in the South were on the same plantations, with the same "rations" instead of wages, and still with few rights which a white man was bound to respect. But was there not hope? Perhaps not in South Carolina nor in Louisiana nor in Arkansas nor in western Tennessee. But Kansas! Fabulous Kansas! Land of the free, land of John Brown's free men!

Aunt Betsy knew of this black movement west; not distinctly nor in detail but in that curiously broad way in which she knew so much of the surrounding world. She had actually seen and heard black soldiers marching down Meeting Street in old Charleston on the great day of surrender, to the tune of "John Brown's body lies a'mouldering in the grave but his soul goes marching on!" She remembered the day when this fabled John Brown had been crucified and nailed to a bloody cross, with five black men. More dimly, before this, she had heard of his bloody crusade in Kansas. Kansas thereupon became a great word in her ears. It was that Golden West whither men of all sorts were streaming to seek for the Promised Land; and Atlanta was on the way westward and held out schools for her grandson.

Then came other rumors of movements among the Negro masses. There was the weird old man, Pappy Singleton, the Moses of Tennessee, who with his own hard-earned cash, his white hair, strong voice and outstretched hand, led ten thousand black folk to Kansas. Later there was the younger, stronger Henry Adams of Louisiana who actually signed up a hundred thousand dissatisfied black workers for migration.

The Southern planters were furious and alarmed. They called a meeting in Nashville in 1879. Colonel Breckinridge was invited but never answered the letter, if he ever read it. The planters made fair promises, but this proved hardly called for. The forty thousand penniless, ragged Negroes who crept to Kansas found cold welcome. The sturdy western pioneers wanted nothing like this; boats refused them passage; trains passed them by, and mobs threatened them. Some died, some turned back; seven thousand stayed and struggled; but the net loss to the Southern planters was small; they still had millions of cheap black labor.

Negro leaders were divided in council. The first colored graduate of Harvard College and his kind encouraged the migration: "Come north," they said, "leave the slave South and be free!" But Frederick Douglass, the intrepid leader, now in ripe manhood, and others, contradicted these leaders. "Stay South," he pleaded, "possess the land where you have labored for 250 years. Let no one run you away. Fight it out." To the great rank and file there was doubt and hesitancy, but most Negroes stayed and worked on the same plantations where once they were bond slaves. Aunt Betsy, who watched this struggle but knew the details only vaguely, held to the movement westward at least as far as Atlanta where her grandson must get an education. He must escape slavery not perhaps physically so much as in his mind.

The little black boy born in his father's blood in Charleston, 1876, lived in Augusta and Athens during his first ten years of life. He was a beautiful child; physically perfect, with dark velvet skin, black and ivory eyes, white teeth and short, black, delicately crinkled hair. He was always spotlessly clean and well-fed, but the black women always near him did not encourage outside intimacies. He laughed and played in a narrow but well-protected world.

He had hardly begun to walk when his mother left the alleys of Charleston and went to Augusta, where they lived in the rear of Dr. Baldwin's house, in a little cottage which seemed to the child the loveliest home one could wish for. Dr. Baldwin's Academy was on the outskirts of the city, an old and rambling group of buildings where Manuel, peeping eagerly through the fence, could see groups of very elegant young men walking to and fro. This was, he was told, an old and famous school, and Dr. Baldwin had always been its head.

There, after a year, his grandmother joined them—thinner than he remembered and more grim of face, but always kind and thoughtful to him. At her coming there began that talk of school for him which continued for a long time. He asked why he could not go to Dr. Baldwin's school. But his mother said he was too young; and Dr. Baldwin himself when approached on the subject by this black baby hesitated a moment and said,

"Well, well! Perhaps! Who can tell? —Stranger things have happened!"

Still his mother did not seem to think much of the idea. She kept talking of Atlanta, where it seemed a very fine school was ready for him, young as he was.

Naturally, for five or six years, up to the time he first saw Colonel Breckinridge, Manuel was blissfully ignorant of being a problem in the midst of problems. He was a happy little boy, living in a lovely world, surrounded by nice people who looked at his beautiful face and sturdy body and smiled. To some that dark color somewhat clouded their sense of beauty. He was to their minds, black "but" beautiful. But to most he was just a lovely boy, with dancing eyes, soft, smooth skin and bubbling spirits. He whistled and sang and went skipping happily to school; came home to delicious meals of cornbread, molasses, and collards, with now and then a bit of pork. Then there were interesting chores to do for Mammy, like splitting kindling, fetching water or running errands. And last there was delicious sleep long and deep, with sometimes magnificent dreams, when he was a king giving his mother and playmates pearls and gold and large pork-chops.

He noticed, of course, but with no particular interest at first, that people were of different height, dress and color of skin. To him these differences were of no significance. Some persons had more things than he, and different; but everything considered, the things he had were more satisfactory and were those which he preferred. It was much nicer he was sure, to eat in the little kitchen near delectable odors, than in that vast dining room of the Big House which he had inspected and which smelled flat and was otherwise uninviting. A horse and carriage to ride in was certainly desirable at times, but not usually near as much fun as hopping and running with freedom to stop, turn aside and climb; all of which horses could not do.

As between white people and black, he had no generalizations which were fixed. Old Pop Jenkins, black as night, was nasty to everybody and said mean things. Mrs. Baldwin was "sometimey"; he did not pay her any particular attention. He liked Old Man Baldwin and the attraction was mutual. White folk had things to give away and gave him pennies, candy and sometimes dimes. That was nice of them as they did not seem to need these things themselves.

Dr. Baldwin eventually accepted the call to the University of Georgia. He was not made Chancellor, as the titular head was called. This place was left vacant. He was called "Dean" with the essential powers of a president. This arrangement satisfied many conflicting elements, and he moved to Athens.

This moving proved a most exciting event to Manuel. He was six when it happened and had just started going to school in Augusta. Mr. Porter, a yellow colored man, had run a school before the war, where the Free Negroes educated their children. After the war this school became a Public School and here Manuel's mother had promised him that he should go. He had looked forward to this with great impatience, and had only just begun school when his mother announced that they were going to give up their lovely little cottage and move to a strange city. Was it Atlanta? No, but it was near Atlanta.

"But why, Mammy? I like it here and this has always been our home."

"We are going where there are better schools and nicer people."

"But our people are as nice as they can be. And I don't want to leave, I . . ."

"Hush, boy! You'll do as you're told. You don't know nothing about people yet. You're going to get an education. Not by 'niggers' but by good white folks. You're going to make something of yourself, or I'll beat the daylights out of you. Now, march and help me pack!"

So everything was packed except a number of his prized possessions, for which there was no room. The dog, who was his dearest friend was only saved at the last moment by his own frenzied burst of grief. But of course they could not take the yard, nor the rosebush and honeysuckle; nor the great live oak under which he had passed his most wonderful hours and dreamed his mightiest dreams.

There must have been many reasons for going, but nobody explained them all to a little boy who was awfully interested. Something very strange was happening and his mother and grandmother talked excitedly long into the night. He tried to listen, but only got boxed ears. He asked questions but got no answers.

Manuel did not regard his new home as nearly so nice as the one in Augusta. The cabin where he and his family lived was too near the Big House to be so pleasant; the white workmen who were renovating the president's rather dilapidated house were not kind, and his mother would not let him play in the yard. But his school was nice, and he liked the teacher, a pretty colored girl from Atlanta University; and she liked him.

Colonel Breckinridge finally came to visit his daughter. He arrived unannounced purposely and spent some time looking at the little town. He found the surroundings as he approached the university rather pleasant; rolling hills without the voluptuous verdure of Charleston but with trees and grass. He approached the house where he was told the president lived; and then came that curious interlude—which marked the end of his life. As he was walking along leisurely in the Spring sunshine he saw for the first time, Manuel Mansart.

Of course he did not know the boy; he had no idea that Tom Mansart had a son. But he did see a little black boy, five or six years of age, chubby and well-nourished, with lovely brown skin and the brightest of black eyes. His hair, close curled, lay on his well-shaped head like a mat, and he was walking along whistling happily, with books under his arm.

He looked up at the elderly white gentleman and said pleasantly, "Good morning, Sir."

This rather intrigued the Colonel, because he had noticed recently that the Negro children did not greet white folk. They acted sullen or afraid. So the Colonel responded pleasantly and stopped to talk a while. Where was the young man going?

"To school, Sir."

"Well, well, and what are you studying?"

"Reading, Arithmetic and Geography."

"And what are you going to be; a farmer, a carpenter, or a minister?"

"No, Sir, I am going to be a lawyer."

"A lawyer? Well, well; where did you get that idea?"

"My mammy says that she wants me to be a lawyer."

"Well, if I were you, I would tell your mammy that there are better things to do in the world than following the law." Then the Colonel smiled, and putting his hand slowly in his pocket, took out a bill.

"What is your name?"

"Manuel Mansart."

Colonel Breckinridge stared, but slowly handed the bill to the boy. Just as the boy reached to take it the Colonel sensed that a woman, slim, dark, had come out of the gate and approached them silently. She stopped and stared at him, and then reached down and took the bill before the child could touch it.

"We do not want your money, Colonel Breckinridge," she said. "There is blood on it." And taking the boy by the hand she walked swiftly away, almost dragging the surprised child.

The Colonel walked slowly on; it was as though on this bright morning a fatal cord had snapped in his mind. He remembered his dead wife. He remembered the Battery; he remembered Meeting House Street. He remembered that dark and fateful gathering far off from the haunts of man, on the lonely ocean isle at midnight. And he knew that in some way a dark fate was still following him. He went on to the house. He was greeted with joy and a warm welcome.

Dinner was not altogether a successful meal, because it seemed that the servants had suddenly left. Dr. Baldwin was mystified and annoyed; but Betty was philosophical.

"Father," she said, "Did you meet any of the servants as you came in?"

He was silent a while and then told of meeting the little boy. "Oh yes, and there was a woman, too."

"Did you know who that woman was?"

"No."

"It was Tom Mansart's widow. I suppose she has run away because she does not like your presence here."

The Colonel apologized. But Betty Lou shrugged it off; she was disgusted, of course.

"You just cannot depend upon Negroes; here this woman has been with Dr. Baldwin over four years, and now for nothing she picks up and leaves. They are utterly unreliable! All of them ought to be back in slavery where they belong!"

But silently Colonel Breckinridge had made a vow. In his will he would leave a sum of money for the education of this child.

The doorbell rang and Dr. Baldwin himself answered. It was the sheriff. He said that he had held up two wenches and a child, with a lot of house plunder. They were at the depot trying to get passage to Atlanta. He was told they were Dr. Baldwin's folk and probably making off with his property. If the President said so, he'd put a lien on the stuff and bring them back here or lodge them in jail. Dr. Baldwin with some difficulty convinced him that the women and their goods were free to go.

So little Manuel was torn again from his roots. There was one consolation. It turned out that the nice colored teacher was returning to Atlanta and might meet him again in the Mitchell Street School which he would probably attend, near Atlanta University. But nearly all the rest of this moving was tragedy. They sat in the dirty "Jim-Crow" part of the depot for hours, until the sheriff returned and sullenly let them board the train. The conductor shunted them to the little half of a coach next to the engine. Then he spied the little dog which Manuel was concealing beneath his coat. He seized the terrified little animal and tossed him off the platform just as the train started.

"No dogs in here!" he growled.

Mansart screamed, but his grandmother grabbed him and cuddled him in her lap. Struggling, he stuck his head out of the window and called. The bewildered dog heard him and with a yelp of joy started down the platform and leaped to the track. He stopped barking, but ran with every ounce of his strength and more. He ran until he staggered blindly and his heart broke and he died. Manuel gasped and crawled back into his grandmother's arms. It was the greatest tragedy of his long and tragic life.

They travelled long into the night. Then in the clear morning the great railway shrieked and flew to a city so large that Manuel stared and gasped. They landed half underground, pushed their way through what seemed millions of people, rode and rode, until past vast red buildings and wide lawns they came to a street, a little lane, and a house. And this again was home.

At first he did not like his new home in the least. It was strange and unfamiliar; he did not know a single soul; there were no real big trees nor grass. But over, around and above all this stood the school, a plain wooden New England building not far from the campus of Atlanta University, whose grass and ivy and beautiful red buildings loomed to the west. This was the Mitchell Street Public School, a regular grade school for children. The teachers were young men and women, students or graduates of the university.

The children were mostly dirty and stupid; but some, like Manuel, soon made the work interesting. He was a dear; so bright and eager; so good-tempered and delighted with school and life. His former Athens teacher soon appeared. His advancement was phenomenal, his application amazing, and his happiness and contentment complete until an incident with the poor whites, which awakened him to new aspects of the world.

The case of that dollar which his mother had made him return to Colonel Breckinridge excited his curiosity; first because it was more money then had ever before been offered him; and secondly because his mother had acted so funny. He began to suspect there might be white people who were in some way dangerous and must be inspected carefully before their friendship was accepted. This of course applied to only a few.

Manuel was too good-tempered to easily take offense or seek always to have his own way. He gradually evolved a philosophy of action. If a white boy blocked his path he walked around him and smiled. If he saw a crowd of whites approaching he waited until they passed or crossed the street. But sometimes the whites were truculent and sought trouble. Manuel had always avoided any difficulties. He was a child of sunny disposition. He very seldom lost his temper; but when a hulking white boy much larger than he (the name he found out afterwards was Scroggs), slapped him for no reason whatever and then seized his new geography recently purchased by his mother at great cost, Manuel lost his poise. Suddenly the little fellow saw red; he fought like a demon; he tore the clothes off the older boy and brought blood. The white children, screaming, leaped upon him and when the policeman appeared upon the scene running, it was to extract a bedraggled, torn and bloody black child from beneath a heap of bitter, cursing whites.

Manuel was pulled and held while the outraged whites began to beat him. Just then Manuel's mother appeared as it seemed to him, right out of heaven. She seized him and began to plead with the officer. This astonished and enraged Manuel. He started to explain, only to receive a blow across his bruised face from his own mother that made him scream in pain. Then in a daze he heard his mother's voice:

"Please, Mr. Officer, don't arrest him; he's such a little boy. He don't mean no harm. You just leave him to me and I'll whale him so he won't never touch no white child again. And I'll pay his fine and work for you if you want me, or do anything—please, Mr. Officer, just let him go this time."

The officer reluctantly released him, and the white children gradually slipped away.

Slowly mother and boy descended the little hill toward home; they entered and without a word his mother stripped him and beat him until he was faint with pain. He stared up at her through wild tears, and saw to his terror the tears that were streaming down her face. He stopped crying and struggling; suddenly she stopped beating him and said brokenly:

"Manuel, don't you never dast strike a white boy. Take what they give, bow, run away. Don't hit 'em. Don't fight. You can't. They'se got the power. We got to wait."

She turned and went out. He crept to his bed and lay very still.

In after life Manuel always dated his understanding of white folks and the Negro problem to this incident. He concluded that white folks were dangerous and unreliable people; that they hated Negroes and were determined to injure them. There were, of course, exceptions. But the rule was avoid white folk and never trust them. Of course they must be met and met pleasantly so as to avoid retaliation and to keep their good-will. They had the power; they had the wealth; they owned the earth. From their wrath his mother was trying to save him at the sacrifice of her own love. He resolved to thwart them. He would carefully avoid offense. He would always be polite, smile pleasantly and give a good word to those who spoke. To those like the poor whites who were rude or cruel he would avoid all contact whenever possible, or get back at them surreptitiously so as to avoid the law.

That law he concluded was to protect white people and annoy and hurt colored people. The police were its agents and were at all costs to be avoided. They must be treated with great personal respect but never trusted, never given any information or help if possible. This extreme position, as he grew older, he modified in particular cases and situations. But its basic principles he never entirely forgot even to the day of his death.

Putting these principles into practice, he received both corroboration and correction. He saw the chain-gangs on the streets and realized that this was what his mother had feared for him. He knew that neither tender age nor innocence kept Negroes from its clutches; for this was a way of restoring the old slavery and stopping the education of Negroes.

The moral conclusions bothered him not a little. His mother was always telling him to be "a good boy" and he wanted to be. But here was a concrete case: that same hulking red-faced Scroggs who had beaten him he came to recognize as liking especially to pick on little colored children and to chase, kick and scare them. This was not right, but he must not oppose him openly; he might himself get licked, or worse, arrested.

So one day he hit on a strategem: He slipped up on the wall which separated the university campus into two parts to let a street run through below. Climbing up carefully one morning he lay prone until Scroggs swaggered by. Then he quietly dropped a large brick squarely on the bully's head.

He was safe at school before a policeman found the unconscious victim and carried him to a hospital where white folk could be treated. Manuel for a time was scared; suppose the boy died? Or was crippled permanently in some way? But no, he saw him about again in a few days; a little whiter but all right. Then, too, Manuel noticed that the little colored children walked more safely to school; there were fewer quarrels.

That was good, but still Manuel's conscience bothered him. In stories he had read, the rescuing hero always paraded and boasted. Well, perhaps that wasn't necessary—perhaps Brer Rabbit, about whom Joel Chandler Harris had begun to write in an Atlanta newspaper, was right in being cunning rather than forthright. Yet it would be nice at least to be sure you were right. Just where did white folk fit into this world? Were they all essentially evil? Or were some fairly good?

He felt the need of spiritual advice and encouragement in matters like this and took advantage of an opportunity at Sunday school. He attended Friendship Baptist Church further up the street, where a new young minister, Dr. Carter, was beginning a long pastorate of 55 years. His class was in charge of a young colored girl who followed the international lessons carefully and avoided straying beyond their printed conclusions. This morning, however, the slim brown minister himself was visiting and dropped by this class for a word of encouragement. He smiled on the bright little faces of the eight children.

"Does you love your neighbor as yo'self?" he asked, a bit unctuously.

Nobody answered. The young teacher fidgeted, and then silently appealed to Manuel, who often helped her over hard places. Manuel stood up.

"Do you mean white neighbors?" he asked.

The minister peered over his glasses and hesitated. "They special needs it," he said finally.

But Manuel persisted, despite the restraint in the eyes of his teacher.

"But, Sir, you said last Sunday, speaking about that lynching—"

The preacher wiped his glasses and glanced toward the next class; then he turned and looked at Manuel severely.

"What yo' name? Oh yes, Sister Mansart's child. Hum! Well, Manuel, them lynchers weren't no neighbors of mine nor yourn. An' tell you the truth, I loves my neighbors as well as may be, considering who they is. But if some white folks is going to heaven, I'd druther go some place else."

And he strode away, leaving a most astonished teacher, some puzzled boys, but one who thought he understood.

Not that Manuel even now was entirely satisfied. The answer was too pat, too smart; ethically he was still uneasy; he wanted more unity in his world; he did not want to leave even most white folks out, and he saw reasons for some of their acts. That Scroggs boy just didn't know much; he lived in the factory district and was about as poorly off and as ignorant as most colored people. And then there were some white folk, like that man who had wanted to give him a whole dollar—well, it was very puzzling and he continued to give much thought to it.

So more or less unconsciously Manuel Mansart worked out a pragmatic solution of the race problem. He was going to avoid white folks when he could. When brought in contact with them he was going to be pleasant. He noted that a smile or cheerful greeting often changed the whole atmosphere. People, especially white people, liked his frank, black face and his ingenuous way. Part of his attitude was quite honest and natural, and part of it was more or less unconscious hypocrisy. He did not smile at white people because he liked them; in fact he usually smiled because he did not trust them, because he was watching to see what they were going to do, either to hurt him or in some way to stop his natural impulses. This did not always happen. Sometimes, in fact most of the time, he met very nice white people; they were kind to him; they gave him things and helped him. But he did not trust them too much. He knew that a time would come and often did, when they would be wretchedly unjust and he would have no method of defense. So he was careful of them; he cajoled them; he kept his temper; he kept out of their way.

What was happening all around Manuel Mansart was a vast social revolution of which he was only a partly-conscious part and groping for solutions and personal adjustments where much of the essential elements were quite unknown to him.

Normally Mansart was a good-natured, frank and affectionate person. He liked people and he was neither selfish nor envious. His mother had made him a simple, homely, but neat little home. He enjoyed it. It was down a lane from the University—a lane of either dust or mud and of course unpaved and untended by the city. Then up a red clay bank one entered a closely fenced and hedged yard, tiny, but full of roses, honeysuckle and bougainvillea in season. One stumbled right up to a tiny porch with an easy chair and a bench. Then came the "parlor," a bit stiff; and the larger, delectable kitchen crowded with table, stove, tubs, coalbin, chairs and an ancient couch. Here he, his mother and grandmother lived; the mother washing and cooking; he eating and talking and studying; the grandmother sitting very still on the porch.

To young Manuel Mansart at the age of twelve came change guised as Death, and almost unrecognizable for what it really meant. His grandmother died. Nobody ever knew much of Aunt Betsy. She was black, tall and gaunt. On her once handsome face, beneath its mane of coarse black hair now faded to gray, Time and Pain had carved deep and angry grooves of bitterness. Yet over it lay and ruled an iron will and a clear head. Of the past she said not a word. How or where Love had touched that magnificent body she never said. Where she was born and where she travelled no one knew. She bowed regally to her slavery and yet bent its masters to her own designs. She knew nursing. She knew cures. She knew the human body. She used her knowledge as power. Once and only once had a white man whipped her. He died soon and silence marked his memory.

Her plan was to stay in Carolina—in Charleston, and make its black folk rule, together with white aristocrats. Both parties failed her: the white aristocrats lowered themselves to compromise with the riff-raff and to midnight murder; the Negroes ran and hid. She followed her daughter and grandson to Augusta for money paid in memory of Clarice Du Bignon. She stopped in Athens until on her very threshold appeared that Colonel Breckinridge, once her ideal, who had descended into Hell.

Her march from the sea to Atlanta was the beginning of death. She said nothing but began to sit all day on the front porch and stare at the setting sun, growing frail and silent. To Manuel, she never seemed to die. She just sat still and ceased to speak. Then one day they buried her in a Negro cemetery amid bare sand and little boards with waving strings. Life went on. His mother worked hard. Just how the money to support even this simple home came, Manuel seldom inquired. He worked at odd jobs—bellboy and waiter in hotels during vacations and on emergency. His mother took in washing and went out to day's work. When he needed clothes or books there was anxiety; and when the time to pay taxes rolled around disaster repeatedly faced them frankly.

Compared to the lovely homes in the white part of town this cottage was assessed at ten times its value. In no sense was it worth the $2000 it was valued at by the white officials, who always were ready to sell it to white landlords and let black tenants rent it forever. But the mother by hard work, pinching and saving at every crevice; and at last by borrowing of unregulated loan sharks at exorbitant interest, managed to keep it until Manuel entered college. Then she, too, lay wearily down one night and never awoke. The loan sharks seized everything greedily and Manuel went into the Dormitory to finish his course.

Thus at the age of 14 Manuel entered the "University," as the High School and embryonic college of Negro school was called. Here he came into contact with a new kind of white folks; Northerners, both men and women, as teachers. It was both astonishing and disconcerting. They were different—in speech and manners. They did not have the haughty and overbearing manners which he had always associated with "quality" white folks; nor on the other hand the slovenliness, cruelty and dirt which he associated with "poor whites." These whites dressed rather plainly but were painfully neat; terribly, and as he thought, quite unnecessarily punctual and strict in little things. He began to make a new category of whites. This made the racial problem less a matter of color and more a question of sort. He began to emerge from his racial world.

But it was in his studies that he approached emancipation. Emerging from "dead" languages which began to show signs of life, they began to read literature and stress what it said, instead of how it said it; they read history of the current world; mathematics became more tangible and less theoretic. There was the morning news bulletin and the discussions of a geography which was real and not a dumb map. The world began to be a fascinating place where one wanted to live, travel and act, and not merely eat.

What Manuel did not realize until many years later was that

this school was curiously different from most schools of its day. It had poor equipment—how poor Manuel never knew; but it had sincerity, it had object and high ideal; it was quite uninfluenced by wealth or renown; no professor was using this low pedestal for a stepping-stone to high places; no degree taken here would be recognized in the world of letters. But out of this simple fellowship of souls, this close acquaintanceship and deep sympathy, came something like that which once blossomed in the groves of Academus.

Viewing thus the worlds about him, the larger and more powerful and the smaller and closer, Manuel's attitude hardened. From the white South he withdrew into his own world. He began to think black; white people had less and less place in his dreams. He was building a separate world for himself and his. As he saw the whites in hotels, on the streets, in stores, they seemed a narrow, sordid, often vicious lot. They stole from Negroes without a thought, cheating them of their earnings, of their hard-earned property, of their good name. It was often difficult for a decent, hardworking Negro to keep from arrest and even jail. The word of any white man was sufficient to convict him summarily. The only thing that could save him was the counter-testimony of some influential white. One must have white friends. Also, for whites it was advantageous to have Negro clients willing to serve, work cheaply and do as told.

This Southern world, however, now came to face a new world where Manuel felt at home and under deep obligation: this was the contact with his white teachers. Their friendship, and especially their unselfish encouragement and advice, made him avoid seeing the white world as wholly a hateful thing. On the contrary, he began to think that this Northern world might be the normal world of real people, while the white South was the abnormal fungus. Nevertheless he must not ignore nor under-rate the power of the South. At present it represented and really was the World, so far as he was concerned.

This made the advent of Miss Freiburg in 1890 so momentous. His other teachers were mostly people born before the war, and not well acquainted with the newly dawning world of the late 19th century. Miss Freiburg was intensely modern. She was a tall, scrawny, keen-eyed woman from Minnesota who came to teach history and economics and knew what she was teaching. She understood what was going on in the world and for that reason had lost her instructorship at Wellesley and took the only thing that was offered. The President of Wellesley said frankly that Miss Freiburg's evident animus against Great Britain must arise from her German descent, and while understandable it was of course impossible for the college to allow such a picture of the British Empire to be drawn on the campus. The harried President of Atlanta University was too glad to get a good teacher for little or nothing to pay much attention to the criticism.

This was a God-send for Manuel Mansart. Miss Freiburg had been educated in Germany, had studied in France and England, and had actually been to Africa and the West Indies. Like all the Atlanta University teachers most of her students were in the high school rather than college grades. She brought them a sort of world view of race, which she applied to Georgia. Under her tuition Manuel began to learn what was going on in the last decade of the 19th century, which was of interest to him as a black man. The Black Mahdi had arisen and driven the British Empire out of the Sudan. In South Africa a consumptive who had listened to Ruskin's appeal at Oxford for young Englishmen to go out and rule the world, had become a millionaire by grace of black labor and gold, and now controlled the diamonds of the world.

He read of the Rand, with its ramshackle, corrugated iron houses, a few brick hotels and saloons, and wide open brothels; mines with wired-in compounds for the black laborers. Second-rate magnates were drinking champagne, and bewildered Boers, who had sold their farms for next to nothing, were coming in with their ox-drawn produce and watching a city spring up. Bewildered Kaffirs shot up and down in cages to work in the bowels of the earth. London bar-maids and prostitutes auctioned themselves off to the highest bidder and sometimes found themselves married ladies.

Manuel read of Lobengula, chief of the Matabele, cheated out of the richest mineral hoard in the world by young Rhodes,— Rhodes, who set the British Empire on the path from Cape to Cairo. Kitchener—with the newly invented machine gun, then recaptured Khartoun and desecrated the ashes of the great Mahdi. Ethiopia and France, about to meet on the headwaters of the Nile, were warned off, and now Britain ruled half Africa.

Then his indefatigable and hard-driving teacher brought her classes back home. She pointed out the wave of strikes in the North beginning with 1877. She read from the newspapers of the Homestead strike of 1892 and the rise of Populism.

The students talked frankly about white people in the surrounding world; they did not like them; they did not trust them. There were always exceptions, and favorite white teachers like

Spence and Freiburg were in some subtle, unexplained way incorporated into their own black race—a method all the easier since they too, suffered under the Southern white world's ostracism and persecution. Among Southern whites they had few friends and acknowledged these cautiously. These Southern whites, therefore, in all student conversations almost invariably figured as born enemies. Students talked over ways of getting even with the whites and over-reaching them. They weighed future conspiracies and what they were going to do when once they were out in the world. They had no doubt but that in the long run they were going to get the best of the white folk of the world, who always figured in their imaginations as conspiring to thwart the colored groups.

Some, like Mansart, expected to come into their own by excelling white people in all lines of endeavor. They were convinced that given freedom of opportunity they would prove to have as much brains, energy and determination as the whites. Others ridiculed and scoffed at this. Negroes did not have more brains and did not need them; they did not want hard work. No! They proposed to get the best of the whites by fooling them; by taking advantage of their mistakes; by undercover conspiracy and hidden deeds. The whites were not so smart at that. This group of students were always laughing at the whites; at their pretense and strutting. They laughed in their faces with solemn mien, innocent looks and sanctified air. When pretentious white visitors appeared and especially important Southern city and state officials, they would ridicule and mock them with perfectly straight faces and then when they stalked off, go into reels of hysterical laughter.

Mansart did not follow this line of thought. He saw it based really on self-distrust; on a complex of deep-felt inferiority, at least in many essential respects. He rejected this. Negroes had brains, but they lacked decent primary schools; sanitary homes; parents. They had small chance to learn English even from Southern whites. If, with this handicap of poverty, ignorance and disease, the blacks were forging forward, as they certainly were, it needed no admission of inferiority and no subterfuge of deceit to gain a place in the world. Their half-trained teachers in the elementary schools knew no English nor even elementary mathematics. Their training had been piece-meal and incidental. Negroes had as much ability as whites. Not for a moment could white folk stand what Negroes daily must endure.

When Mansart in 1890 was entering his second year of High School, the Populist movement started in Georgia and Tom Watson was swept into Congress. It was not the policy in the Southern mission schools for Negroes to say much about politics. But Miss Freiburg, from her own keen interest in this Southern situation, talked freely with her brighter students. She told them about Tom Watson; how he had come to the legislature in 1880 by advocating free schools for all and attacking the Convict Lease system. She stressed the rise of the Farmers Alliance in the West and South and its cooperatives.

Mansart was particularly attracted by her explanation of the basic reasons for the current uprising of the farmers. It was not as he assumed, simply a race problem; white farmers were facing the same sort of oppression that Negroes faced. The same remedies applied to both. Indeed, it began to dawn on Manuel that more often than not what he called "problems" of his race were in essence problems of all men in similar positions.

Miss Freiburg, sitting primly and yet speaking so clearly and concisely, talked nearly an hour after class to a group of students in the beginning of the campaign of 1891.

"There is Want, Hurt and Fear among masses of Americans, black and white today. The cause is not easy to explain and we have no scientific social leadership in this country. But we do know certain facts. Not all know all the facts, but various facts are known by all, each in his own narrow experience. Farmers need land and land is owned in great unused quantities by people who never earned the right to own it and do not need it nor use it now. The prices of goods raised by farmers have been falling for thirty years. Laborers, North and South, black and white are not in many cases paid enough to feed, clothe and house their families well. Some are mistreated, beaten and shot when they protest; especially in the South and among the new immigrants in the coal and iron mines. Some actually fear starvation.

"On the other hand, prices of goods in general are going up. Why? For many reasons, some of which are clear, some only guessed at. For instance, more gold and silver are being mined. Gold especially, silver sometimes, are measures of value. When they increase their value falls and the prices of all other goods compared with them rise. Again, new ways of making goods may raise their prices, and new supplies of workers may lower wages.

"But no matter what the cause, farm products drop in price, and goods which farmers want rise in price. At the same time owners of land and valuable goods grow rich. Millionaires have multiplied. The masses, led by various sorts of men, have suggested remedies; they saw rich men buy a dollar's worth of goods for 33c, but later when they themselves spent their hard-earned dollars they got only 33 cents worth of goods. They said that the government should remedy this by printing cheap greenback money. This Greenback movement arose in the seventies and lasted until 1884. Then the farmers took hold: in the Grange movement against railroad rates and then in the Farmers Alliance. Last came the Populist Party."

During the campaign of 1892, when Mansart was 16, he followed the work of Sebastian Doyle. Doyle was then a preacher in southeast Georgia, near where the radical Congressman, Tom Watson lived. Doyle had advised and influenced Watson, and was speaking all over the state in the campaign of 1892 for the Populist ticket. The tall, cream-colored mulatto, with flying black hair, tremendously impressed Manuel. He attended his rallies whenever they took place in or near Atlanta, and several times they talked together. Doyle found this boy both intelligent and inspiring. Both believed that political power must be restored to the Negro if he was to survive, but Doyle insisted that this must come from alliance with the poor whites—the small farmers and city mill-hands. He told how he had forced this idea on Tom Watson, the new leader of the poor whites and had made him see the truth. Mansart strongly disagreed here. He believed with his dead grandmother that the salvation of the Negro rested in the hands of the "Quality," the heirs, spiritual and temporal of the planters.

Later, in Mansart's freshman year Doyle was again in Atlanta, stumping for the Populists. Miss Freiburg heard Doyle speak. She pointed out:

"Doyle represents the application of Democracy to politics. Negroes are suffering under present conditions. They should have opportunity to state and explain just where the shoe pinches in their case. Then when remedies are proposed, these remedies must include the righting of Negroes' wrongs."

She distinctly sniffed in class when Mansart expressed his doubt about the use of bringing the wrongs of Negroes to the attention of the poor whites.

"They want Negroes to suffer," he maintained.

She retorted, "Until they learn that they are in the same boat with Negroes."

It looked for a while as though the stars in their courses were fighting for Democracy in the South. But facing the stars, the forces of reaction and status quo rallied. They held the political State;

they ruled the Church; they had the Press; they had the money and credit and held the mortgages; they had long controlled and manipulated the elections, and they counted the ballots.

Young Negroes like Mansart were convinced that in the South at least, Honesty did not pay and that "poor whites" could never be trusted by blacks. Miss Freiburg clung to her belief in the ultimate triumph of Democracy. In 1895 she particularly called his attention to the new Negro leader who was to speak at the Cotton States Exposition. She hoped a new prophet would reinforce Doyle.

Mansart sat in that great auditorium on Negro night. His heart swelled with pride. The leading men of the North were there sitting beside the best blood of the South. Never before had so many whites and Negroes sat together since 1876. It was, he firmly believed, an omen of world significance. One could, of course, see the Color Line as whites filled the auditorium and blacks a part of the gallery; but what of that? One must see things in perspective, and while he had become used to sitting side by side with Northern whites at table and in class, after all, he argued, what was that? Peace, Work, Good-will—that was first. So they were separately seated of course, but they were there—the Old South, the New South, the North—liberal and conservative, with here and there a radical and a reactionary.

The list of colored speakers was impressive; he knew of many of them. He did not know nor had he ever heard of Booker T. Washington who was given prominence probably because he represented rural education. He was principal of an Alabama school called Tuskegee. He spoke well, very well indeed; but to Mansart's mind not better than two or three other colored leaders. Then too, he felt some uneasiness because he feared that Washington's philosophy of seizing opportunities at hand, avoiding politics and making friends with the white folks was yielding too much; was stating plainly his own belief but a belief which he did not want proclaimed too publicly or put too clearly into words.

He still never wanted to forget, or let any children he might have forget that they were men and had rights, and that those rights were being trampled on. Nevertheless he was impressed by the applause and enthusiasm of the whites. They gave Washington a tremendous ovation. They applauded his advice to the Negroes to work and save; but they loved his words on social equality: "Separate as the five fingers." Ladies stood on their chairs and waved their handkerchiefs, while men threw up their hats, danced and gave the Rebel yell.

Again next morning the absolutely unexpected happened. The *Atlanta Constitution*, which usually relegated all news about Negroes to the inner pages and small type, displayed Washington's speech on the front page and praised it editorially as marking an epoch in the South. The other colored speakers were almost ignored.

Mansart thought this over carefully on his trip home. Here was something unusual. It must be the result of deliberate plan. It could not have been accidental. There was thought and movement back of it. The white South was yielding and ready to bargain. Practically all his fellow-students disagreed; they criticized Washington roundly; they said he was an "Uncle Tom" and ready to surrender all the Negro's rights. Mansart veered increasingly the other way. It was a shrewd speech, it was an answer to some counter-proposal not fully revealed; it was an offer to make great sacrifices which would be followed by yielding on the part of the best whites. When the matter was discussed in class, as it was repeatedly, the teacher said little. Manuel challenged her.

"Don't you think his talk was good political strategy?" he asked.

"Do you?"

"Yes, Ma'am!"

"Well, I think most Southern white people will agree with you," she answered crisply.

The speech had taken place the 18th of September 1895, just as Atlanta University opened its Fall term. The class discussed Washington's speech all the year; the colored people discussed it; the nation discussed it. Perhaps no American speech before or since has been so widely considered. It was six months later, on the first of March, 1896, that an answer to the Washington philosophy came, so terrible and portentous that men scarce dared mention it. There was nothing in the newspapers about Italy in Ethiopia. Miss Freiburg noted it almost negligently at the close of class:

"By the by, you might be interested in this bit of news: yesterday Menelik of Abyssinia overthrew the invading Italian army at Adua and slew 25,000."

The students sat very still. The evening sun burned red through the western windows. Manuel sat entranced, almost unconscious, staring east. He heard faintly his departing classmates. He saw the Citadel of Africa, its mighty snowswept crags facing sun and sea. He heard the fury of its waters leaping from crag to precipice, rushing down to feed the Nile—the endless and eternal Nile. Over the black land streamed the dark thousands, grim and terrible, red-eyed and foaming at the mouth; with the vast bulk of the black Emperor Menelik riding ahead, plumed with lion skin and corsetted with steel. Almost abreast paced the mounted brown magnificence of the Empress Taitou, flowing with silk and gold. He heard wild cries that shook the skies as clamor of hoof and brass thundered on the earth. He saw the Italian host, proud with the axe and fasces of ancient Rome halt, shiver and then turning, flee like wild and hunted things down the gorge of death. He saw 25,000 bleeding and festering corpses. Dear God, let that cup pass—

"Mansart, are you ill — or asleep?" came the voice of Miss Freiburg.

Manuel rose shamefacedly in the empty room. "No, ma'am, no — I was never so much awake."

Chapter VIII

JOHN PIERCE AND HENRY GRADY

Atlanta is a city set on three hills of the Blue Ridge, a thousand feet above Charleston and New Orleans. It is a city which had little to do with slavery and which grew into real being after the Civil War. It is a child not of plantation owners but of poor Southern whites and Northern capital, planned by railroads before it had any inhabitants. John C. Calhoun, the bitter professional Southerner, predicted its birth in Memphis when less than a hundred human beings lived anywhere near it! "From the course of the Tennessee, Cumberland and Alleghany rivers" and the "chains of the Alleghany Mountains" the railroads between the Mississippi valley and the Atlantic "must necessarily meet here."

Here then they met, 300 miles each way from the Atlantic ocean, the Mississippi River and the Great Lakes. A railroad ran from Atlanta east in 1845; a road opened south in 1846; roads west and southwest were built in 1852; and an "airline" north in 1857. Around the railway station grew a village of railway hands, with four streets: Peachtree and Whitehall running west and east; Marietta and Decatur north and south; meeting at Five Points.

Above this hamlet hovered a black murk, swathed in white veils of mountain mist. When shivering rain and cold prevail a cloud descends and blankets the mountain tops above where Atlanta lurks in dim discomfort. But when awakening and rising, the sun burns through, men see the glory of sundrenched life in this city set above the seas.

The town grew crazily into a frontier center of cursing, fighting, whiskey-drinking and tobacco-chewing brawlers until the merchants and workers, about 1850, brought the bums of Slabtown and Snake Nation to heel. In 1860 Atlanta was the fourth city in the state with 8,000 whites and 2,000 colored. Atlanta cared nothing about slavery. Its few black servants were owned, of course, but there was also a small knot of free Negroes ten years before the war. The city, however, was in the South and felt it must be Southern in sentiment. In 1858 there was a movement to establish public schools and considerable interest was aroused. A citizen was even sent to Rhode Island to see how the curious system worked. Several mass meetings were held, but at the last one, held during the October Fair, the forces against this Northern innovation got control and killed the scheme.

As the war scare increased, Atlanta was not interested. It was the commercial center of a territory extending down toward the cotton belt, out toward the West and up toward Yankee notions. The railroads brought in goods, wagons distributed them, and trade was brisk. Nevertheless, a thriving Southern city had to notice current events and in March, 1858, a "Kansas Meeting" was held and resolutions adopted opposing the admission of Kansas as a free state.

"The safety of our Southern institutions, and the peace and quiet of our truly patriotic, liberty-loving and law-abiding citizens are in danger . . . by the interfering and aggressive policy of abolition fanatics."

None of the mass of people, however, contemplated secession. That would have been fatal to trade. But when secession actually took place and war was imminent, Atlanta began to take notice. In February, 1861, Jefferson Davis found that Atlanta was his shortest route from Washington to Montgomery. He stopped off and said a word. Later Alexander Stephens dropped by. He had fought a duel here in 1848 but now was a cripple on crutches and was on his way to Savannah. At Savannah he made his celebrated declaration on slavery as the "cornerstone" of the new South.

As the war neared, Atlanta, far from the front and centrally located, with means of communication, experienced a wartime boom. It became a military center and supply depot for the Confederate Army. Arms and ammunition were manufactured extensively, and in 1861 the city became the headquarters of the Confederate quartermaster and commissaries, as well as a chief hospital point.

During the year 1863 Atlanta became a base for Federal prisoners. In 1864 it was announced that Federal generals were preparing to attack Atlanta as the last connecting link between the East and the Mississippi Valley. If the Confederates lost Atlanta they would lose their food supply. At first it was feared that General Grant would stop and attack on his way to Richmond. Characteristically during this time of anxiety great religious revivals took place. By June it was evident that Sherman was preparing to march southward to the city. And Sherman came.

In July there were two battles: in August the city was bombarded, and was three-fourths destroyed in September when Sherman's army entered the city. The citizens were ordered to leave and 12,000 of them walked and rode away, laden with furniture and household goods. Most of the Negroes remained and two regiments of Negro soldiers were immediately organized. Then Sherman marched to the sea, followed by a vast crowd of Negroes, including Tom Mansart, and cutting a path straight through the Confederacy wide in miles and wider in significance.

Slowly the people of Atlanta, after the surrender, came trooping back. Out of 4,000 buildings, only 400 were left. But Atlanta had lost little else by the war. Her charred ruins after Sherman's bombardment were picturesque and good talking points; after all, the destruction of a few thousand old wooden buildings only gave opportunity for brick, steel and concrete, on land still intact and rapidly increasing in value to almost fantastic heights. Moreover, Atlanta had had none of the spiritual losses and psychoses that paralyzed the southern South. Atlantans had lost no picturesque plantation mansions, having never owned any; they had lost no faithful "retainers," having owned few slaves and hating the sacred "institution" because it took bread from the mouths and work from the hands of most Atlanta settlers. Atlanta had no old family bonds of blood, nor aristocratic traditions. Instead of nourishing insane hate of the North and bewailing a lost civilization, this busy, energetic and ruthless town began a new culture designed to bring North and South together in profitable partnership.

First of all Atlanta, to the disgust of the old and aristocratic cities of Macon and Savannah, became capital of Georgia, removing it from the inaccessible compromise town of Milledgeville where local rivalry had hidden it since before the war. Atlanta had every advantage at the time which a capital of Georgia needed; accessibility, nearness to West and North, established trade and industry, wide-awake citizens not averse to hard work, and close alliance with Northern capital.

Her Negro population was small and there were none of the ties of blood and association which made Negroes an integral part of Charleston and Augusta. The transition from United States control was accomplished so precipitously that it had to be done twice. It ended both times in the same way: Southern whites and representatives of Northern capital in complete political and economic control of the state; Negroes almost completely disfranchised; little disorder, and business "as usual," before the rest of the South realized what was doing.

Thus Atlanta in 1881 was a rapidly developing city. It had 60,000 inhabitants, ten lines of railway, and real estate which had tripled its value since Mansart was born. It was attracting men of ability, push and shrewdness from the plantations South and the business North. Even writers and artists were sucked into the Atlanta maelstrom. A little modest man, born in middle Georgia and driven out by Sherman, wandered about, worked in Savannah and finally came to Atlanta in 1876. Seven years later his folk tales of "Uncle Remus" began to appear in the *Atlanta Constitution*. Henry Grady, grandchild of Irish peasants got his education in Virginia, worked on papers in New York, and then bought part of the leading Atlanta daily.

Atlanta in 1880 was handling a hundred thousand bales of high-priced cotton a year. The coal, iron and steel possibilities of the Birmingham district had been tapped. The labor problem had been quietly and legally settled by deliberately planned and widespread arrest of Negro offenders, together with a few white vagrants, and leasing their services to private corporations. These corporations became in 1889 the "Georgia Penitentiary" and the state received an income of nearly a million dollars a year from this new slave trade.

The panic of 1873 which rocked the country did not greatly disturb Atlanta. No banks failed and business continued to flourish. Three large new churches were built by the Episcopalians, the Presbyterians and Lutherans. This prosperity called the nation's attention to the Southerner's industrial paradise and to Atlanta as its center.

Fired by the example of the Great Centennial Exposition at Philadelphia in 1876, Atlanta began a series of shows to advertise Atlanta to the North and to bolster and encourage the spirit of the South which was still sulky and reminiscent. In 1879 came the visit of President Hayes to the city. There followed in 1881 the "International Cotton Exposition" to celebrate the beginning of the transfer of cotton spinning from New England to the South, the opening of the Atlanta Cotton Mills, and the completion of the railroad which linked Atlanta to the West. Alfred Colquit, clad in his shining cotton suit, told the world of the "untarnished and untarnishable glory" of the "Imperishable Cotton Kingdom!" Young John Pierce, a New York merchant, investor and banker, was especially interested when he arrived in Atlanta in 1881.

There was a town in northwest Massachusetts where for many decades the leading store had borne the sign, "John Pierce and

Son." By 1880 not only the leading store but most of the factories
and other industries of the growing city and indeed many of those
of New England and the whole country might have had the same
legend flung across them, so far as control was concerned. At this
time the firm consisted of Old John, a tough industrial warrior of
77, and Young John, a well-groomed business man of 30.

The main offices of John Pierce and Son were now in New York
City, in what was then "uptown" in one of the newer office buildings. And there in 1880 sat the head of the firm, angry and bitter.
The world appeared going to the Devil, with no real reason. There
was money, plenty of money in the North, accumulated from war
activities, investments, speculating. Recovering from the recent
Crisis, it sought new investment for future power and security. The
conquered South with boundless opportunities lay at last open
for development. Then difficulties began to appear. The Rebels
set a stiff price on cooperation with Northern business—namely,
restoration of slavery in all but name, and a Poor White president
who tried to push this through. To stop this plan Negroes were
given the vote to outvote their former masters. Silly thing to do,
said Pierce, but it wasn't intended to last long.

Ignorant black labor in the South, instead of doing as they
were told, tried to use political power to control industry and spend
the money of employers. These laborers had to be put in their
places by force and violence as John Pierce agreed; but just as that
method was succeeding here came in 1873 one of the worst of those
breakdowns of the whole industrial system, which are so frequent
in the growth of modern capitalism that some scientists have sought
to plot their ten-year cycles and measure the inevitable mathemat-
ical course, or even to link them to sunspots.

But, as in all social phenomena, here were clear causes rising
from human thought and desire and expressed in human action.
The panic of 1873 was caused by a bloody, cruel and costly war
which ruined lives and plans, destroyed and misused hard-earned
property, interfered with education, lowered morals and dealt civilization mortal blows. It was useless to seek to ignore all this and
place blame on a mechanical money system, or to try to go forward
with old plans and methods just as though nothing had happened.

Something had happened and more was happening of tremendous and lasting import. John Pierce did not understand it. He
tried to interpret it by applying old moral judgments on wholesale cheating—as when the Whiskey Ring came to light; railway
building graft which besmirched Blaine; a cabinet official hastily

resigning to prevent sordid scandal from actually reaching the presidential chair.

Meantime those who owned and controlled capital arranged for a new and rising stream of cheap labor. Immigration, which stopped during the Civil War, now rushed up to a flood, attracted by pictures of new freedom and free land. A half million immigrants in 1880 became in two years 750,000 and for two decades remained at flood tide; and there was work shrieking to be done.

Then came other unawaited complications. White Northern laborers, pressed to the wall by low paid immigrants, began a desperate fight to keep up their income until the strikes and riots from 1876 to 1880 became, as one said, "a rising against society itself." Revolution was in the air, and John Pierce did not like it.

John Pierce did not like Negroes and the reason was in its beginning small but in the end momentous. There were, before the Civil War, less than 300,000 black folk in the North and West and only 23,000 among the 270,000 whites of New England. They formed a rather lonely group, attached as old house servants to some well-to-do families, or hidden away in small, segregated groups where they lived by small farming or as servants and laborers.

One such family lived near the farm of John Pierce's father and were annoying. Three brothers owned three small adjoining farms which they had inherited from their father who had been brought to New York by Dutch traders. They had in some way become recognized as "free" and here they were at the Pierce's doorstep. They were quiet and kept to themselves, but they were outsiders and in the way of progress.

The Pierces wanted their bit of good bottom land around a tiny lake, and they wouldn't sell even for a good price. John remembered his father's last offer.

"Jack," he said as he stood glowering at the Negro, "I want this land and I'm tired of dickering for it. How much do you want for it?"

The old man was black and tall. He wore earrings, which vastly intrigued little John. He answered briefly, for himself and brothers.

"Won't sell!" Then they stalked away.

Old Pierce was furious. He called this mere "nigger stubbornness."

It was more. If the Negroes sold their land where would they go? What would they do for a living? But little John grew up despising Negroes as stubborn and thriftless. They did not send their children to school and the whites were glad they didn't. They did not attend town meetings nor vote, and the whites did not ask them to. They just let them alone or sometimes hired them at trifling wage when labor was scarce.

When the slavery controversy spread John Pierce, grown to manhood, saw that this Negro clan had lost most of their land, disintegrated and scattered. Some went South with the 54th colored volunteers.

Then the Pierce interests moved its headquarters to New York. John Pierce during the war had been a "copperhead." He did not believe in abolition and tried desperately to prevent Civil War. As a businessman he considered such a war suicide. It interfered with business. He himself had avoided participation in the war by buying himself a substitute; and one of young John's first experiences at the age of 12 was a brief view of the draft riot in New York, with blood running, and dying Negroes, and some hanging to lamp posts.

When in 1877 strikes broke out over his far-flung railway properties, Old John dismissed his employees, hired private police to shoot them, and appealed to the Government, which responded with alacrity; until suddenly the country faced another Civil War. Farmers in the West forced laws through actually giving states the right to fix railway rates; the despicable Supreme Court upheld these Granger laws, and they spread. The laborers formed unions and actually demanded a voice in settling the rate of wages. Although the reliable Democratic Party, shorn of its slavery heritage, came into power again in both House and Senate in 1878, yet beside them sat 15 Independent members elected by farmers and laborers.

Pierce was, by his own lights, an honest and deserving citizen. He was a typical, hard-bitten New England business man, and sitting in his simple but costly New York office this spring morning of 1880 he was a very angry man. He was talking to his close friend and business associate, Cyrus Field, who had just rebuilt the New York elevated railway system.

"By God, Cyrus, I've done as much for this country as the next man. I bought bonds, and loads of them, when they were down to 33. I supported the war; sent substitutes to the front and ran my enterprises at a loss. My money helped the Centennial in '76, and now just as business is picking up and things getting normal and profits beginning to appear, the damned workers on my railroads go on strike and try to start a revolution. I tell you, Cyrus, my business belongs to me and I'll run it as I damned please. I'll pay such wages as I think right and if anybody don't like them they can get out and let others who want to work take their places. If this God-damned government won't protect the right of a laborer to work, then I want to know it."

Pierce had been an exporter before the War; then had turned to manufacturing for the tariff-protected domestic market; then to transportation and railroads, especially the new Pennsylvania system which had just suffered from the strike of 1877. Just now he had entered the banking field to finance his own and other ventures.

"No lazy labor leader, nor dirty foreigner, nor slimy Catholic is going to tell me what wages to pay, what hours to work, or pry into my private income and ask how I earn or spend it."

Field called attention, as he had often before, to the South and especially Atlanta. "I was talking only yesterday to a bright young Southerner. The name was Grady—yes, Henry Grady, an impudent, hustling, self-confident Irishman —"

"Irishman!" growled old John Pierce.

"Oh, by descent only, second or third generation; but a fierce American and Southerner with new ideas. John must meet him."

"Meet whom?" asked John, the son, entering the office.

"Henry Grady of Atlanta—"

"Grady? Oh, I know him. He represents the *Herald* in the South. I'll have him in to dinner next time he's in town."

Young John had met Henry Grady on his first visit to Atlanta— a chunky, ebullient newspaper reporter who literally worshipped Northern Big Business and saw salvation in its advent into the postwar South. At 30, he was boyish-looking, with a round, kewpie-like head, and near-sighted. He had graduated from the University of Georgia in 1866 and then gone to the University of Virginia. College to Grady meant two things: oratory and writing. Nothing else mattered. His time was spent in effort and intrigue to gain some envied chance for an "Oration"; and a year after graduation he was writing for the *Atlanta Constitution* and editing a paper in a neighboring town. With true Southern gallantry he married his boyhood sweetheart and they lived together contentedly with several children until he died.

He investigated election frauds in Florida and was mixed up with the Ku Klux Klan in Georgia. He gave popular lectures. Writing and talking were his life, and it always seemed that he regarded events as things to write and talk about rather than as the real life of real people. He was positively thrilled when he saw the New York Stock Exchange. "Railroads as cards and millions for stakes," he sang.

He worshipped Industry as he saw it in action. He got a position as Southern correspondent on James Gordon Bennett's *Herald*, and then boldly approached Cyrus Field for a loan to buy a third interest in the *Atlanta Constitution*, the most thriving daily in the South. This loan he repaid from a "flier" on the stock exchange, and he began a fabulous career as prophet of the "New South." By his sheer drive and enthusiasm he burned himself out before he was fifty.

Grady first sharpened young Pierce's conception of the South and induced him to consider settling in Atlanta. For a long time the situation in Georgia had Pierce baffled and repelled. He saw the most astonishing gang rule of which he had ever known. It surpassed in many ways Tammany in New York.

He heard of the Triumvirate which had ruled Georgia before the War—straightforward men but hopelessly antediluvian in thought and outlook; the huge pro-consul, Cobb, who owned a thousand slaves and actually believed slavery was the ideal industrial system. He died with the war. Then Toombs, a robber baron of Falstaffian proportions who, ranting in Boston, threatened to auction his slaves on Bunker Hill. He was never reconstructed and fought Northern capital as he fought abolition. He was now a vast and tottering wreck of a drunkard, and Grady acted as his proud secretary, along with his newspaper work. Finally there was Alexander Stephens, a high hat, a vast black coat and a thin white face between, hiding a brain far too keen to be consistent. These had ruled Georgia until after the war.

As these leaders stepped off the stage, there came the most awful gang of which Pierce ever dreamed: shrewd, slick, courtly, who played the game of popular control to the limit. There was Joe Brown, the unctuous, conscienceless Puritan from Carolina; a stern, God-fearing Presbyterian who neither smoked nor drank and was successively unionist, secessionist, carpet-bagger, scalawag and professional Southerner. He served as governor, chief justice, railroad manipulator, lessee of state convicts, and United States Senator. He was rich and ostentatiously charitable.

His buddy Alfred Colquit, played the Southern planter; a Princeton graduate who raised 1000 bales of cotton on his ancestral Macon plantation; governor, railroad speculator, United States Senator, and courtly gentleman of the old school, whose fellow travellers, no more guilty than he, went to jail for bond frauds.

And finally, General John B. Gordon, the magnificent figure who played the Old Soldier game as it never has been played before or since. He had fought with Lee and surrendered with him at Appomattox; he was governor of Georgia and fellow-grafter with Huntington and old John Pierce in the Southern Pacific deal. By parading with the aged Jefferson Davis at the Confederate reunion at Montgomery, and later exhibiting his tottering guest at Atlanta, he secured for himself the United States Senatorship from the very hands of the triumphant Populists.

All this the enthusiastic Grady discussed with young Pierce and tried to convince him that the South was the place for him to settle. Grady represented the poorer white element of the South rather than the planters; but not the farming peasant, rather the emerging bourgeoisie, the trader, middleman and industrialist. He stood for the new Southern entrepreneur, needing capital, furnishing cheap labor and promising large returns with no squeamishness as to method.

Grady was a "natural" for this job because he believed in capitalist exploitation as he believed in God. He declared that "the self-made business man had sunk the cornerstone of the only aristocracy that America should know." He saw salvation in unhampered business development in the South. He knew but laughed off the present political gang rule. To be sure, the Triumvirate ruled the state, when one is governor, the other is chief justice, and the third United States senator; then the senator becomes governor and the governor, senator, and so on they toss the ball of power back and forth until the state, that is the mass of poor farmers and workers, are rising in arms—.

But Grady brushed this off. They could be controlled by influx of Northern capital and Northern business ideas. He ignored the fact that under Northern capital a quarter of the Georgia white mill-hands were under 17. Naturally the Farmers Alliance was growing in the state and now Populism. It had been growing for a decade.

"And it had reason. The basis of the Georgia farmer's life is cotton. Cotton has been falling continuously from 20 cents a pound in 1870 to 6 cents today. Not only that, land bears the brunt of taxation while stocks and bonds pay nothing. We must head off radicalism by increasing business. We must interest the North in a New South."

John from time to time let out some doubts which had arisen in his college days and had been emphasized by his travels South:

"Of one thing, Grady, I cannot feel as sure as you Southerners, and that is the future of Africa and Africans. I wonder if they can be written off as easily as you assume. Have you been watching Africa? I tell you the black world is stirring. Three big six-foot men are fighting. One is European and dead white from tuberculosis. He is rushing from the death which pursues him. The other is thick, stolid and red from the South African sun. He is fighting modern capital. The third is a black king calling his warriors and his witch gods to hold back the white flood."

Grady was impatient. "The blacks have no chance in the world. They lack brains. The Boers will be crushed by the invincible British Empire."

"I fear for that Empire," said Pierce. "I fear for White Supremacy. Of course, Rhodes firmly believes that the British are 'the first race in the world and the more of the world we inhabit the better it is for humanity.' He believes this, and shrinks at nothing to make it come true. He will crush Kruger and plant his own tomb on the heights of the royal Matoppos beside the murdered Lobengula—"

Grady laughed. "Stop ranting. Darkies will never rule; they can't. They can work and make the South rich. Come and help."

"How are you going to handle the Negroes in the South today?"

"All we got to do with them is to make them go to work, and get in enough capital to employ them and the whites. But the present triumvirate in Georgia is ruining the chances of our getting capital. They are manipulating the railroads for gain; exploiting the mines with convict labor and squeezing the farmers. Hell will be to pay unless we can pry them from their grip on the state and its resources and get an honest regime in power."

"Will that be easy?"

"Yes and no. Easy to dislodge them but difficult to replace them with honest men who know commerce and industry and what they require. If we replace them by radicals and anarchists we'll only get rid of thieves to welcome fools."

"I still don't see just where the Negroes come in."

"So far as the political picture is concerned they don't count. They've neither the brains nor morals. But as laborers they come in as the best, most docile and if well treated, the most willing labor force in America. Now see the danger: if they are brought back into politics you spoil your best workers and drive away capital. On the other hand, if we can ease out the white grafters, attract capital and placate and guide the farmers, a New South is born."

So Grady dined with the Pierces the next time he came to New York. Several Southerners sat down with them.

"Mr. Pierce," began a Charlestonian, "you think you got troubles; just look at us. Your laborers at least want to work. Ours don't. Ours want to go to college and learn Greek. And you Northerners are furnishing them with colleges. They want to vote and control our money and get themselves good-paying public offices. They want to sit at our tables and marry our daughters. And by God, Sir, we won't have it! I'll tell you the truth, we've stopped them voting; we've made them work or go to jail. We are going to force them to keep to themselves; live together, marry each other, have their own churches and schools. They can be as free as they want to be with themselves, but they can't force their company on us.

"We are glad to be rid of slavery. I used to support more lazy old 'niggers' than I could afford. Made and kept me poor. Now I'm tickled to death to have them take care of themselves. But they got to work. They can't loaf at other people's expense. If they'll work half as hard as the old 'niggers' used to work, I tell you Sir, we'll have a rich and prosperous South, and there won't be no strikes neither, and no trade unions."

Old John nodded complete agreement.

"And," added a Congressman from North Carolina, "there'll be the best opportunity for Northern investment on this continent, if not in the world."

"Let me add another idea," said young John Pierce. "I have spent considerable time in the South in the last two or three years. First of all, industry has begun a rush forward in the South. Your railroads have twice the mileage they had in 1860; industry like cotton spinning is increasing by leaps; other industries are rising. Prosperity faces you if you can get capital. Northern capital, afraid of labor unions here, will come to you if your labor conditions get better.

"What I see there is the responsibility not only of building up a satisfied Negro laboring class, but one which could be trained to keep white workers, North and South, from making unreasonable demands. We could say to the white labor leaders in the North: 'There are Negroes who can take your place and who ask less wage than you demand.' We could say to the Southern white artisan: 'There are Negroes right here ready to work for less than we pay you, therefore it would be wise if you refused to listen to revolutionary Northern union organizers.' Finally, we could say to the blacks: 'We are offering you work and wages which whites want; as long as you work faithfully and avoid unreasonable demands you'll have good jobs.' "

The South Carolinian gave enthusiastic assent. The other Congressmen were a bit disturbed. Said one: "I wouldn't favor threatening white labor with black competition."

"I'll threaten the damned Socialists with any weapon I can get before I'll let them interfere with my property," said old John tersely.

But young John added a further suggestion. "The blacks could never really compete," he said, "if they were disfranchised."

"Of course not," retorted a North Carolinian, "but ain't Negro suffrage a main demand of the North?"

John spoke slowly in answer. He was really searching his own mind for his conclusions as to Democracy. "We Northerners of course believe in Democracy. But Democracy is not suited to all people at all times. There must be a period of apprenticeship. It would have been better if this trial period in the case of the Negroes had been longer, much longer. But as it is, we are not helpless. The courts can interpret the unseemly haste of Congress. I think you see how this will work. Already, in the Slaughterhouse cases in 1873, the extreme interpretation of the 14th Amendment has been tempered. In fact, it will now protect our investments better than the rights of Negroes."

"The Supreme Court is a set of fools," retorted Old John, thinking of the Railway Commissions.

"Yet," answered one of his directors, "they are usually on the right side. When they are not, we can get better appointments."

"Certainly," Young John agreed. "Just yesterday I had assurances that the outrageous Civil Rights Legislation will soon be annulled by the Supreme Court. I think I do not exaggerate when I say that the North, led by business interests which have suffered grievously from extreme democracy at home, will acquiesce in this new interpretation of Negro rights."

The Southerners looked gratified; but John added, "Of course a main prerequisite will be a satisfied mass of black labor. They must not feel abused, as they undoubtedly do at present. We must yield to their laudable desire for education, but temper it with common sense, giving a reasonable amount and kind. We must above all see that they get proper leadership within their own ranks."

Old John was gratified at his son's words. It showed a ripening of judgment and a sureness of decision which had hitherto been lacking. Young John himself was a bit surprised. His mind had been half-consciously coming to conclusions over which he had long hesitated. He was going to cast his lot in the South. His friendship with Henry Grady helped his decision.

Young John was a contrast to his father. Old John was tall and thin, scraggly, carelessly dressed, with an abrupt if not gruff manner. Young John was dressed well in tailored clothes. He looked prosperous without being showy, and he gave one a certain feeling of confidence in his judgments. He had been trained at Andover and Princeton and sent South after graduation to look over this new territory for industrial expansion. Old John Pierce believed in early marriage and half hoped young John would marry one of those pretty and aristocratic Southern girls whom he himself so admired. But to his disgust John had married Kate Gibbons, an Irish girl.

New England was liberal and anti-slavery, but it disliked the Irish and the Catholic church intensely. Had it not been for the railroad strikes and the adaptability of young John's wife, he and his father might have seriously quarrelled. But the old man needed his son's experience and help and Kate helped by promptly dropping her religion and joining the Congregational Church. The appearance of a healthy boy in 1881 halted hostilities, although old John was never quite reconciled. Nor were the young couple satisfied. New York society ignored the Irish wife even of a rich Pierce, and John for some time was not decided whether to settle down here or in the South. His decision came after that dinner in New York to which he invited Grady.

"We'll have the Democrats in the White House in a few years," Field assured them, "but we must keep them from fighting the war over again."

"Yes," said old John Pierce, "but what about labor? We've got good laborers rushing to us by the hundreds of thousands and being ruined and turned into anarchists by these damned unions. You've got millions of Negroes—can they work and will they?"

Grady became earnest: "They can work and they must if they want to eat. But they must be kept out of politics. Just as you Northerners must and will control the Labor vote, so we Southerners must control Negroes in politics."

After dinner, with the older man gone, young John Pierce and Grady, with Kate and the awakened baby, sat long and talked.

Kate was fed up on New York. "I'll never get a chance here and I'll keep John back. The Dutch will never recognize the Irish. I want John to go South. How would I be received in the South?"

"Well," said Grady, "both of you must remember one thing. If you go South you must conform. It will be difficult but it is inevitable. The South has been hurt to its guts. It has been fed for a century on tales of its bravery, beauty and culture. Then in a war where victory was certain, it was whipped not simply by Yankees but actually by help of armed 'niggers.'

"As a spiritual upset this was simply unendurable. Now comes the Cult and Creed: 'The South was right; the Negro is fit only for slavery and must not vote; the South was never conquered and never will be.' If you grant these propositions you can help build a new South with docile black labor, Northern capital and white brains. But you must grant the propositions; you must conform; you must talk and make speeches in support of this. Otherwise you're a 'Damnyankee' and a 'nigger' lover and can never belong."

Kate laughed. "I might get my daddy's Confederate Commission and his forage cap and pose as an honest-to-goodness Secessionist—"

"What!" exclaimed Grady, and John scowled. The frank Kate explained:

"It's all a joke. You see, my Dad, Pat Gibbons, a little down at the heels in 1860, was representing a loan-shark outfit in Georgia when the war broke. He tried desperately to get away but was caught in the draft, and making a virtue of necessity joined the company, became its captain, and was 'missing' after the first fray."

Kate and her frail little mother had been hard put. The mother went into house service until 1864 when Pat Gibbons, after an incredible series of adventures, made his way through the army lines and turned up in New York with a small bank roll derived from illegal trade. There, with irrepressible energy and impudence he became a member of Tammany and got hold of a profitable street contract.

In ten years he had made a modest fortune by methods not to be inquired into; had installed his weary wife and little daughter into a west-side brownstone front, and then died of drink just before Tammany Tweed burst into infamy. His sad little Irish wife obediently followed him, leaving Kate lonely but fairly well-to-do in cruel postwar New York. Kate met John in one of the innumerable bazaars which swarmed in the city for relief of the soldiers, the South and the Freedmen. The Vandeventer debutante whom John was escorting looked down her thin, straight nose at Kate's pert snubbiness when the Irish girl inveigled herself into their company uninvited. The Vandeventer girl soon found excuse to withdraw.

This was a tactical error, for John was fed up with her cold, high breeding, and fell willing victim to the good-looking, healthy and terribly frank Kate. They were soon laughing at the deserter, the whole company, and the world in general. Kate threw herself at the young banker without reserve. He was the only gentleman of the new order she had met after the dubious politicians of the East Side, and she wanted terribly to be a lady with such a husband. While John, just past the wilder and unsatisfactory indulgences of early youth was drawn to this honest, red-blooded, even if slightly over-dressed and vulgar girl. He found himself gradually forsaking prim and snobbish society for Kate's welcome warmth and joy in life; until one night they ran over to Connecticut, married, and spent a delirious week's honeymoon.

Old John was furious. He glared at the returned couple in grim anger. "My God! My son hitched to an Irish paddy and a damned Catholic!" But old John was no fool. After all, the boy was married, the girl was no drab nor mere fortune-hunter, and this was his only son. The boy had ability and John Pierce and Son needed all the ability and hard work they could muster.

This miserable escapade gave the old man a handle to put the screws on the young one, to taunt him with dilettante indifference to real energy and interest in the affairs of the firm. In this he found he had a firm and intelligent ally in Kate. Moreover, Kate could cook. So an offensive and defensive alliance was achieved quietly in the Fifth Avenue mansion of the Pierces. Society bowed unenthusiastically and slowly to wealth, and business began to boom. It was, old John decided, not so bad after all.

It was the outline of this story which Kate, at first to John's discomfort and then to his inevitable enjoyment, insisted on telling to young Henry Grady. Grady shouted with laughter.

"Listen," he said as he left, "bring that Commission and the forage cap along when you come to Atlanta. As a Daughter of the Confederacy you'll go further than your banker husband."

Thus young John and Kate settled in Atlanta the year that Cleveland became the first Democratic president since the war. John entered the largest bank in this city as an official and in charge of his father's railroad and investment interests. He came South with an increasingly clear program: control labor in the South without disorder; make the Negroes a satisfied working class with good paying jobs and education limited to their needs; develop Southern industry, trade and commerce and tie it in with Northern investment. The South was the critical area of the modern world. He gradually forgot Africa. He had few actual contacts with Negroes. He was in close touch with Grady.

"I tell you, Grady, how to begin. I'll get the New England Society of New York to invite you as speaker at their next dinner. We'll get the biggest capitalists of the country to be present. You lay the 'New South' on the line thick. Treat the planters and the carpet-baggers as dead, and the Negro Problem as settled. Grady, we'll start a new era!"

"Good, I'll try it. But there's one hitch. There is a man here in Georgia who may upset the apple cart. He's a little red-headed shrimp named Watson. He's a curious mixture: son of an Augusta cotton mill hand and a small south Georgia farmer. He's served one term in the Legislature and put up a fierce fight against Colquit, the gang governor. Then he got discouraged and sulked ten years. Now he's hobnobbing with the Farmers Alliance and the western malcontents who are causing you and your father so much uneasiness. They are piling into the crazy farmers' cooperative movement.

"If some combination including these elements should gain control of Georgia and the South it would repel instead of attract Northern capital and sound industrial organization. We've got to watch this. Right now there's a deal on foot between Gordon and Colquit which, if it goes through, may raise such a stink as to put the radicals in power before we can head them off. Populism is growing fast in Georgia."

Pierce and Grady kept in close conference as soon as young John was permanently settled in Atlanta. Pierce decided:

"As a long range project we must rush legal disfranchisement of Negroes. Otherwise we'll have a labor revolt in the South to join the wild west. Mississippi has started. Tillman is at work in South Carolina. We must push it in Louisiana and Georgia and Alabama. The Republicans are pushing a Force Bill to give the Federal government charge of national elections. This is so unpopular it should help us disfranchise Negroes.

"Remember, we've got all the money back of us that the situation calls for. And now to this other business: I'm going to settle down here as a full-fledged Atlantan. I want to buy or build a house and get to know the proper people, clubs, etc."

"I'll help; but be careful. Even I am a social outsider. Just because Atlanta has no society like Augusta or Macon, it's sensitive and snooty, especially in the case of Yankees. You'll have to go whole hog with them for success.

"Now it happens I have a good starting point. There is a woman in town with money to invest. She is a Breckinridge of Charleston, married to the old fogy who's at the University of Georgia. She wants financial advice and came to Clark Howell, my boss, who runs with quality. He told her of you as a new official at what will soon be our biggest bank, and since I know you, I'm to bring her to your office tomorrow afternoon. You give her inside financial advice in return for a social steer. Of course, you'll do this with care."

Thus Betty Lou Breckinridge Baldwin came to know John Pierce and they liked each other. Betty Lou left a check for over $100,000 for investment; also, she gave John sound social advice.

"Of course, as you doubtless know, Atlanta has no real society. It is a poor-white town, energetic and commendable but unknown in the best Southern circles. But I have some friends to whom I shall be glad to present you and especially your wife who, I understand, is a Daughter of the Confederacy. That's good! You must, of course, build far out on Peachtree among the more select folk. I and my son live out there. But where is Dr. Baldwin? He's getting so old and forgetful.

"I brought some papers of settlement which I want signed and put in a safe-deposit box. You understand that the money in our family is mine, but I want to make suitable arrangements for my elderly husband, a precious soul—a close friend of my dear father —but a scholarly fogy and always late. You'll smile when I tell you that this minute he is visiting the colored college near here and I fear has quite forgotten me and the Board meeting."

Meantime the double plan of Pierce and Grady for North and South both matured and lost ground. In the South the groundwork of race division on which Grady depended as immovable began to give way under Watson's drive. While on the other hand, Grady's influence in the North flourished and spread. The orator was a Southern institution. He was more emotional and less reasoning than the Greek who was his prototype. Before the war he adopted the great voice, majestic mien and broad gestures. He was strongly emotional but carefully tempered this with disciplined culture. After the Civil War came orators from nearer the masses who had been deeply imbued with the methods of the Negro preacher. The full voice now chanted in rhythm, the gestures were more frequent and wilder, and the emotions were frankly shown in tears and physical gyrations.

Henry Grady was invited north in 1896 to address the New England Society of New York, of which old John Pierce was president. He had Irish wit and Southern fire. He applied Southern oratory to Northern business. He was the first to sentimentalize on the "Black Mammy." He earnestly poured this philosophy of a new business South into eager ears. This elaborate gathering of well-fed diners represented millions seeking safe investment and only afraid of labor revolt. Grady reassured his audience:

"There was a South of Secession and Slavery. That South is dead!" He added, "The Negro as a political force has dropped out of serious consideration."

And the unspoken corollary followed: with five million disfranchised black workers, five million white workers would not dare to strike.

The North received this speech with wide acclaim. It sighed with relief. It liked the unaccustomed oratory applied to hard, dull business. The results were soon evident. Between 1880 and 1890 the number of spindles in the cotton mills in the South doubled and the value of their products quadrupled. In Georgia railway mileage tripled and property value jumped from $250 million to $820 million. Grady howled with delight.

"We have sowed towns and cities in the place of theories, and put business in place of politics. We have challenged your spinners in Massachusetts and your ironmakers in Pennsylvania . . . wiped out the place where Mason and Dixon's line used to be, and hung out a latchstring to you and yours. . . . We have fallen in love with work. Every train brings manufacturers from the East and West seeking to establish themselves or their sons near the raw material in this growing market. Let the fullness of the tide roll in. Plenty rides on the springing harvests."

McClure and "Pig-Iron" Kelly applauded. President Cleveland and his bride came to Atlanta, received guests under Grady's chaperonage and characteristically dined with Gordon and Colquit.

The employers who listened to Grady knew that their control of the labor vote in the North was waning. The Knights of Labor had been formed in 1869, but grew rapidly after 1881 and welcomed Negroes after 1883 when it had over a half million members. It began to win strikes, but the employers fought back bitterly and killed it with the Haymarket Riot in 1886 for which it was not responsible. That year the American Federation of Labor was formed, less radical and for the most part excluding Negroes.

But despite labor revolt Capital was riding high. One great industrialist said, "The public be damned!" Another added, "If a workman sticks up his head, hit it!" Another: "Law? What do I care for the law?" And the King of Bankers declared, "I owe the public nothing. Men owning property should do what they like with it."

By 1880 Standard Oil was in control of the whole industry. In two decades the railroads tripled in mileage, quadrupled in capital and shrunk in number of owners. Trusts controlled sugar, whiskey, tobacco, salt, tinplate and steel; and by 1890, 157 of them had three billions of capital. There were 4000 millionaires. But revolution loomed and in the South Tom Watson was becoming its embodiment.

Grady, although alarmed at the Populist movement in Georgia, was not discouraged. He rushed wildly on with his writing, travel and speaking. He had kept close touch with the Farmers Alliance in Georgia, addressing them annually and devoting a column of the *Constitution* to them.

But Grady was tired. He had been speaking to vast audiences over the nation for years. To him speaking was great physical effort and nervous tension. A speech was always preceded by endless conversation with all kinds of persons; and with eating elaborate dinners. Then there were the long trips almost invariably at night; and he never got real rest in a Pullman.

He was worried. His wife had had a miscarriage and he had lost $8,000 gambling in cotton futures. In 1889 he had spoken in Georgia in March, in New York in April, in Virginia in June, in South Carolina in July, and in Georgia in August. Then at the Piedmont Second Exposition in October, just before the primary vote, he spoke on Farmers Alliance day in Atlanta and made his supreme appeal not to economics nor politics but to race prejudice. He warned against union of blacks and whites in Georgia politics.

"Whom God has separated, let no man bring together!"

Chapter IX

OLD DR. BALDWIN AND HIS FAMILY

For Dr. Baldwin a new life had begun. The State University was an old institution; but had for years been poorly supported, with tumbledown buildings and yet with certain tradition. Dr. Baldwin loved the institution where he first studied; it was something to build on and he liked to dream of what it could become for guiding the South to a new destiny.

Quite characteristically his mind had worked on, with little interruption because of the marriage. They had rebuilt and refurnished the old presidential mansion, using some of the funds which the Colonel had given them. They had social contacts with members of the faculty and the community and a few of the older students. On the whole, life had renewed interest for Dr. Baldwin, and as for Betty Lou it was more livable than anything she had expected. She did not pretend that she was exactly happy, but she was at peace and safe.

Colonel Breckinridge too, liked the old rambling neglected place which had a niche in the hearts of a large number of alumni. He liked to talk again with Dr. Baldwin about the world. He sat in some of his classes. He heard with distress about the Mahdi in the Sudan, and his driving out of the British. He was astonished at the efforts of Italy to annex Ethiopia. But he was not sure that the world was going right even when by accident a gentleman like Arthur became president and the Democratic party for the first time since the Civil War might in a few years return to power. World commerce was increasing, railroads were pushing all over the country; life insurance had doubled and telephones were coming into use.

But gradually the Colonel became uneasy. He could not forget that Mansart boy. He began to have the shadow of a headache, which was not quite a headache yet would not go away. He was not as aware of the world about him as he had been. He became forgetful in annoying and inexplicable ways. Then he began to have startling dreams, when he could sleep at all. He began to see things which others apparently did not see. He had visions. It was not sudden or startling, but people began to ask after his health solicitously, which annoyed him more than it should have. Once or twice he lost his bearings in broad daylight.

Once he found himself almost raving at a stranger because of a blood stain which was not there. Once he shouted and shrieked at a band of mounted murderers, who were but white hunters returning from the country. Once he found his wife lying bloody and dead among the lilacs of a public park. The doctors who were called in advised rest and later, travel, perhaps abroad. But Betty Lou revealed another remedy.

At dinner one night, after the maid had withdrawn, she announced to her father and husband that she was expecting to have a baby in a couple of months. Then she kissed them and went upstairs. Both men were astounded, but neither so astonished as Betty Lou herself. Betty was thirty and her husband sixty-five. She had never been promiscuous; never but once had she forgotten her birth and blood. But especially here in Athens she had close and personal friends. Her husband's caresses had been rare and she had endured them with composure if not enthusiasm.

Dr. Baldwin himself knew that the prospective child might be his. He also did not try to hide from himself the fact that it might not be. In that case he did not care. There was always gossip in a university town. Betty Lou was young and loved company. This child would be company to her. After all, physical paternity was unimportant. It was education that counted and he would have the privilege of training this child.

The Colonel was at first shocked and then uplifted. For a moment black suspicion engulfed him; but the complacency of the father and his own firm faith in the women of his family drove this instantly away. There followed a flood of exaltation. The Breckinridge family would live again. His name was redeemed. He had become used to thinking of his family as dying out with him; of then himself escaping from settling the problems of the world. And now miraculously he was to live again. His health became better and he began to plan.

He could not help but think of that healthy little black boy and to wonder how his and his own grandchild's lives were going to meet and intertwine in the world. He altered his will both for the benefit of his grandchild who would get the bulk of his fortune, and to insert a sum of $2500 for Mirandy Mansart and her child.

The long days and months went slowly by, with exaltation and disgust for Betty Lou. She soon made up her mind that she would never live permanently in Athens. It was a stodgy little university town, full of gossip and envy. Betty Lou knew that she, especially, was the subject of slighting remarks and unpleasant glances, along with perfect courtesy for the Dean, as Dr. Baldwin was designated. There had even been some cases of social ostracism, which Dr. Baldwin never noticed but which she would never forget.

The question of the future of the university dragged on, but Betty Lou was thrilled by the activities of a group of alumni who insisted that the place of the old university was in the new city of Atlanta which had no institution of higher learning, unless one counted the Negro college, which one did not. A committee on this matter met several times at the University and Betty Lou saw to it that they were pleasantly entertained; and the legislature in Atlanta helped things on by refusing decent and necessary appropriations for the University. It was openly whispered that the legislature might be more generous to an Atlanta institution.

Then at last the strain of waiting was over. In an Atlanta hospital Betty Lou in blood, pain and filth gave birth to a little boy in the summer of 1881. A few days later, in the beautiful suite of a new Peachtree Street hotel, Colonel John Breckinridge held in his arms at a baptismal font, John Breckinridge Du Bignon Baldwin; while old Dr. Baldwin stood smiling by. The Colonel gave his grandson to the arms of radiant Betty Lou, turned slowly to sit down, and died of a cerebral hemorrhage.

Betty Lou was sincerely grieved. In the last months she had come to know and sympathize with her father as never before in their lives. She wanted him to travel and meet more men of his kind. But the baby intervened and now he was dead.

But of another plan Betty Lou was now certain. She was going to live in Atlanta, this developing giant of a city; her boy was going to grow up there. The social advantage of Breckrinridge and Du Bignon aristocratic blood in a poor white city could not be ignored. To this Betty Lou insisted on adding a rumored relationship of her husband to Abraham Baldwin, founder of the University of Georgia. Next, Betty Lou helped the alumni committee to finance offices of the University in Atlanta where her husband could spend part of his time, meet business men and legislators, and prepare for the final transformation.

To this Betty Lou added a calculation and re-investment of her new wealth. She was rich and sole executive, and did business with an old banking house which had just taken into partnership young

John Pierce of the well-known firm of John Pierce and Son of nationwide fame. With this young man about her own age, who had a son also just born, she consulted. She was affronted to learn that her father had left $2,500 to the Mansart boy. Of course, her father never knew that old Aunt Betsy had bilked her out of five hundred dollars for a nursing job some years ago; and Betty Lou had never forgiven this pair for daring to leave her employ at such short notice when her father came to visit. She arranged without difficulty for the Mansart bequest to be reduced to five hundred dollars. With the other two thousand she bought a fur coat which she had glimpsed at Rich's department store. What, after all, did Negroes need of all that money?

Dr. Baldwin meantime was seeking to build a real university with headquarters at Athens or possibly later at Atlanta. He really did not care which, if the plans were right. What he was trying to do was readjust his thinking and teaching to a new situation. He had seen the Carolina experiment fail; the attempt to build a new agriculture with free, educated, enfranchised black laborers. He saw it die a bloody death in 1876.

In its wake came a harvest of lawlessness, lynching and misuse of the courts to reestablish slavery, which he knew must eventually fail, or establish a new, modern caste system which he doubted could succeed. And it was all so unnecessary. He still stuck to his thesis that nothing was to be feared from a little education given to a few Negroes of moderate ability.

This new city of Atlanta was situated between the old aristocracy of Carolina and the newer cotton kingdom of the Mississippi valley. And it was the natural highway for the incoming Northern industrial invasion. This prospective change vastly interested Dr. Baldwin.

Dr. Baldwin had not finally been confirmed as head of the University of Georgia. That functionary was called the "Chancellor" and had long been a figurehead for advertising purposes. Recently it had even been proposed to make the aging Jefferson Davis chancellor. But there was need of a real head and director of education at the university, which the former students of Dr. Baldwin knew he was fitted to fill. He therefore became "Dean" at a fair salary, and was in charge of educational policy and teaching while money-raising and speech-making remained with the unfilled office of Chancellor.

Matters moved very slowly from 1880 to 1890. Industry and capital rolled into Atlanta and politics grew grim. Old Man Baldwin was repelled. He had seen politicians try to settle human problems and the mess they had made of it. Of Economics he knew nothing. Work was natural, wage was necessary; but this rising cry of the farmers could not be a matter of politics. It was a matter of work. He regarded Watson as a demagogue and was attracted by the young Grady. In 1889, during one of his visits to Atlanta to see his young son now eight years of age, and to consult with the University committee, he slipped out to Piedmont Exposition Park one golden October afternoon and listened to Henry Grady.

Grady was standing before the 10,000 farmers and their wives, a bulky, beaming cherub, exuding good nature.

"Hello, folks!" He told two rattling good stories and had them yelling with laughter. Then he roared; he raised himself on his toes and flailed with his arms. He thundered; his hair flew and the sweat poured down his face. Blood suffused his fat cheeks.

There came a sudden calm as the audience bent forward in tense expectation. With tremolo in his voice he turned to God and religion. His finger pointed to heaven, he raised himself on his toes. His deep voice swelled again with emotion and tears were in his eyes as he shrieked.

"Whom God has separated, let no man bring together!"

Baldwin was repelled. He did not like emotional appeal in political speeches. It was to his mind too negroid, a white imitation of Negro methods.

Grady's speech was the studied histrionics of an experienced actor who believed in his role. Every gesture, every cadence was calculated, and the real man was hidden watchfully behind the act to weigh its effect on his audience. And that effect was not satisfactory.

Baldwin noted the considerable number of Negroes present, mostly segregated in groups by themselves, but not entirely. Down in front he saw the handsome Negro Doyle, Watson's confederate, looking at Grady with concentrated unwinking attention. Grady himself must have felt that his climactic final appeal to race separation did not go over so well as usual and the applause, while heavy, was not tumultuous.

Baldwin could see that Grady was exhausted. He must have known that he was ill and perhaps feared that he and his party would be beaten in the next election. He saw black and white labor hand in hand marching to victory. They would not win. With the Gang in control of elections they could not win no matter how many votes they cast. But they would be beaten by force, not as he planned by capital, industry and prosperity in a New South.

As Baldwin later heard, Grady had an attack of vertigo after the speech and went to bed. But he would not rest. In December he rushed to Boston to address the Merchants Association; and then, of all places and times, he went to Plymouth Rock where, standing barehead, he made his last speech. With a cold and chill he returned south, and within a week was dead.

Dr. Baldwin was deeply disappointed; nor did the election of Tom Watson to Congress the next year make him any happier. He regarded Watson as a demagogue and would not listen to his tirades. He insisted that education, not politics, was the panacea for the South. He was therefore encouraged when a new development to his university plans began to evolve. Hitherto the push to Atlanta as the future seat of a state university had come from the alumni of the Athens institution. Now came a pull from Atlanta itself. Atlanta had money. It had no white college. Atlanta needed a university.

The captains of industry, conspiring with Betty Lou Baldwin, proposed, back of the facade of old Dr. Baldwin's reputation, to transfer the University of Georgia—or at least its more substantial departments, to Atlanta. For this object a Committee for the Expansion and Development of the University of Georgia was formed and installed in appropriate offices in Atlanta which Betty Lou kindly furnished. Here meetings were held, and to attend one of these Dr. Baldwin was in town in the Spring of 1890.

He was educating his young men to take part in a new developing world and in that world he was against lawlessness, dishonesty and graft; and against poor and careless government; against courts which were being diverted from their normal function and used to keep Negroes in slavery. Also, he was interested in the rising Negro. To Dr. Baldwin life was education; to the training of reason and knowing of facts all human problems would yield. Thus the Negro Problem was a problem of education and as such was simple: Negroes could not be educated; that is, most Negroes. A few—a very few—might take some training. It would be interesting to know how many; just what proportion of the overwhelming mass.

He talked frankly to his young men. This attempt to put the Negro down was all so unnecessary.

"You do not have to organize and fight in order to keep people down who are naturally down, who are born down, and who by no possibility can rise very far. What you have to do is to be patient and intelligent. You must understand the tragedy, especially the tragedy of the few Negroes, the very few, who are above the mass; they must have a chance. You don't need to segregate them or to crucify they. They would not go very far, or if a few of them did, what of it? It was rather to their credit and to the advantage of the world. Let them have their little chance. All this turmoil and fear and fighting was ridiculous. The great mass of Negroes would always stay in their places.

"If some persons try to lift themselves by their bootstraps, it is not necessary to argue with them or seek to stop them. The effort would stop itself in time and in a comparatively short time. The capacity of Negroes is small. I have known them all my life. They were funny, bizarre, faithful, imitative; but they did not have brains."

Of course, Dr. Baldwin admitted there were some exceptions; a few here and there. He admitted that as a matter of fact he really knew very few Negroes intimately. His contacts had been narrow, and contacts of opinions and beliefs rather than of persons. He was rather interested in seeking to learn how far these new Northern teachers agreed with his conclusions. He did not wait to be introduced; he sought out one or two teachers in Augusta and talked with them. Some of them he concluded were frustrated old maids, teaching more or less mechanically what they had learned in the North; sincere and honest, but having indifferent results.

He had once visited one or two colored schools in Carolina and South Georgia and laughed at what they were doing. A few pupils were learning to read and write. Most of them were floundering helplessly. Negro colleges were entirely unnecessary, and probably high school education for the great mass would be unsuccessful. He didn't think much of the people who were educating the Negroes. Some of them he met and recognized as good-hearted folk without very sound classical training. He was quite willing to cooperate with them, and he liked to talk about their Negro students.

There was, of course, some capacity there, certain exceptions, but the exceptions were few. Some of the white Northern teachers agreed with him; others seemed to him fanatical and wanted to establish colleges. He saw their argument, so far as it was valid. You must have teachers for these Negro schools and that implied some education but not a regular college course; a normal school of some sort, yes, that certainly should be established.

For some time after coming to his new work he lost touch with Negro education. But today he was in town on business for the

University of Georgia and incidentally to visit with his wife and infant son in the new house they had built far out on Peachtree. He was received casually and hurried off so as not to be late for a University Board meeting which was to convene at three. He found he had plenty of time and it occurred to him to drop out Mitchell Street and visit the Negro campus, with its high green lawn. Just as he was about to mount the stone steps he met a young man and stopped him to ask directions. The young man was Manuel Mansart.

Dr. Baldwin was quite evidently out of place on the campus of Atlanta University. He looked the Southern gentleman of the old school; rather more carelessly dressed than was customary, and peering about nearsightedly and undecidedly. He saw Manuel and hailed him in his high, shrill voice.

"Hey, Boy!"

This was, of course, the wrong beginning and stamped him as a white Southerner. College students at Atlanta University were not "boys." They were men. Then Manuel recognized Dr. Baldwin, but of course the old man did not know him after ten years. He looked the "boy" over and was favorably impressed. He forgot his original query and began to talk.

"You a student here?"

"Yes, Sir."

"Like it?"

"Very much, Sir."

"What are you going to be when you finish?"

"I don't know, Sir. Grandmother wanted me to be a preacher; Mammy wanted me to be a lawyer. I think I'll probably teach."

"Because you want to tell what you know, or because it's the easiest job to get?"

"Because I want to learn."

Dr. Baldwin stopped and stared. "Well, young man (no more 'boy'), you are on the right track. But—(remembering his color again), there are other things to do: carpentry, cooking—" He peered at the boy.

Manuel stiffened and started to say, "But I don't want to work for white folk." But he caught himself and remembered that Dr. Baldwin was white as well as Southern. He ended by saying, "I'd prefer teaching, Sir."

"Hm!" said Dr. Baldwin. "I was just looking about—"

"Wouldn't you like to meet our professor of Greek?" Of course Manuel knew that Greek was Dr. Baldwin's hobby.

"Greek?" said the old man. "Do you have Greek here?"

"Oh, yes Sir." And then Manuel reeled off the learning of Professor Spence. "He was, Sir, a pupil of the great D'Ooge."

Baldwin stared, then said eagerly, "Take me to him. I'd like to see him." And to himself, "What on earth can a pupil of D'Ooge find to do here?"

Then he had an experience which he always remembered. He met Professor Spence, and Professor Spence was a man from the University of Michigan who knew Greek. He knew an extraordinary amount of Greek. He was a great Greek scholar! Dr. Baldwin thrilled to converse with him and almost forgot the real reason for which he had scraped his acquaintance. He said finally, as he turned back to it, "But Spence, why on earth did you leave your professorship to come down here and teach Negroes?"

Professor Spence was a little man, and kindly. He smiled and said, "I like Negroes and enjoy teaching."

"But teaching them what?" asked Dr. Baldwin.

"Stay over for my class this afternoon."

So Dr. Baldwin stayed; he found himself to his dismay eating lunch in a basement dining room with Professor Spence and his frail wife, his little daughter and six Negro students. The students did not eat with their knives, and talked frankly to him, to the Spences and to each other. They used good English. Dr. Baldwin smiled at this situation and wondered what his students would say; and his wife? Then he accompanied the sprightly Spence to his rather bare classroom and sat down with the professor, three young men and a young woman. They were all colors from white to black, and indifferently dressed; but old Dr. Baldwin being a scholar at heart and knowing Greek, forgot all about who they were.

To Dr. Baldwin that was an unforgettable afternoon meeting with a great student of the matchless Greek tongue; marching once more and in dark companionship with Xenophon down to the sea. But with it went the scholarship of Spence,—the exact knowledge, the broad background, the human sympathy—it was not often one could know such an afternoon.

As he thought the matter over later, he honestly concluded that his experience there was about the same thing as his experience in his own classes. Except there were two masters of Greek and one black boy who—well, if he hadn't been black would have made a third master of Greek! Yes, he certainly would! Baldwin mused. There might be a great many more exceptional Negroes than he had thought formerly was in any way possible. In fact, he began carefully to examine the idea of the possibility that the mass of Negroes were much more susceptible to training and capable of attaining higher status than he had ever dreamed. He wanted to talk, to question, but— He happened to glance at his watch. It was four o'clock. Good lord! His wife! He was to have met her at three. —He telephoned immediately.

John Pierce and Betty Lou drove up to Atlanta University to summon Dr. Baldwin from Professor Spence's Greek class. He was was all apologies for his tardiness and started to explain. Betty Lou was a bit short but hastened to introduce Mr. Pierce of New York, the well-known member of the staff of the First National Bank. Dr. Baldwin then turned to introduce Professor Spence; but Spence had discreetly slipped away and President Sheldon of Atlanta University stepped up to take his place. Betty Lou acknowledged the introduction stiffly and was evidently in a hurry to depart. John Pierce was glad to meet Sheldon and see this Negro school to which his father had contributed, but evidently this was not the time to linger. He shook Sheldon's hand cordially and they drove rapidly away. Sheldon was glad of this opportunity to meet one of the rich Northern donors to his poor school.

Dr. Baldwin climbed awkwardly into the carriage and entertained him and his wife with a dissertation on the possibilities of the Negro brain and indeed, any brain, under a man like Spence. Betty Lou was speechless and Pierce monosyllabic. The colored coachman seemed curiously pleased.

Dr. Baldwin had listened to Booker Washington. He thought him shrewd and tactful, but wise only if the South was ready generously to respond to his proffered compromise. This, Dr. Baldwin feared, was not the case. He had learned much since his visits to Atlanta had brought him in touch with current events in the South. He saw proposals being made which argued ill for any real education for Negroes. He could not forget that class in Greek at Atlanta University. What would happen to a disfranchised, servile caste, deprived of having any of its genius free to soar? He was afraid.

His theories on race and progress came to be seriously at odds with those of his trustees and many of the alumni. He could not be summarily dismissed from his position; he had become an institution and a legend. It was better to leave him alone, while narrowing his power and limiting his salary. Meantime, to his family he was an increasing annoyance. The young mother and son lived in

Atlanta, where their own fortune and his increasing income enabled them to live in simple elegance. They referred to the father with a shrug; a difficult person, not quite normal. In fact, the boy at 14 had been brought up always to regard his father as queer and negligible.

One thing alone made the family and friends of Dr. Baldwin patient. He was 75 years old and while still in apparent good health, it would be necessary to retire him soon if he did not die. Meantime, he was becoming difficult because of his outspoken words and theories. It was reported that at one of the Board meetings Baldwin had actually suggested that the new university include the Negro Atlanta University as an integral part. As everybody was too astonished to open his mouth, the heretical remark went by without comment. Later the Doctor in class commented on the rising Populist Movement as "perhaps the voice of the People conscious of a new democracy, including the Poor and Black."

This set off a bitter discussion which reverberated over the State. The resignation or dismissal of the Dean was seriously considered. But wiser counsels prevailed.

However, hearing of this, it occurred to young Mansart that in some way he ought to arrange for Dr. Baldwin to meet and talk with Sebastian Doyle. This took some manipulation, for the meeting of black and white in the South on any level above that of race subordination, was difficult. However, Manuel finally wrote to Dr. Baldwin inviting him to attend a conference at Atlanta University, the Negro college, to meet and talk with Dr. Crogman, Miss Freiburg and Sebastian Doyle. Dr. Baldwin was delighted and came, telling his wife frankly where he was going.

Betty Lou was beside herself with rage, but the old man took no notice of it. When he returned after lunch he reported a very interesting time. Betty fumed, "Why in God's name doesn't the old fossil die?"

Chapter X

THE VISION OF SEBASTIAN DOYLE

Young Sebastian Doyle was a handsome man. He was one of those dark blonds of Negro and white blood which sometimes makes the most beautiful beings on earth. He was physically perfect, with erect carriage and resonant, well-modulated musical voice. He had a brilliant mind, trained under wise old Dr. Crogman at Clark University, a colored Methodist school in South Atlanta. Here too, he got his ideal of moral integrity.

He was in college at Ohio Wesleyan with the son of Governor Foraker and other young westerners who received him as friend and equal. Here he got his vision of life and his knight-errantry for real sacrifice and hard work. He went out into rural Georgia in 1890 at the age of 23 as a teacher, and in 1892 took his first charge as a Methodist preacher in Waynesboro, not far from Thomson where Tom Watson lived.

Doyle had not only studied the Negro problem, he embodied the Negro Problem. It was bone of his bone and flesh of his flesh. It made his world and filled his thought. He knew something of modern history and followed current events. He had especially read economics and social reform; he knew about Owens' consumers' cooperation and Fourier's communities. He had read the "Wealth of Nations" and the "Communist Manifesto," and dipped into Ricardo and Malthus. He had read "Progress and Poverty." He was not a profound scholar but he was an intelligent reader and an earnest thinker. All he read or thought went to the solution of the question of how American Negroes were going to find place as men in this country and the world.

On many matters he was still at sea and knew that he needed more reading and experience. But on one point he was sure he had reached the rock-bottom of truth and that was that the only salvation for the Negro in the United States was the right to vote. On this foundation stone all else must be built. His religion was a rather vague philosophy built on real life and work. He had small belief in dogma, doubted miracles and smiled at theological phrases. But he believed in honesty, he hated lying; he did not drink liquor

162

and he respected women. His sermons avoided doctrine and were aimed at good conduct, courage and search for truth. One of his young listeners wrote:

"As a youngster I was greatly impressed by his learning, his eloquence and his courage. While his sermons were shot through with emotion, he never stooped to the methods of some ministers who played upon the emotions of the people in order to get their support.

"He was the one minister who had the courage to challenge racial discrimination, even though he knew that his statements might be used against him by the so-called 'Uncle Tom' Negro type of leadership so prevalent at the time. Not only had he the courage to challenge jim-crowism, he also had the courage to challenge the effectiveness of the dominant political parties."

He became excited as he followed the career of Tom Watson. While still in school in middle Georgia and at Clark University in south Atlanta, at the age of 15, he watched him.

Tom Watson was a scrawny poor white from south Georgia, son of a woman who worked in the cotton mills of Augusta and of a small farmer. Near him lived Alexander Stephens and the great Bob Toombs. He worshipped them in his youth and even later their spell gripped him.

He got his sketchy education by toil and study at the University of Georgia during its war difficulties, and then "read" law. He became a flamboyant orator but for years remained at heart honest and sincere. He sensed the revolt of farmers and laborers against capital and industry and began a fight in Georgia when he was elected to the Legislature in 1880.

He faced an unholy mess. The state was in the firm grip of a triumvirate of politicians unrivalled in finesse and power. Watson could do little against the open rule of wealth in the Legislature. Corporations ruled the state. Combinations increased. The rural districts were discriminated against in favor of the large cities in railway rates. The landholder paid the taxes and the bondholder went free. A tenant could give a mortgage to a merchant on a non-existent crop raised on land which he did not own. In vain Watson attacked the Convict Lease system. He finally resigned from the Legislature, disillusioned and discouraged.

Ten years went by in which Grady's "New South" rose and flourished. Capital was invited to come and reign. A picture of fabulous future for the South was painted and for a while even

Watson was attracted. But soon he began to hesitate in his devotion to the "New South." He knew that he himself had been a plow-boy and his brother was still a helpless tenant. He began to talk.

"Here is a tenant—I do not know or care whether he is white or black, I know his story. He starts in and pays $25 for a mule, 1000 pounds of cotton for rent, and two bales for supplies. By the time he pays for that mule, and the store account, and the guano, he has not enough money left to buy a bottle of laudanum, and not enough cotton to stuff his old lady's ear."

Then he began to appeal: "To you who grounded your muskets twenty-five years ago I make my appeal. The fight is upon you— not bloody as then—but as bitter; not with men who come to free your slaves, but who come to make slaves of you."

Money and capital continued to rule the Georgia legislature and nothing was done to stop corporate combinations, discriminations by railroads against small way stations in favor of the great cities, and especially the mortgage and crop lien situation and the tax structure were not touched.

At Atlanta University Miss Freiburg, who had just then begun teaching there, was frankly puzzled at the two figures: Tom Watson and Henry Grady. She was not satisfied with the current pictures of both. The North saw Watson as a crazy socialist; the South saw him as a popular leader who was valuable but must be guided. The North saw Grady as a prophet of Triumphant Capitalism; the South knew him as a brilliant editor and orator. These pictures were not contradictory, but they were not complete nor supplementary.

She was eager to get the impression these men had on Negroes. She heard Doyle speak and, learning that he was teaching not far from the city, invited him to come to the university for a conference. He usually stayed with his favorite teacher, Dr. Crogman, when in town, so she asked Crogman also. He, as one of the first graduates of Atlanta University, gladly accepted. Miss Freiburg arranged for high tea and invited the Dean and a few college students. She included Manuel Mansart, who although only in high school, was intelligent and especially interested in Doyle. She was a bit startled when Mansart proposed to invite also the President of the University of Georgia, Old Dr. Baldwin. After consultation with the president, she asked Dr. Baldwin to step in "after lunch." He accepted.

Dr. Crogman was easily drawn out. "You must remember, Miss

Freiburg," he said, "that Watson and Grady are both Southern orators. In the South for reasons I will not stop to examine now, the orator is a species of poet. He seeks on a basis of fact to build a picture of Life which is satisfying, even beautiful. His method is the orotund voice, the forceful presence, wide gestures and flashing eye. He differs from the Greek orator because he lets emotion override reason. He differs from the conventional poet in his object. While the poet seeks Beauty or Clarity for its own sake, the orator, especially in the South, has always a distinct political or social object. He wants folk to believe his interpretation of fact so that they will do as he directs. His basis of fact may be incomplete or even distorted; but his belief in his cure-all is complete. Remember the flood of pro-slavery orations, with their pictures of happy slaves and philanthropic masters?"

Doyle added: "Grady knew nothing of Negroes. Brought up beside them, he has never seen them or realized they are human. To him they are always lay figures—Labor; Service; The Black Race. When he lauds the 'Black Mammy,' he is talking of a fanciful picture of his imagination. But worse than that, he doesn't even know the mass of whites. He idealizes or fails to see them.

"For instance, he once discovered a white girl in the chain-gang along with Negro prisoners. He was incensed. He wrote a sentimental plea to the public and had her released forthwith. He wept over this 'poor and lovely girl,' and the white state wept with him.

"Now, if Grady had really known the South he would have realized that no white woman would even have been arrested, much less jailed, unless she was degraded beyond hope; while blacks, male or female, young or old, are jailed on the slightest pretense. This poor white girl, debased, freed, publicized and promptly forgotten, fell back into the depths and was soon on the streets as a public prostitute, living by the only profession she ever knew.

"Grady was outraged and discouraged. He protested to heaven the ingratitude of human beings. He never knew or utterly ignored the innocent Negroes in chain gangs at whom none even looked. In the same way, while Grady was ranting of the new wealth and happiness of the South, the same South was festering in poverty, ignorance, violence and disease."

"Watson's knowledge of ugly facts," added Crogman, "was deeper and better than that of Grady. He knew poverty and bitter toil on the plantations. He had labored there long, hot days. Despite his later boasting of a rich grandfather with droves of slaves, he and his family were poverty-stricken, half-starved tenants and laborers.

"On the other hand, in his long and difficult quest for knowledge he learned what the world was trying to do to abolish poverty and ignorance. He became therefore the champion of equal taxation, just control of money, rural mail delivery and cooperative buying. But he did not realize that knowing and doing are not the same. He had not experienced the slowness and difficulty of the democratic process. When with loud voice, winged words and furious gesture he had driven home the truth to cheering thousands, he thought that the battle was won. If reform did not quickly follow, fools and scoundrels were to blame, and Watson went into angry hiding and sulked."

"With both these men," said Doyle, "the Negro problem was an impasse. Grady simply ignored it or said it was not there. Watson knew it was there and always would be. His inherited reaction was to despise if not hate Negroes. But knowing too well what poverty and ignorance had done to the white world, he had the courage to ask earnestly if the Negro was not only suffering from the same oppression, which re-inforced white degradation. I'm going to talk to him. I'm going to see if Tom Watson cannot be led to try solving the Negro Problem."

"Remember one thing," said Dr. Crogman, "Watson is sick. He was starved as a child. He has a bad digestion. He suffers from migraine. His nerves are on edge, which explains his fighting, his crazy hyperbole, his hiding for rest and recovery."

"So you know him personally?" asked Miss Freiburg.

"No. Few Negroes who are not servants get to know white people in the South. But I've seen him and read accounts of his behavior. He's sick. Some day he'll go crazy."

Old Dr. Baldwin came in before luncheon was over. He sat with them and listened to every word. He made almost no comment of his own, but several times injected a question or asked further explanation. In fact this was the most illuminating contact and conversation this Southern white man had ever had. He sat continually saying to himself, "What race problem—what human problem would be left if all Southerners, white and black, could now and then meet and talk like this!"

It came to be more and more openly declared in Georgia that a labor party must be formed in opposition to capital, and there was open discussion of the necessity of a Third Party. Throughout the

South the Farmers Alliance grew. Over forty congressmen and several senators from the South were committed to the Alliance program. In a national meeting held in Florida in 1890 a Third People's Party was openly advocated.

Tom Watson joined the Alliance. He was a pronounced free trader and campaigned for Cleveland in 1888, but afterward thought the money question most important and became a candidate for Congress on the regular Democratic ticket, but with a straight Farmers Alliance platform.

The Farmers Alliance was formed by cattle men in Texas in 1879. It merged ten years later with state groups to form the National Farmers Alliance, limited to whites. The Alliance entered Georgia in 1887 and set up cooperatives. The next year the Jute Bag Trust was formed in St. Louis and a meeting of 800 farmers in Tom Watson's town, Thomson, started a boycott.

This national Alliance and certain northern Alliance bodies which admitted Negroes, met in St. Louis in 1889. That year Watson entered the race for Congress against the rich Major Barnes, nearly two years before the primaries of the 10th Congressional district were to take place.

Grady's death this very year determined Doyle in 1890, at the beginning of the Congressional campaign, to seek personal conference with Tom Watson. If the approach of a self-respecting Negro to a planter aristocrat had its difficulties, so too the attempt of an educated Negro to approach a Poor White who had ambitions was equally hazardous. Fortunately for Doyle, Watson was sitting out of doors in his front yard so that the question of approach by front or back door did not arise. Doyle was purposely bareheaded so that the matter of lifting his hat was eliminated. He simply entered the gate and said:

"Mr. Watson, may I have a word with you?"

Watson was sitting in an old rocker, surrounded by books. One large volume was in his hands. He glanced up from it slowly, noting the blacked boots with a film of road dust; then the well-fitting trousers; the vest, coat and tie. He was about to rise and welcome some well-to-do constituent when he saw the golden face and curly hair. He paused and sat still; his face hardened and he said curtly, "Well?"

"Mr. Watson, I want to sell you some votes."

"I ain't got no money to buy 'niggers.' "

"In this case the price is low; in fact the deal will pay you as much or more than it brings us."

"And what do you expect it to bring you?"

"Schools, homes, no convict lease, decent wages and land."

Watson stared and rose to his feet. "That's a hell of a lot, fellow. Who are you, anyway?"

"I'm from upstate. My name is Doyle and I've followed your campaigns since I was a boy."

Watson glanced about and then led the way to the backyard. "Come with me," he said. He walked around back of the house to the garden, where they would not be conspicuous to chance passersby. He seated himself on a pile of wood and indicated an old chair. "Sit down," he said. "Doyle, you're too young to know Georgia."

"I was born and educated in Georgia and my fathers before me. I'm teaching upstate and expect to preach in Waynesboro. I've travelled over much of the state."

"Well, you're in for a jolt. You've got ideas, but 'niggers' won't follow you. They ain't got sense enough. I know 'em. I can buy a thousand 'nigger' votes at a dollar apiece."

"Of course you can, because a dollar is as much as they have ever been offered, and they must strive hard to get a dollar by honest work. Try offering more and not in cash but in rights."

They talked a couple of hours. Watson told of his disappointing experience with Negro voters in Augusta, but was astonished to learn of the growth of the Farmers Alliance in other parts of the state and in the South.

Doyle strove to bring to Watson's attention the extent to which the Alliance owed its increasing triumph to Negro support. He pointed out that as far back as 1875 the Negro head of a Virginia tobacco union had attended the convention of the Greenback Labor Party in Cleveland; that three years later, in Texas, there were ten Negroes among the forty delegates to the first state convention of the Greenback clubs; and that at a convention of the Greenback Labor Party that same year 70 Negro clubs were among the 482 clubs represented.

"But," asked Watson, "does the Northern Farmers Alliance admit Negroes?"

"Yes," said Doyle, "although of course there are comparatively few Negro farmers in the North. But the Southern Alliance early became interested in the organization of Negro farmers, and in 1886 the Colored Farmers National Alliance was formed in Houston, Texas. A white Baptist missionary became its secretary, but its other officials were Negroes."

"How many members are there today in the Colored Farmers Alliance?" asked Watson. He was astonished to know that the membership was nearly a million and a quarter and that already cooperative exchanges had been started in five southern cities. Moreover, at the Ocala meeting two Negroes, representing the Colored Alliance, had been made members of a Standing Committee in the Southern Alliance, and a column of news about the Colored Alliance was published weekly in their regular organ.

In the election of 1890 Watson was swept back to Congress by the triumphant Farmers Alliance; the Alliance won six out of the ten congressional districts of the state, controlled the state convention, chose the governor, and elected three-fourths of the members of the legislature. There was, however, one fly in the ointment. It was necessary that year to elect a senator to succeed the notorious Joe Brown. Gordon wanted to go back to the Senate; Grady groomed him, and even Watson finally gave him his support to avoid supporting the grandson of John C. Calhoun who was a railway attorney.

That year the meeting of the Farmers Alliance at Ocala, Florida, turned decisively away from the Democrats toward a Third Party movement; and the following year the Third Party was launched at a Cincinnati meeting. All over the south and west the Farmers Alliance and the Populist movement was victorious. It looked as though they might sweep the country in 1892.

The Colored Alliance began to establish schools and academies, but as Doyle was free to acknowledge, there were some differences cropping out between whites and blacks. The Colored Alliance, for instance, backed the Force Bill, which the white Southern Alliance opposed. But at the same time it advocated votes for Negroes. The Colored Alliance in 1891 proposed a strike of cotton pickers which the Southern Alliance, representing many employing farmers, naturally opposed. The strike was not called.

During the meeting in Ocala of both the white Southern Alliance and the Colored Alliance, committees for mutual greeting were appointed; and in Louisiana in 1891 the address for a Third Party conference went to both colored and white groups; and local organizations fraternized.

In May, 1891, there was a Third Party convention at which the Southern Alliance, the Colored Alliance and other alliances, together with the Knights of Labor and others met. Color segregation was defeated overwhelmingly, and when Confederate and Union veterans clasped hands a Negro delegate stood with them.

In Congress Watson bolted the Democratic party and openly sided with the Populists and the leaders of the St. Louis convention. Doyle pointed out to Watson this growth of understanding between white and black. He emphasized the growth of Negroes in education and general intelligence. He offered his own services in Watson's campaign. Watson was attracted. He had never been thrown with a Negro who was his intellectual equal if not his superior, with ideals that were essentially the same. They sought the company of each other and Doyle threw himself into the campaign.

His help, however, was with advice, and he seldom appeared as a speaker. Watson had thought it was not yet time openly to ask for the Negro vote in 1890, although at Doyle's suggestion his statements became increasingly bold and clear. Watson's triumph in the campaign of 1890 had been complete, not only in his district but in the state. Doyle now counselled open effort to attract the Negro vote in the future, and complete union with the labor vote of the nation.

Doyle knew that laborers in other lands were getting leadership. It had been long incubating among the thinkers of Europe. Plans, elaborate, sometimes utopian but often practical, had developed. Revolution had been attempted, and in many ways the idea of independent, self-defending workers emancipated from grinding poverty, had spread. In America came the growth of the Greenback and the People's Party, now strengthened by the sending of Tom Watson to Congress from a state where the Farmers Alliance had triumphed. This and Watson's career in Congress brought the critical fight between labor control and reaction into the open. Doyle's advice was for Watson to make an out and out bid for the Negro vote. If the rest of the South followed his lead and they undoubtedly would, a tremendous victory would be gained. The Negro would gain an undisputed place in the political picture as partner in the labor upsurge.

Watson took a stand in 1891: "Now the People's Party says to the white man and the black, 'You are kept apart that you may be separately fleeced of your earnings. You are made to hate each other because upon that hatred is rested the keystone of the arch of financial despotism which enslaves you both. You are deceived and blinded that you may not see how this race antagonism perpetuates a monetary system which beggars both!' "

There were undoubtedly difficulties which Doyle and Watson both realized. The Negro vote, being the vote of workers earning low wages, with some semi-paupers, was in part purchasable. Negroes would be herded to the polls in droves and voted by the reactionaries. Other Negroes would be driven away by force and fear. This was inevitable but Doyle argued that reliance on Right and Courage, full publicity and wide appeal would offset this largely.

Watson not only feared that the average poor Negro would sell his vote, but that force and deliberate fraud to suppress any vote would be undertaken. But the die was cast, and Watson was now leading the Third Party movement in the South. His confederate, Doyle, was seeking to unite the white and black workers against the industrialists; to give the black worker the vote and political office; to give him protection against lynching and the chain gang.

There was double difficulty here. Big Business itself in the South would suffer unless law and order prevailed. The white South could not hope to continue to win elections by force and fraud. But now the crisis was on them. Unless the Negro vote was legally disfranchised, the united white and black vote might be victorious over Big Business. This was a real danger.

Even the die-hard Rebels were out of line and attacking the North. "The Great Barbecue invited a second generation of Carpet-baggers as Northern business men invading the South in search of profits."

Watson started with furious energy to organize the white farmers and show them how the cheating and false promise of the '80's had brought them only increased subjection of labor to corporate wealth. Doyle supplemented this by cooperating with the Colored Farmers Alliance. Watson and Doyle both attacked lynching; they denounced the Ku Klux; they demanded the abolition of the convict lease system which was the modern slave trade.

Negroes, led by Doyle, became prominent organizers of the new Third Party. He demanded Negro education and praised the black King Lobengula then fighting Cecil Rhodes and the British grip on Africa. The few Negro members of the legislature exposed the abuse of Negroes in the newly developing coal mines in the Birmingham district. The white workers pledged themselves to protect Negro rights.

Doyle risked his life in the campaign of 1892, beginning late in 1891. He offered his own services, and against the advice of his bishop practically gave up his church work for three months to take part in the campaign. He made 63 speeches for Watson. Fifteen Negroes were killed, but increasing numbers of them worshipped Watson.

Said Doyle: "The poor, ignorant Negro men and women who so long had been oppressed were anxious even to touch Mr. Watson's hand."

But it was the hand of Doyle that held Watson's steady. Doyle's life was threatened and he often spoke with loaded pistols beside him. To guard him, Watson once barricaded Doyle on his own plantation and summoned two thousand white farmers to protect him from lynching. They came in buggies and on horseback, travelling in some cases all night. They filled the village, they lined the streets, they marched to the Court House under arms, with the county sheriff accompanying them. Watson addressed them:

"We are determined in this free country that the humblest white or black man that wants to talk our doctrine can do it, and the man does not live who shall touch a hair of his head without fighting every man in the People's Party."

In Watson's county lived the Scroggs family of poor white tenant farmers. It was really an old Scotch-Irish family transported as indentured servants early in the 18th century. One of their number, Sam Scroggs, had been killed in Charleston in the campaign of 1876. He had become leader of a group of white workers who had tried to make alliance with the planters in the election, and help offset the Negro vote. As it proved, the planters did not need their aid or at least were not compelled to recognize it. Scroggs was killed mysteriously in the Negro quarter on the night that the Negro leader, Tom Mansart was lynched. The Scroggs widow remained in Georgia and tried to farm. In 1891 the oldest boy, Abe Scroggs, was 18 and the main support of the large family.

An older brother of Sam Scroggs left south Georgia after his brother's death, and settled in Atlanta. His son, Jim, was the one who annoyed little Manuel Mansart as he was attending school and on whom Manuel wreaked vengeance. Eventually Jim's son, born in 1880 will come to our notice again. It is, however, now with Abe that we have to do.

Abe Scroggs went into politics by running with the Klan. He tried to keep Negroes from voting and stole from them systematically. His hatred of the aristocracy of land and capital increased when one night as he was looting a Negro home during a raid, a prominent white man stopped him.

"Here, put that back, what do you mean by stealing from these people?"

Scroggs stared at him in surprise. "But they're 'niggers,'" he said.

"Doesn't make any difference what they are; put that stuff back and get out of here."

From that time Scroggs realized that certain whites were still teaming up with the Negroes as they had in slavery times. He could not understand. Scroggs, living near Tom Watson's home town of Thomson, soon was attracted by him. He seemed a fellow-sufferer of the right sort, and Scroggs began to attend meetings of the Farmers Alliance, especially when the price of jute bagging went up on account of the St. Louis combine. He wildly applauded the proposal of a boycott.

In quest for a job he had once crossed the Carolina border and attended a political meeting presided over by a big, middle-aged, one-eyed man. Someone arose and made a plea for inviting Negroes into the Alliance. He tried to point out that Negroes had to work for low wages or starve; that if black and white labor stood together in union—. He got no further, for Ben Tillman, presiding, suddenly became a profane monster who almost leaped down the speaker's throat.

"We want nothing to do with 'niggers,'" he yelled. "We don't recognize them as men. We are going to keep them on the farms where they belong at the wages they are worth. We are going to kill and lynch them if they dare to look at our women. We want union, yes, but union among white men, not with black. There can be no union between white and black. Negroes must be disfranchised; they must be kept in their places. They are the servants of the whites, the Bible says so!"

This was but one of his bitter tirades, and they greatly impressed Scroggs. With his meeting with Tillman Scroggs' outlook upon life began to change. He talked with the rough upstate leader and Tillman warned him. He told Tillman how disappointed he was with his own poor white friends and associates.

"The mistake you fools are making," growled Tillman, "is in trying to destroy the aristocracy. That ain't what you've got to do. You've got to take its place; and that means that everybody can't rule, everybody can't become an aristocrat; they ain't fit; only a few. You and me can break a way into this closed circle and let the others take their chances. Some of the whites will never get up; but above all, 'niggers' must have no chance; they must be kept down under the feet of all whites."

Scroggs mentioned Watson but Tillman scoffed. "Watson is a

sulky coward; he gets beat and then runs home and shuts himself up to spin theories and write poetry. That ain't no way to lick this game. You've got to fight and then fight some more; and you've got to know what you are fighting for. I am going to lick these aristocrats, but I am not going to drive them out. I am just going to take my place beside them. I am going to be elected governor of the state."

Scroggs almost laughed but didn't dare because Tillman was glaring at him with his one eye. "Remember," Tillman admonished him, "some of us are going to climb to the top, but we ain't going to tear away that top. We want it for ourselves!"

Tillman was cool toward organizing farmers' alliances. He said it was an idea from the North and thus suspect.

When the election of 1890 swept Watson into Congress Scroggs attended a rally to celebrate the triumph of Watson and the small white farmer. In the crowd he was astonished to recognize Tillman, governor-elect of South Carolina, but evidently unknown to most of the crowd. Scroggs had jostled the big, rough, one-eyed farmer and both bristled, ready for a fight, when Tillman grinned and held out his hand, at the same time warning Scroggs not to disclose his identity.

Then he growled: "What the hell are you celebrating?"

"The victory of Watson and the people," answered Scroggs truculently, remembering that Tillman was a big landholder and not sympathetic with Watson.

"You mean Watson and his 'niggers.'"

"He might as well buy up the 'nigger' vote as the landholders."

"Hell, he ain't buying—he's selling us to the darkies. Treating 'em equal. First thing you know if this goes on your sister will be marrying a 'nigger.'"

Scroggs was impressed by the "us" and alarmed by the unthinkable prospect. "Don't believe it," he asserted vehemently.

"Look," said Tillman, pointing to the platform where a young Negro was starting to address the throng. Scroggs was appalled; he turned away.

"If that there 'nigger' stays about here," he muttered, "he'll get lynched."

Tillman smiled. "What's your name? Scroggs? Oh yes. Well, Scroggs, listen. I'm a poor white like you. One of these days I'm going to take the vote away from 'niggers' 'legal'; Mississippi will lead off and the South will follow. Then I'm going to the United States Senate and see that Southern whites rule this nation from now on. Already we've made the Supreme Court say that 'niggers' ain't got no rights! Stick around! Get your buddies; lynch that 'nigger,' Doyle!"

Scroggs stared at him. "I don't believe you," he gasped. But from this moment Scroggs began to waver from Watson and Populism toward Tillman. Especially was he incensed at the phenomenon which Doyle, the Negro companion of Watson, represented. If he hated Negroes in general, his hate of educated Negroes was emphasized by fear. They wanted to be white; they talked white. Once they got a chance they would be white, lord it over poor whites and marry their sisters. It must never happen. This Doyle must be lynched!

It was Scroggs who led the mob to lynch Doyle late in October, 1891. It was a night never to be forgotten. The moon was full, the magnolias scented the world, and the slow, sullen river ran like blood to the sea. On the platform in the center of a vast throng stood the tall, handsome mulatto, on whose winged words a host of armed whites and Negroes listened breathlessly. Beside him stood little Tom Watson, red-haired and scrawny.

Scroggs marshalled his mob of a thousand armed men silently back in the shadow of the moss-dripped trees. Suddenly his men let out the shrill Rebel yell and started forward cursing, with guns waving. Just as suddenly an answering yell shrieked up from the listening throng; guns glistened and clicked and horsemen whirled and then stopped. Then came a dead silence; an awful silence that held death in a breath. One heard a nightingale singing.

Scroggs was appalled. This crowd was ready to fight for a "nigger"; they were ready to kill. Slowly, slowly, Scroggs paused and lowered his gun, glanced at his followers and began to move backward. Then, without a sound they all turned, disappeared and rode wildly homeward.

Scroggs that night saw an awful vision: black and white labor united and black equal to white. It must never happen. He would starve first. He would surrender to landlord or Yankee rather than see a Negro considered his equal. Two nights the crowd remained on guard. Nothing like this had ever happened in the South. It was revolution. It was culmination of what Abraham Lincoln started.

Labor, North and South, was out of hand and even revolutionary. Its radicalism was at the point of ignoring and forgetting race hate, one of the strongest of human motives. Men talked in club and family circle; in Church and in the secret societies which in the South rose from solemn mummery to become carefully calculated centers of white propaganda and action.

The South said: The trend to a Third Party must be stopped by splitting the labor movement. The obvious way to do this was by using the "natural and doubtless God-given difference of race" in the laboring class to keep them separated. Race difference must be emphasized and enforced by law. This, pleaded Science, was in the long run legitimate and would lead to the best human stock; this, argued Religion, is not hate and suppression but recognition of the "divine purpose" in history.

In 1890 Populism had swept the South. In Georgia, Alabama, Mississippi, Louisiana and Texas it had received the majority of votes. But only in Georgia had the Populists gained actual control. In other states they were counted out by cheating, violence and fraud. But the situation was now ominous and the South girded itself for the next election. The West watched.

Reaction and race hate in Georgia wheeled into line. Watson's congressional district in the campaign of 1891 preliminary to the 1892 election was quietly gerrymandered by cutting off a strong Negro district. Campaign funds poured in even from corporations in New York. Voters were threatened, intimidated, assaulted and at least fifteen Negroes were killed outright. At the polls votes were openly bought, forced and stolen. Watson said, "It was almost a miracle that I was not killed." The governor of the state added that he ought to have been killed. The newspapers cried, "Watson has gone mad." "The South is threatened with anarchy and Communism."

Thus the Georgia election of 1892 proved a farce, with terror, fraud, corruption and trickery. Federal supervisors under United States marshals attended the election in Augusta but could not prevent repeatings, bribery, ballot-box stuffing, voting of minors and intimidation. Negro plantation hands and laborers were hauled to town in wagon loads that were brought across from South Carolina and voted. They were paid in whiskey and cash. The total vote in Augusta was double the number of legal voters.

Watson and Doyle had campaigned in 37 counties and addressed hundreds of thousands of people. His "People's Party Paper" stood in circulation second only to the *Atlanta Constitution*. Still, officially he was declared defeated, on the face of the returns. A delegation marched 35 miles from Augusta to Watson's home and raised money to finance a contest in the House of Representatives. Watson announced that he would carry on the Third Party fight. "I am determined never to give it up as long as I live!"

His contest of the election, however, was not allowed to come up until the second session of Congress and then, for the first time in history he, as contestant, was not allowed to speak in his own behalf. The report was a complete whitewash and declared that the committee in charge of the election "were the very first citizens of Georgia and were representing every business and profession, and were all men of the highest character, none higher."

In 1893 came Panic. Banks failed, money disappeared, factories closed, unemployment spread. The prices of farm produce continued to fall and hunger and misery were more widespread in the South than even in 1873. Yet there was a Democratic president in the White House. The next year was called the "Terrible Year of American History." The Depression persisted, with strikes, brutality and distress. Coxey's Army of the Hopeless marched on Washington. Men were reading "Looking Backward" and "Wealth vs. Commonwealth." The President sent troops to break a Chicago strike and put Eugene Debs in jail.

Revolt was in the air and nothing but stern counter-revolutionary measures could prevent the triumph of the Populist Party throughout the nation in the fall of 1894. Again the Populists won. They doubled their vote in Georgia; they increased it 40% in the nation. They carried the whole southern South. Yet they lost. They lost again by fraud and force; by deliberate overthrow of the democratic process, by giving to the minority nominees offices which they did not win.

Watson had run in the 10th District of Georgia. But he faced a new "registration law." Watson carried nine counties and his opponent carried two. But in those two was the city of Augusta. There, with only 11,000 voters, Black, who ran against Watson, got a majority of 14,000. Black was declared elected. The cry of fraud was so loud that he resigned there months later and a special election was staged. When it came in 1895 Black, now for "Free Silver" and helped by an outrageous primary registration law, won again.

For a third time Watson was officially defeated. But he cried: "Discouraged? Bosh! Let the fight of 1896 begin now!" Watson gave up the hopeless struggle in Georgia and looked toward national recognition. The Populist Party stood for government ownership of railroads and other national utilities; for an income tax; against Federal suppression of strikes; against imperial expansion in Hawaii and Venezuela and for cheap money not dependent on the Gold Monopoly.

The silver barons in Western rotten boroughs bought control of the Democratic party and sought to stop Populist socialism by advocating "Free Silver." They nominated Bryan, a political orator who ranted over Free Silver but about little else among the measures which the Populists favored. With him they named a rich railroad man from Maine. The Republicans, with the help of Mark Hanna, nominated a smooth-faced politician ready to take orders, and they poured money into a campaign aimed at warning the rich, the comfortable and the respectable.

The Populists, meeting last, were asked and subtly cajoled into accepting Bryan. The forces of Populism rallied for a final effort, and 1400 delegates met in St. Louis. Watson acted coy; he not only did not attend the convention but kept out of all direct touch. Yet the leaderless crowd first nominated him unanimously as Vice-President, and then accepted Bryan on condition that the Democrats accept Watson and Populist Socialism. This the Democrats dared not do and thus lost nine-tenths of the Populist two million votes.

Too late Watson tried to retrieve his ill-advised absence and regain support in the West. He demanded government ownership of railroads and other public interests; control of trusts; an entirely new system of money and credit; and finally remembering Doyle: "A ballot free from corruption, and political rights for Negroes." He added that there "was never a greater unrest than that which stirs the masses today," and that "free silver" was too easy an answer.

But South and West could not mix. There were fundamental differences that made this impossible and they stemmed from Negro slavery. Even with slavery partially abolished, slave labor in the South with low wage or none at all persisted; no Democracy could thrive on ignorance, and the South, black and white, had few and poor schools; and post-war lawlessness, built on "white" supremacy, had become endemic.

In the West, on the contrary, there had developed a democracy based on landowning farmers of essentially equal social status, with good schools. Industry, organized and becoming monopolized, united its efforts and descended on South and West. In the South it was opposed by the attempt to unite labor and small farmers. But labor was split by the Color Line and the small farmer was dominated by the big planter. There was no real union there. In the West united farmers beat the banks and railroads but the mining corporations tempted them with "cheap money."

Watson was beaten, Bryan was beaten, Socialism was buried, and triumphant organized private industry won the election and rushed into Colonial Imperialism through the Spanish-American War. So Revolution failed. So Tom Watson went mad. After 1896 he said:

"Politically I was ruined. Financially I was flat on my back. How near I came to loss of mind only God knows. I was as near distraction as any mortal could safely be."

Ten years he hid, scribbled and brooded. Then he roared, raving, into the Atlanta Riot and the fury and flame of the San Francisco Earthquake.

Sebastian Doyle faded into silence after the campaign of 1892. He had planted the seed. He had given all his strength and risked his life career. His own people distrusted his breach with the Republican Party and his alliance with Democrats and poor whites. He faced his church conference, deficient in his report on dollar money on which the church lived. His Bishop scowled and growled.

"Son, this is a bad report, and our church in Augusta still needs a new building. I ought to send you to the woods. But you're a good preacher and mean well. So see here: drop politics. Preach Christ crucified and raise money. I'm sending you to Alabama."

Doyle could not rebel. He had a young family. He knew no other work. He bowed his head and went west. Ten years he aroused growing congregations to fervent prayer for the Grace of God and new church buildings. Then a tubercle bacillus crept into his golden voice. Ten more laggard years he fought back its ravages in ever failing effort; until discouraged and forgotten, he died in Texas where the Farmers Alliance had been born.

Chapter XI

MANUEL GRADUATES

Manuel missed his mother more than he thought he would. She was not talkative nor widely informed. But she took care of him, gave him much from her store of experience, and above all listened to him. After her death he missed the intimacy of a home and began to dream of one of his own. Life in the men's dormitory was pleasant but not satisfying. He began in his sophomore year to talk of his plans and dreams to Susan Sanders, a student in the Normal School, as the large high school conducted by the University was called. Just why he chose Susan it was hard to say. In some unconscious memory of his mother's attitude, he avoided the prettier girls with tawny skins and flowing hair. He feared they might not care for a man so dark as he. For the students' ideals not only of dress and behavior but of beauty were based on the judgement of the white world. To them a light skin and straight hair must be beautiful because whites thought so. In unconscious submission to this judgment, both Manuel and the student body thought Manuel ugly.

Susan was a small brown girl from Savannah. She was timid and retiring and it was easy to find her sitting apart and alone at the social gatherings. By chance more than choice they found themselves often talking together and finding common ground in criticism of erratic and unpleasant conduct on the part of fellow students and teachers. They were among the first to note the attraction of President Sheldon's daughter to the brilliant and rather nice young Tommy Hendricks, whose colored blood had not reached his sandy hair. They saw how her brother John resented this, for they resented it, too.

But the interest of Manuel in Susan was not confined to attitudes toward others. He noticed how smooth and unblemished was her dark skin; how her hair crinkled prettily on her neck and how she listened to what he said and dreamed. Manuel felt very grown and manly to see her depend on him for company and advice.

Since the average age of these colored college students was rather higher than among northern white students, engagements were more common as graduation approached. So during his junior year, almost without conscious decision on their own part, the student body regarded Manuel and Susan as engaged and they accepted public opinion. They became formally engaged in the Spring by means of an engagement ring which left Manuel almost penniless, and worried him because of his debt to the University for unpaid board and tuition.

Just before Commencement in 1897, President Sheldon asked Manuel to go north for the summer in charge of the College Quartet. The former manager had got a job and married. Manuel was to arrange concerts and make the collection speeches as was the custom. This was one of the many ways to which the college turned to make ends meet. It yielded something in cash but more in publicity; for summer vacationists loved the Negro folk songs and were willing in turn to hear about conditions in the South.

For Manuel, also, this was a path to the future. He would work this summer, pay his debts and then during his senior year look for a job teaching. Susan expected that her family would maintain her in school until her graduation in 1898. Then they would both get jobs and as soon as possible get married. Manuel went north with high hopes. He had never before been out of the South. He now had double incentive.

The white president of Atlanta University was in serious trouble about funds to keep the school running. Poverty for an individual is understandable. There is, however, something mystic and peculiarly appalling in the poverty of an institution; it is more than the poverty of an individual or even of a large family. It is a huge and perpetually recurring burden which can be shifted only by miracle and that miracle usually assumes the guise of a very rich and benevolent man.

President Sheldon, tall, white-bearded, anemic and devoted to great causes, came South during the War. He was unwilling to enlist as a soldier but eager to work and he found in educating Negroes an ideal task. He gathered them in old and drafty army barracks, in rickety church basements; at last in a fine new building which the Freedmen's Bureau furnished out of unclaimed bounty money due dead or missing Negro soldiers. Finally, after the death of the founder, he came to Atlanta University.

His dream was of schools supported by the new state, in which whites and Negroes shared in government. He was not bothered by

what seemed to him the purely academic question as to whether
the schools would be open to all or separated by race. In time, of
course, the schools must be biracial, because anything else would
be fatally costly.

Then his plans were changed by the necessity of having more
and more and better trained teachers. For a while war enthusiasm,
adventure, "The coming of the Lord," furnished a flow of fairly
good Northern teachers, mostly women forced to celibacy by the
bloody toil of war and the waste of savings and property in organized destruction. But as this stream began to dry up because of
postwar prosperity, so too, simultaneously, the demand for teachers in Negro schools increased enormously. Such teachers must be
trained, and well-trained. The need of teachers of highest and
most careful training was greater in the South and among Negroes
than in the North among whites, where social environment furnished much that the school need not attempt. Thus Sheldon's
school became a "University" in ideal and forced purpose before
there was any provision for its rapidly increasing costs.

The disfranchisement of the Negro, therefore, which to the
Southern whites seemed absolutely necessary to quick reconstruction of their disrupted economy, and to the charitable North an
unimportant, postponed ideal of some far-off democracy, was to
President Sheldon the destruction of the foundation of Negro
Education. So long as the blacks had the power to make the state
support schools for them, charity was temporary. But if Negroes
lost all control over public moneys, became a disfranchised working
class with starvation wages, whence was support for their schools
to come? Not only for public elementary schools but even more,
support for the higher schools on which the lower must depend?

Therefore, between the Southern devil of disfranchisement and
the deep Northern sea of profitable investment, the cause of Negro
education began to suffer grievously. Not only did the new Southern masters begin a campaign to curtail and starve Negro schools,
but the Northern supply of Missionary funds for higher Negro
education also began to fail. Once the thrill of war had passed and
the victory won in the Southern United States, the lure of missionary effort in Asia, Africa and the South Seas began to make
larger drafts on imagination and charity. Wealthy church officials
of the North who were also investors in Southern industries could
not see why the South should not now support its own schools, and
were disposed to argue that the white South knew better how to

educate its workers than the white North.

Men like President Sheldon of Atlanta University were therefore in an increasingly difficult position. He had to spend more and more of his time begging funds in the North. Student singers, carrying on the fame of the earlier celebrated Fisk singers who spread Negro music across the world, were used to help this begging campaign.

Sheldon too, in this work, was compelled to assume an attitude antagonistic to the new Southern leadership which increasingly had the ears of the rich and powerful. After Henry Grady spoke in New York in 1886 the reception given President Sheldon, as he wearily passed the hat in Northern churches and especially among business men, became distinctly chilly. Was it not time that "free and equal" Negroes supported themselves and their institutions?

Old John Pierce was especially annoyed when his secretary brought in President Sheldon's card in 1895. Here it was again! "University" for lazy Negroes to toast their heels in. He knew Sheldon and liked him personally. But Negro education, so-called, was encroaching on business and bidding fair to get in the way of sectional understanding. He must ask Young John to talk frankly to Sheldon and either pound sense into his head or withdraw his support. So he put Sheldon off with a smaller contribution than usual and referred him to Young John who now lived in Atlanta and was better situated to judge of his southern charities.

It was not until after the election of 1896 that Young John Pierce, now quite at home in Atlanta, was approached by President Sheldon and reminded of the talk on Negro education which Old John Pierce wanted him to hold. He got hold of some general data concerning Atlanta University and had another talk with Old Doctor Baldwin. Baldwin was now 76 but still hearty and intellectually alert. He spent much of his time with his wife and son in Atlanta, rather to their annoyance.

John Pierce and his wife were often guests of Betty Lou and it was easy—indeed hard to avoid—having talks with the old president. He strongly advised conference with President Sheldon. He thought the colored school promising, in the sense that Negro students could be found capable of the highest training; but naturally it would be silly to develop two systems of universities, one for whites and one for Negroes. Eventually there must be one system open to all.

Eventually—perhaps; but what now?

Dr. Baldwin had no ready answer, and so John Pierce went out and talked with President Sheldon. His own feeling was that the urgency for providing university training was not pressing. He put this before President Sheldon. The result of the interview was unpleasant for both men. Pierce's arguments were not so overwhelming as they had appeared to him before the talk.

"You can't begin with colleges," he said. "Primary schools, workshops,—even kitchens and backyards is where children must begin, and Negroes are children."

"And who will teach even children? The ignorant cannot be entirely self-taught," retorted Sheldon.

"Of course not. There must be some teachers, of course; but they don't need to be Ph.D's."

"Except to teach the teachers. That is a high calling and needs the best preparation."

Pierce referred to the great Northern universities, but realized as he was speaking that their white graduates could not be tempted South either by salaries or social conditions. No, there must be a few Negro colleges—

Sheldon then asked: "Mr. Pierce, have you visited a Negro college and examined its work? Why not join our Board of Trustees and come to understand and help direct our program?"

That seemed reasonable; yes, it was a good idea. He glanced at the catalog and noticed the names of several well-known Northern business men among the Atlanta University trustees. Why not add to these some prominent Southerners? Well, he was a Southerner now. He could persuade others.

"Very well, President Sheldon, I'll join and I'll bring in others."

His check was smaller than President Sheldon had hoped for, and his allusion to "others" was ominous. But the President was encouraged. Pierce took his trusteeship seriously, since he proposed to make it fit in with larger and pressing plans of his own. He unexpectedly appeared at Atlanta University at the Trustee Meeting called at Commencement in 1897. He found himself almost the only trustee present from out of town. Northern trustees usually did not bother to attend these meetings.

He gave the University a thorough inspection and the President gladly gave him every facility. Secretly, behind his detached gravity, he was hanging breathlessly on this inspection. He hoped that this might be the turning point and that from this visit the long awaited endowment might come.

Pierce was both gratified and astonished at his inspection. The institution was honestly and efficiently run on a surprisingly small budget. The college students were of good quality, few in number and probably with much less background of training than similar Northern students; and older in years and experience, which had advantages and disadvantages. But their future looked to Pierce uncertain. They ought to be trained to become good artisans, small merchants and intelligent farmers. They were, on the contrary, aiming to be teachers, preachers, physicians and lawyers. The reason was obvious: teaching and the professions offered immediate jobs in their own group. But for the South as a whole this was crazy. This was building for a divided world, with a Black World organized with few producers, and a dominant White World with unlimited demand for consumption and yet not using its chief mass of producers. It was fantastic. This must be changed forthwith.

But one other thing which astonished and affronted Pierce was to see a white boy among these colored students. He was the son of the President and he was a very unhappy boy. John Sheldon, then 16, had grown to dislike Negroes because they hung like a weight around his neck. He had been thrown with them all his life, having been born on the campus. At first he had his friends and playmates among them in a perfectly normal way. Then he became conscious of the surrounding white world and understood what it thought of Negroes and of those who associated with them.

For a short time he and his younger sister, Henrietta, had been sent to the white public elementary school. As soon as teachers and pupils learned who they were the persecution and personal mistreatment became unendurable. It was in vain that President Sheldon intervened, argued and pleaded; the children simply had to be withdrawn. They were entered in the grade school attached to the Negro university.

This the President thought was the best thing to do; he had only tried the public schools on account of the principle involved. Henrietta got on well in the colored school. She liked the colored children and after a period of stiffness they liked her. Indeed, as the age of puberty approached, the President's wife noticed with something like horror that Henrietta was in serious danger of falling in love with a classmate, a beautiful, sandy-haired boy, Tommy Hendrick; white, but "colored" in southern phrase, but as unconscious of race as Henrietta.

If the parents could have looked at the matter impartially they would have seen only the natural result of youthful contact. But even the President was frightened when he realized what a love episode between a colored student and his own daughter might do, not only to Negro education but to the whole race problem. It had been a stock belief in the South that racial coeducation meant miscegenation. So quietly the next term Henrietta was left in Massachusetts and the Atlanta home was broken.

The lonesome brother bitterly resented this. He put the blame on the Negroes and picked quarrels with the innocent and unsuspecting Tommy, who liked John as he had liked Henrietta. For a time he avoided John or yielded to his surly treatment; then he got tired, thrashed John thoroughly and got himself expelled from school. This increased rather than diminished John's bitter distaste for his situation.

The poor President was at his wit's end. Not only was Henrietta exiled from home, but although he wanted to send John away to college he simply could not afford to. He welcomed Pierce's criticism and met it frankly. But he would not yield the principle:

"I maintain that a white child can be educated alongside a black with mutual advantage."

"Do you advocate mixed schools in the South?"

"Yes, in the South and in the North; in all the world; humanity is one and should in its earliest years be made to realize this."

"You know it would lead to intermixture of race—I hear that you feared this in the case of your daughter."

"That is true. Possibly—probably, I was unduly alarmed, and I was not free to take any chances of a happening which would ruin my work here and hurt the Negro race. I still maintain that occasional intermarriage, probably rare in the present feeling about race difference, would be better and wiser than cultivation of race hate as necessary and God-given."

"So you are keeping your boy here to prove your theories?"

"No, I'm keeping him here because I cannot help myself. I do not earn enough to send him away to college, and I'm afraid to turn him into the world without education. He is not at fault. In his environment he was almost compelled to breathe in race hate. He feels himself a victim. I am almost in despair."

John Pierce regarded him with mingled contempt and sympathy. "I'll send him to college," he said briefly.

President Sheldon would have given a fortune to have been able to refuse this offer. But he thanked the philanthropist humbly.

John Pierce now had a brilliant idea due to an encounter he made just as he was leaving the President's office. Manuel Mansart was about to enter for a last interview before departing with the quartet. Manuel courteously stood aside, but the President saw him.

"Oh, Manuel, I want you to meet one of our new trustees. Mr. Pierce, this is Manuel Mansart who is now a junior. He is going north this summer to take charge of our quartet."

"Glad to meet you, Mansart. Walk with me to the gate."

They sauntered together across the green lawn, with ivy-covered Livingstone Hall behind; past the boulder over the grave of the Founder. Pierce paused.

"— that we, our children and our children's children might be blessed," read Pierce thoughtfully, as Manuel watched him. This was to him a new specimen. He knew Southern whites and Northern missionaries. But Northern business men? He cloaked his soul in caution.

"That's an idea," said Pierce. "We seem all to be in this together." An idea sprouted in his mind. He was going to Princeton for a class reunion and taking along his boy of sixteen, John Pierce III. John would enter Princeton in the Fall. He was a rather uncertain, erratic young man. His father wanted to guide him. John Sheldon, the President's son, could also come with them and try to enter Princeton next year. He had just been talking to Betty Lou whose son, John Breckinridge Du Bignon Baldwin, was already at the Hun School near Princeton. How would it do—?

"Say, Mansart, could you bring your quartet to Princeton?"

"Why, yes, Sir, I think so."

"You see, the Princeton commencement will not take place for nearly a month in late June."

"Oh yes Sir, we'd be glad to come."

They talked further. Pierce liked Mansart. Manuel was puzzled at Pierce. Pierce thought it would be both interesting to him and enlightening to the three young men to meet Manuel Mansart. He put the matter before his own son as they rode north. The boy was enthusiastic.

"By Jove! That'll be capital! Three Johns and Feirefiz!"

"Who?"

John did not enlighten him but rushed to find young Baldwin. "Say, I got another Georgia boy, Sheldon, coming. And with him, a darky! My father is a trustee of his school and has sent him here in my care. He's got a quartet or something and is raising money for the school. Let's give him a lift. What do you say? I'm having him in my diggings after his concert. He is older than we are and a college senior, but let's give him a good time."

Baldwin evinced no great enthusiasm but promised to come. When Sheldon arrived Pierce invited him, but assumed that since he was from Atlanta University he knew of Mansart. He therefore only asked him over after the concert and forgot to add that Mansart would be there too.

Thus it was that Manuel Mansart in the Spring of 1897, just after the May commencement at Atlanta and just before the June exercises at Princeton, came to town with the Quartet. Princeton is in many ways an ideal college town. When the noisy, dirty Pennsylvania railroad proposed to run its tracks through this nest of decorous muses, the College rose in its dignity and made it pass the institution three miles to the east, leaving the village to its quiet and dreams.

It had long had a famous Theological School where the Presbyterians ruled in stiff dignity, but did not hesitate to admit a colored student now and then. That black John Chavis, teacher of famous white Carolinians, was trained here in the early 19th century, but of course granted no degree. Later, as the slavery controversy waxed, Southerners, avoiding the abolitionism of Unitarian Harvard and the latitudinarian tendencies of Congregational Yale, began to send their sons to orthodox and reactionary Presbyterian Princeton which became after the war, in a sense, a Southern University. No Negro student gained admittance here for a hundred years after 1840, and Southern gentlemen sent their sons here with confidence, to sit largely under Southern teachers, until well into the 20th century.

Manuel steered his quartet along the Jersey shore to Cape May, Long Branch and Atlantic City. There were the usual difficulties of finding places for colored boys to stay, and suitable food to eat. Manuel talked frankly and clearly about the University and the Negro. He had to answer the usual questions about social equality and intermarriage. He began to learn to parry pleasantly, without too much offense, and to accumulate a stock of funny stories—which were not too funny and went over with only fair success. The collections were small and Manuel was not altogether happy when he reached Princeton late in June. He was astonished at the antics of class day. His boys, however, were comfortably housed. They sang well to a large and generous audience. Then he went to find Pierce. He suddenly confronted the Three Johns.

They were sitting about relaxed, sipping coffee, when the door opened and Manuel was ushered in. A stillness fell on the group. Manuel paused a step within the door, and then stood quite still. He sensed the tension and knew it was their move. One or two of the elder Pierce's classmates were present. One whispered: "A 'nigger' from Georgia? What the hell!" Others were amused. After all, Pierce had not infringed etiquette by inviting the fellow to dinner. What was Mansart going to do? Sing or dance?

But it was the boys that the elder Pierce was watching. Young Pierce arose quickly.

"Hello," he said, extending his hand. "You're from Georgia. Glad to meet you. You know my father. These are some of his classmates."

Young Baldwin came forward. "I'm from Georgia, too. Glad to welcome you."

The third John, John Sheldon, sat frozen in his seat as Manuel appeared. He knew him, of course. They had been in school together for years,—in a Negro school. Manuel glanced at him but made no sign of recognition, but Sheldon quickly recovered.

"We know each other," he said.

"You two know each other? But of course, you're from Atlanta."

"And were in school together," said Sheldon, watching Baldwin. Baldwin looked puzzled and then realized that Sheldon must have attended a Negro school. Probably his father was one of those Carpet-baggers who taught Negroes. He was startled, but not too antagonized. He remembered what his father used to say about these schools and how his mother angrily disputed him and was sure these schools were spoiling Negroes, while their teachers were fleecing them and the North. He had never had opportunity to test these judgments. He was rather glad to talk to a young man of education who happened to be black.

Pierce was quite delighted and noticed nothing. He shook cocktails, which Mansart refused and Sheldon touched sparingly. Pierce started talking.

"Well, how do you like Princeton? Where are you staying?"

"It's a beautiful town; and we got lodging with a nice colored family."

Pierce realized that no hotel would take him, and had to twist his next query as to how it felt to be in the North. He saw that probably the difference was not as great as he was ready to assume. But he turned to the concert.

"Your fellows certainly sing."

Here Baldwin could chime in: "There is nothing like Negro music."

"I wonder," said young Pierce, "if the solution of the race problem does not lie here: music, art and drama for black folk; government, business and manufacture for whites?"

"I doubt if the South would settle for that," said Mansart. "They need labor."

"By George," said Baldwin, "that's just what my mother is always harping on."

"It isn't easy to work out. Labor means wages, security, political power."

"But," said Baldwin, "isn't it better for the upper classes to decide the rate of wage and conditions of work until the workers are ready and intelligent enough to take responsibility?"

"I don't know about that 'upper class' business," rejoined the elder Pierce, touched on a sore point. "I think the owners of industry should direct it, that's natural—"

There was a pause as heritage and power silently clashed. Mansart was too discreet to talk further. After all, his task was to get Pierce to help Atlanta University. Sheldon was silent because he knew too well what he wanted: money, and he cared not how it came. If driving Negro workers was the way, he'd drive. But he devoutly hoped he'd never see another Negro so long as he lived. But young Pierce was inspired by a new line of thought.

"By God! Mansart," he said. "You're lucky." Mansart looked at him. "See, you've got a job! You've got something you must do and want to do. Your life work is laid out and it's splendid. I've never been interested in anything more than a week at a stretch except liquor and girls. A good football match can get me momentarily wild. But you, Mansart, don't have to play games. You've got the real thing. Fellows, I wonder if we couldn't join in and help him. The Three Musketeers to settle the Negro Problem—Boys, is it a deal?"

But the others discounted Pierce's enthusiasm and laid it partially to liquor. On the other hand, Pierce the father wanted further to explore these young minds and especially to draw out the reluctant Mansart.

He said, "It's a big game—worldwide, with the South today in the center." He leaned back, lighted a cigar and began to probe: "Talking about careers for you boys," he began, "Baldwin, I'm wondering if you wouldn't like to go into politics and help govern this land, especially the South?"

Baldwin looked interested. "Well, I don't know, Sir. Mother has been stressing that idea. I think I might like it."

Pierce smiled and remembered the many talks with Betty Lou on this matter. Then he glanced at Sheldon. "Sheldon, you're a Southerner, at least by birth. Now the New South is Industry. How would you like to go into business?"

Sheldon reddened and answered quickly, "I certainly should if I could, and by any route."

Then John turned to his chief worry, his son. But the young man grinned engagingly and raised a deprecating hand. "Now, Dad, no tricks;—'never shake thy gory locks at me.' We've been over all that. You've got your politician and Captain of Industry. Now, I know, you're looking for a banker. No, thank you. Not interested. Couldn't stick it! But how about a little Literature and Art?"

"Well, perhaps, if we've got a young Shakespeare about—"

"Never can tell—could be. But you're not going to forget Mansart; why not see where he's going to fit in."

The father was a little peeved. He wanted, of course, to bring in Mansart's role, but as it was in his own mind fairly humble, he had not decided just how to approach the subject diplomatically. Then young Baldwin had to blurt it out quite innocently:

"Mansart, doesn't it seem to you that your people might train yourselves to furnish the South the faithful, skilled labor force which it will need as it rises to leadership in national and world industry?"

This, of course, was just what the elder Pierce had wanted to ask, and he listened eagerly. His son stared and Sheldon closed his eyes. Mansart glanced at the elder Pierce and saw distinctly above his head a shadow that resembled Miss Freiburg. Then he looked directly at Baldwin and said slowly, as if thinking:

"Labor, hard labor, and skilled, is sure going to be needed. But I'm wondering just what kind of labor I would be allowed to do, and for whom—" he paused imperceptibly, "and why?"

Young Baldwin looked puzzled; the elder Pierce scowled; but young Pierce whooped: "Got you, John; what can you say to that?"

But John Baldwin made no rejoinder.

They talked again about the concert, and Mansart sang one of the songs, with Baldwin at the piano: *"Walk together, children—don't you get weary!"*

Then he cordially thanked them all and pleading an early train, left for his lodging. Here a telegram awaited him: Susan Sanders announced that she was about to marry another man!

It was quite logical. Susan's father had died and there was no money to pay her way next year in school. She was not so promising a student as to warrant keeping her without pay. Her depression had brought on a recurrence of the malaria which she had brought endemic from the coast of Georgia, and Dr. Henry Jones, a hearty, big and well-to-do colored physician who successfully attended her, had persuaded her that she would make an excellent successor to his wife now dead ten years. The dead wife had seen him through his early struggles and paid for it with galloping tuberculosis.

He became fatter and more prosperous. He had learned his job. He wasn't a very good student and his medical art came from the bedside and not from books, hospitals or journals. He was a super-nurse, an unconscious psychoanalyst, and an inspiring and jolly companion; and he got on with the white folks. Especially he got on with the white folks. Once when he had driven through a busy intersection with his showy horse and carriage a policeman yelled at him angrily: "Hey, 'nigger,' where do you think you're going?"

"Ah'm goin' right back t'other side of that street, Sah, and sit there twel you tells me to start again," answered Dr. Jones with purposefully exaggerated accent and a broad smile.

The policeman guffawed and Jones escaped arrest and fine.

He treated laborers, maids and porters and had them quickly back to work; he helped in the colored annex to the white hospital without asking status or recognition as a physician. He elaborately minded his own business and had, so far as whites were concerned, no opinions on the race problem. He never dabbled in politics. Thus he was one of the best liked Negroes in Atlanta, and one of the richest. He could offer Sarah security, a lovely home and nice clothes. Of course she did not love him; he was too old and rough in his ways. But after all, one must live.

There was too another reason which Sarah never voiced even to herself, but which one of her girl friends blurted out: "Old Jones is a fool and Mansart is a dear! Pity that Manuel is black and Jones nearly white. Girl you just can't bring black kids into this

world and see them crucified. Yellow kids have a better chance."
Sarah shrank. But the shaft went home and she made up her mind.
She wired and wrote, returning Manuel's modest ring. He could
not desert the quartet and rush right South as he wanted to, but
he wrote daily, making desperate appeals. He was in the depths of
despair, and the President had to advise him not to paint too
pessimistic a picture of the Negro problem to audiences who
wanted at least the possibility of some return for their contributions.

At last in late September Mansart reached Atlanta and sought
out Susan. She, usually rather phlegmatic, was for her, really exu-
berantly glad to see him. She was working in the dormitory of her
school as maid during the vacation, and sewing rather half-heart-
edly on her trousseau for the October wedding. She wore a dazzling
diamond of which she was, despite circumstances, quite proud. She
had never owned anything half so beautiful. Manuel burst the
rather prim barriers of etiquette in school discipline even in vacation time, and called on Susan daily. Dr. Jones saw and knew it.
But he discreetly kept absent and for the most part silent. Now
and then he sent flowers and delicious candy. But he did not attempt to argue. He waited.

Mansart talked to Susan. No, of course she did not love Jones.
Ye-es, she had long loved Manuel. But after all, what could she
do? She must live and she did not want to be a servant. She wanted
a pretty home and clothes and good food. Did he blame her? He
did not. And all that she should have. But how? He'd get a job now;
he'd teach school; he'd go North.

Of course poor Susan's defenses were easily beaten down as she
was only too willing they should be. It was at last arranged. Manuel
would finish his senior year, meantime looking for a job. Susan
would return to her home in Savannah, helping her mother and
younger sisters wash clothes for white folk if she could find no better employment. Next Commencement they would get married.

So Susan went home, with no opposition from Dr. Jones who
even insisted that she should keep the engagement ring. The year
went slowly. Manuel tried to study; read as widely as time allowed,
but what worried him more than all the clouded writhing of nations was the fact that he had up until April secured no job, no
school to teach, no clerkship, not even an offer in domestic service
that promised a living for two. And Susan's letters were filled with
disappointment bordering on despair.

The President had tried especially to secure a teaching position for one of his best students. The public school authorities were getting chary of Atlanta University and her teaching. The city schools were filled with as many teachers as the city would pay for. The country schools did not want college graduates and paid little or nothing at that. Then, late in April there came a chance, due to young John Baldwin. As he returned from Princeton a year after the meeting of the three Johns he met Mansart on Mitchell Street as he emerged from the railway station and was waiting for a cab.

"Hello, Mansart," called John. His handing his luggage to a redcap made an offer to shake hands unnecessary, and he was a little ashamed to be glad of it. But he paused. "How are things?"

"Rather bad;—about to graduate and hunting for a school!"

"Say! We are to have a town school superintendent at dinner tonight. He wants a teacher. Here, let me talk to him. He lives in Jerusalem, in the southeast part of the state."

John gave Manuel a good recommendation. He was genuinely glad to be able to do something. His effort was successful and Manuel received a letter from the superintendent offering him the colored school for ten months beginning in July.

Manuel was overjoyed. He wrote Susan immediately asking her to arrange the wedding in June. He very much wanted her to come to his graduation in May, but she could not afford it.

Susan was not enthusiastic. She knew the poverty and struggle ahead. But she was fond of Manuel, and life with love in a cottage, even a leaky one, had attractions even to her rather prosaic mind. Moreover, Dr. Jones rather overplayed his hand during Manuel's absence, and her ingrained stubbornness came to reinforce her inclinations. Jones paid several visits to Savannah. But after all, she was not for sale. The doctor, however, did not press her too far. He gave her the diamond engagement ring for her own, to her great joy, and planned to send her a wedding present so as not to suffer any loss of prestige in the community.

Meantime on April 24th war was declared with Spain over Cuba. There had already been much discussion in Miss Freiburg's class over Cuba. In February she called attention to the revolution in Cuba; she reminded the class of the efforts of the Slave Power to annex Cuba and its slaves in the fifties; of the Ten Years War waged by Negroes and Cuban whites against Spain 1868-78, helped by American filibustering expeditions. Then the Americans invested 50 millions in Cuban sugar and when Cubans under Marti and the Mulatto, Maceo, revolted in 1895 the United States was ready to interfere.

Now Manuel proposed to take the Spanish American War as the subject of his commencement oration. He wrote his essay, climaxing the heroism of Maceo with the philanthropy of America the Emancipator.

Miss Freiburg sniffed. "The Sugar Trust," she said, "does not deal in philanthropy. And McKinley forgot to tell the Senate that Spain had surrendered before he demanded war."

Manuel modified his essay but he did not change it much. He lauded the American army and navy.

Chapter XII

JERUSALEM

It would have been wiser if Manuel had first gone to his new school, acquainted himself with the situation and then gone back to marry and bring his bride. But funds were too scarce and Susan might see reason again to change her mind. So Manuel hurried to Savannah and went through a breathless marriage ceremony. They then boarded the dirty "jim-crow" car of the slow local train to Jerusalem. They arrived in the early afternoon at a small, drear depot which had almost no accommodations for colored passengers. Manuel had to leave Susan sitting on a bench of the platform while he hurried to the office of the Superintendent of Schools.

The Superintendent was in and had several white visitors. He caught a glimpse of Manuel and swore under his breath. It would be just like this fool 'nigger' to burst in on him just as he was busy with white folk, and to come all dressed in city clothes. God! But he'd have to learn a lesson if he expected to stay here. He glared at Mansart as he entered. He looked at the letter Manuel brought and dropped his eyes. Of course this city darky would be on time and rush about like a white man. He must be taught his place.

"Wait," he said curtly, and then began to consult successively with several white visitors. One complained of a poor teacher; another of the delayed repairs on the white high school building; a third was impatient at the delay at finding a job for her daughter. " 'Niggers' seem to be getting most of the school funds anyway," she flung back as she left.

Just as the last white person left and the Superintendent was shuffling his papers and trying to think just how to phrase the unpleasant things he must say to this new colored teacher who was better dressed and more upstanding than he had hoped, a white man entered, grasped hands with the superintendent warmly, and they both laughed, sat down, leaned back and smoked leisurely. They conversed a half hour until Manuel, who had been standing, ventured:

"Perhaps, Sir, I'd better return when you have more time?"

The Superintendent scowled and growled, "Wait!"

The visitor started to arise. "Don't let me keep you, I had nothing to do—"

"Sit down, sit down; got plenty of time. When can we go on that fishing trip we planned?" Another quarter hour went by. Then the visitor went and the Superintendent turned and looked Manuel over. "Manuel," he said, "never interrupt me when I have a white visitor! Get this: You are in a Southern town and remember that here a black man, no matter what he is, occupies an inferior place and obeys his betters!"

He looked at Mansart and Manuel without a word looked him straight in the eye. The Superintendent hung his head. "Hell, Manuel, I don't like this no more than you will; but you and I got to bow to white public opinion in Jerusalem, or we'll both lose our jobs. I had to waste time talking about nothing while you stood, because my visitor is very influential in this town. I was ashamed and you were mad. But that's the way it is. Work with me and I'll do my best. Fight back and I'll kick you out. I'll have to. For God's sake, understand if you can."

Manuel said nothing. He would have given his soul's salvation to have walked out and taken the next train. But his new young wife, tired and frightened, was waiting for him on the dirty depot platform. They had yet to find a home. He and the Superintendent talked a half hour as Manuel took his orders and learned "his place." The Superintendent offered Manuel $40 a month for a ten-month term, which was ten dollars more than his predecessor received. She had used $10 of this to bribe two of the white trustees to keep her place. They both would deplore the new extravagance in wage and set themselves to find fault.

Jerusalem was a typical small Georgia town. That meant it was a square, set at the meeting point of four country roads. Around the square was the "City Hall," containing Court House and Jail; the post office, a saloon and pool room, several general stores, with a drug store and bank. Opposite the Court House was the First Methodist Church, an expensive, rococo monstrosity. Down the West Side, leading toward the country, was the colored quarter with a few shops, pool rooms, and churches. Up the other side was the large white Baptist Church, a new white high school, and a hospital.

From the Square three other streets radiated to the country: one with new and elaborate homes of the white town aristocracy; two with more or less drab, old and new homes for humbler whites. A new white elementary schoolhouse had been built near the square. The Negro school was carried on in a rambling Negro church on the outskirts to the west, near a factory and a fertilizer plant.

To understand this community one must remember that it was a group upset and dislocated by war. It was humanity in flux with all its old culture patterns curiously changing and yet clung to desperately. The onlooker might have described seven matters which engaged this little town: first and foremost was money, then race and social standing; third came sex, and then indulgence in liquor and gambling; fifth the courts and police, sixth murder, and seventh religion. There was no question about it: money and earning a living dominated the situation. It had to, because poverty lurked over the land.

Before the War the landed aristocracy lived scattered in the country, usually with city homes which later grew in relative importance as urban life developed. After the war the poorer whites gathered in the small villages and towns like Jerusalem where they could achieve a local importance paralleling the city, as merchants standing between owner and worker; as professional men practicing law and medicine; as artisans and laborers, and as loafers and semi-criminals; all this centered in a sea of black folk.

The merchants drove hard bargains or cheated deliberately; the landed aristocracy neglected its debts from carelessness or necessity; the white and black laborers fought for employment; and the new "democracy" began to function with the Negroes intimidated or forcibly disfranchised or given "friendly" advice by employers.

The square was nearly always well filled with folk, white and black, mingling in good-natured fellowship but with clearly defined lines of cleavage: Negroes lined the curbs and hitching posts; whites occupied the walls and steps. In the stores whites were waited on first and treated with elaborate attention. Negroes were treated more brusquely but with enough condescending comradery to keep them from going to any rival store. There was always a certain tenseness in the air which at times, especially on drunken Saturdays, brought one or two quick police to rush some black man to jail. Whites were seldom arrested.

Here were the white secret orders and the white militia with its well-stocked armory. Horses, mules, dogs and vehicles, with numbers of Negroes were common on the square; while white men of leisure, with strutting and roisterous young blades occupied the porches and ogled the young white girls who paraded by frequently with elaborate casualness. On Saturdays crowds of country Negroes descended on the square and displaced some of the loafing whites.

The Negro quarter slept peacefully most of the week. Tired servants and laborers streamed in and out twice a day. Children swarmed in the dirt and mud. They would soon loiter to and from the shabby school in the church, until the crops drove them into the white planters' fields. On Saturday the black town was wide open. All over town among white and black drinking of cheap whiskey and gin was common, together with gambling and irregular sex intercourse within and across the color line. A half dozen Negro prisoners always went to the jail, to be leased Monday morning to farmers as laborers.

Thus the pattern of race segregation and control was laid down and kept rigid. None transgressed in wages paid, credit given or character of social contacts. Strangers were watched and warned. Crops and wealth were divided by long arranged rule. Mobs could suddenly be gathered and lynchings arranged by whites. Riots and murders were carried out by rule. One or two white policemen watched the Negroes. These towns by the thousands in the South kept the interracial pattern intact, held political control of the state, and were the center of stern religious dogma. It was no empty joke to assert in this land, "Man made the city, God made the country, but the Devil made the small town."

It was not always the actual hunger and dire want that frightened this town as much as the fear of loss of status among the few who were on the edge of security, among the well-to-do who were striving between riches and poverty, and among the rich who realized that their wealth was in continuous danger. Thus came status to increase the meaning of money and of earning a living in this town. To some extent and in certain matters it even replaced money.

First of all there was the real and fabled status of the white former slave-owner. Many who had never owned a slave boasted of their slaves; those who had climbed up by tedious ways of working, cheating and stealing to a place where they could now pretend and tell legends of their father's and grandfather's "estates"; and woe to the person who denied this or who intimated that this or that man's family had been overseers at best and not great landholding aristocrats before the war.

The first part of status was color of skin, and the second was land. In town most people were white; in the neighboring country most people were black. In town a considerable number of folk

were light brown, yellow or almost white; in the country the number of mixed bloods was smaller.

The fierce fight to keep land and to get land was foremost in the
minds and acts of men. Some estates like that of Colonel Breckinridge which lay across the river, were going down in ruins. Parts
had been sold at prices far below the real value even in post-slavery
times. Other parts were lying fallow; some were ruined by white
and black tenants who could hardly make food and shelter out of
long hours of work without machinery or fertilizer.

There were whites who had struggled up through overseerships
and storekeeping and were beginning to buy up such land. One
method was to sell it to Negroes who were desperately hungry for
land and who wanted to become landholders and farmers. Through
mortgages with high interest, and through faked debts and fore-
closure and even by brute force, most Negroes simply succeeded
eventually in losing their land and paying the middlemen fabulous prices. Then came the storekeepers with their systems of
credit; with their "furnishing" the tenants and laborers, white and
black, with goods before their crops were in or their wages paid;
and then charging them exorbitant prices so that they remained always in debt.

Beyond race and landholding, education was a sign of status,
and here the Negroes were fierce in their desire to learn to read and
write. They could not be entirely deprived of this chance. Yankees
demanded it and sent money and missionaries whom the Southern
whites believed were sneaking hypocrites; but they had influence
in the North, so that Negro schools were carried on although not
very effectively outside the cities.

The Jerusalem Negro school was housed in a half-ruined old
wooden church. It had no desks nor proper chairs and its teacher
had always been one selected by the local whites for his subserviency
and ignorance. After two or three months of school in the middle
of winter, when the children learned little but reading by rote,
sketchy writing and almost no arithmetic, they were dragged out
of school to pull weeds and pick cotton on the country farms and
to help in the homes of white housewives. Most of the white children went to school six months and learned to read and write. Few
went further.

Above all, next to race, land and education came house service
to prove and maintain status. Every white woman who had any
claim to standing or even decency must have at least one black
servant: someone to cook, wash dishes, clean house and care for

the babies. In some cases, where there was money to pay them, servants were efficient but dissatisfied because service was still near slavery. Many of them got away to the cities as quickly as possible. Most of the whites could not afford to pay decent wages and have well-serviced homes. Nevertheless, few Negro women dared refuse to work at service; if they did they were liable to be arrested and jailed as "vagrants." They worked therefore, and subsisted by pilfering of food, wearing cast-off clothes, and malingering on the jobs as much as they could.

Male Negro workers and their families were mostly serfs on the farms around about at nominal wages and under conditions of work inherited from slavery. Black laborers were always in fierce dispute with white labor which demanded and usually got preferential return even for inferior performance. This made always a state of competition where low Negro wage lowered white wage. The employers gained accordingly. In house service, where no whites competed, wages touched bottom.

Next to money and status in Jerusalem was Sex: the thought, the planning, the dreaming of Sex. It was not so much the fact that in this town sexual acts were more common than in other towns, north and west; but thought and talk about it was much more common. Above all in thought, talk and imagination loomed the sex rivalry of race. Every white man of any pretension was expected to have a white wife and at least one colored concubine. Each colored man could have a colored wife but he might be asked to share her with a white man. On the other hand, he must not dare even think of touching a white woman even accidentally; actual sexual commerce between black men and white women called for riot and murder even if the woman was a known prostitute. This theory, of course, varied in practice but its very uncertainty lent a perpetual nervousness to the life of the town.

Sex was looked upon as a matter of privilege, as escape from the deadly boredom of the town. Life presented itself vividly as Sex, and the owning of women was characteristic of the men's dreams. Conversation centered on it in bar and parlor.

Especially colored women had the most difficult time. If they were pretty and comely they must marry early and even then their husbands had a hard time protecting them from white men. If they did not marry they were fair prey for both white and colored men. If they went into house service they were fairly certain to become concubines, and in a few cases colored women were supported openly in the town and everyone knew what white man was their master. Sometimes the colored women fought furiously to ward off white men even to maiming and murder. In other cases they flaunted their sex attraction for white men in the very faces of white women, who could but helplessly hate, and hate they did.

On the other hand, white women were guarded fiercely in physical and mental harems; they must avoid not only the evil of sexual life outside of marriage but the very suspicion or implication of it. They must pose as "pure" and absolutely unsophisticated. They therefore indulged themselves increasingly in gossip and imagination. For they talked Sex, they thought Sex, they dreamed Sex. Always they were shrinking from white aggressors and running wildly from black rapists. Always white men were making advances, and often they were affronted when a bold-eyed black man even looked squarely at them.

Among the black youth there was not only the natural sex attention to his own dark girls but beyond that the lure and temptation of the unattainable, of the ivory colored limbs and scented bodies of women whom they could not own but might force. Such rape was the greatest conceivable crime on earth in the eyes of white men. Now and then a white woman willingly had a black paramour, but if the truth ever became known or even suspected she must cry "rape" and he would be lynched without having a chance to open his mouth.

About a situation so unreal and false as this must come forms of indulgence in appetites and excess; and in Jerusalem it took the path of drunkenness, gambling and fighting. One only had to visit the Square of a Saturday night, when the meager wages had been paid or money been borrowed and the liquor cheap. The air was tense; brawls and fights broke out, usually within the race groups but sometimes between the races. Then it meant riot, if not murder.

The Courts were curiously handicapped. They could do very little with regard to crime because their first business was to protect status; to give the white man, even the poor whites, a preferred position in the community which under no circumstances could be questioned or invaded by blacks. So that Negroes were arrested because they were Negroes, and whites allowed to do almost as they pleased because they were whites. The demand for forced labor made arrests and summary imprisonment absolutely necessary for the economic progress of the community. The chain gangs were filled because official orders were sent down for such and such a number of Negro laborers.

On the other hand, among the whites it was almost impossible to punish crime—not even murder, certainly not theft. White criminals could not be adequately punished without insulting some white man or encroaching upon his preferred status. The judges sat therefore bound hand and foot, and those were most successful who were callous in sentencing Negroes to forty years, death or life imprisonment.

Naturally this made murder characteristic of the town. The taking of life was a little thing. Part of this stemmed from war and force which had swept over the community for long years. Part of it came from status and feud. Some of it came from the necessity of forced labor, but most of it came because men did not hesitate at killing each other. Everybody went armed and if a man was killed the only question was: what was the murderer's race? If he was white, in nine cases out of ten nothing was done, even though he killed another white man. If the murderer was black he was hanged or sentenced for life. The only semblance of justice was between Negroes where the white judge, above and outside the quarrel, was now and then free to give justice.

Finally, over all this of necessity came Religion: the frantic effort to escape this life as it lay around all people; the sense of almost universal guilt: guilt of white people for murdering human beings, for cheating labor, for forcing women to their lust, for lying and stealing and libeling each other. The universal sense of guilt was also among the Negroes who knew of their own stealing and lying and refusal to do work for what little they got. So that everybody wanted to be "saved"; they wanted to be "washed in the blood of the Lamb!" They wanted supernatural assurance that they would not be punished for what they had done or were doing. Everybody was conscious of "sin" and hypnotized themselves in religious orgy or in logical subtleties.

Religion was as universal as crime. Everybody belonged to a church: to one of the four Negro churches, where shouting and singing filled the day and night on Sunday and at least one week-day night; to one of the three white churches where the quality of worship varied from the orthodox but fervently evangelical address of the Reverend Dr. Swain of the First Methodist, to the more enthusiastic and unctuous discourses at the First Baptist, down to the wildly orgiastic yelling of the Hard-shell Baptists who often outshouted the Negroes, but with less melody.

Above everything, the prime product of this town was Gossip; stories told, whispered, screamed about everybody and everything:

guesses, slanders, lies and nasty truth. The gossiping habit was a festering sore. It poisoned the air and frightened everybody. It gripped and held the decent, normal core of honest white people, the simple lives of people who tried to be good and honest, who dressed, cooked, ate, washed and ironed or toiled with one or two black servants to make a home, and went to church to serve God.

But fear gripped them, and especially fear of the Negro; especially the black ghost of a past they did not dare forget—why, they could not say. But the Problem was there like a vast, dark hand. They were always conscious of it; their lives were efforts at pretending to escape its grip, but they never could, they never dared.

And fear gripped the Negroes: whether they were humble drudges, striving desperately to please their masters; or bitter, hating serfs driven by hunger or blows or threat of the chain gang; or hard-working laborers, glimpsing a far-off freedom for their children. All these feared white folk, good as well as bad—feared them as they feared God and often more.

Over all this hung two veils which blurred all true views of life: over the whites a pretense and desperate assumption of superority, of natural inborn privilege, to be shown in strutting walk, loud talk and swagger. This pretense in solitude or among cronies might fall away, but it especially soared and swelled in the presence of Negroes, even when these Negroes were most elaborately ignored. The white always felt a Negro was watching him and he acted his assumed part accordingly.

And Negroes did watch them from behind another veil. This was a veil of amusement or feigned, impudent humility. Through gay laughter ran a vein of cynical contempt and "shaden-freude"; of cutting, jeering mockery. Thus happy, careless guffaws hid bitter hate and even despair with impenetrable good humor.

The Superintendent of City Schools in Jerusalem, elected by the white people of the city, was in the summer of 1898 at his wit's ends. He wanted desperately to get a better job and to escape from this God-forgotten town. This depended on his local popularity and on his superior, the State Superintendent. That official was putting pressure on him to build up the colored school, which had never been more than a farce. It had been taught last year in an old Baptist church by a decrepit old woman who had inconsiderately died of chronic starvation just at the end of the school term.

The Superintendent was a well-intentioned man, but he knew that his real bosses and the source of his bread and butter was the local white electorate. He also knew that his chances for promotion and escape from this dead community rested in the good will of the state educational officials. For some reason, he did not quite know what, the state was putting pressure on officials to improve the Negro elementary school system.

He did not believe it was pure philanthropy. More probably it was Business and not unconnected with the new playing up to the North. Whatever it was, why should they pick on him? They knew his predicament; he did not have nearly enough funds for his wretched white school system. How was he to get funds for a new Negro schoolhouse and equipment and salaries for at least three teachers needed to teach 300 children?

He laid his troubles before old Dr. Baldwin as he dined with his old teacher and his charming wife and growing son in Atlanta. They had no real solution, but when Young Baldwin recommended Manuel Mansart to his mother's astonishment, the Superintendent was glad. Here at least was a well-trained Negro, vouched for by good white folks and not disposed to haggle over wages. This certainly would be put down in Atlanta to his credit. He hoped Mansart would have sense enough to realize that he as white superintendent had as great difficulties as the colored teacher. If the Negro had sense and would play along they might accomplish something—not much but enough to bring escape for both.

Manuel had to beg a half month's advance of his salary, and then began to hunt for a house. For a couple of weeks they boarded in discomfort with a colored family who did all they could to accommodate them. The home finally found was poor. It was drab in appearance, with two rooms and a barren, half-fenced yard. The roof leaked and windows did not fit or glass was missing. The running water was in the back yard not far from the primitive outdoor toilet. Of course there were no set tubs nor clothes closets.

So in this town of Jerusalem, Manuel Mansart began his active life. It soon revealed certain geographical connections of which Mansart had not at first been aware. It was not far from Thomson where Tom Watson lived. He had begun to wonder at Watson's silence and to inquire after Doyle. Caste and disfranchisement were rapidly spreading over the South and Mansart began to realize one of its causes when he learned that Jerusalem was the home of the Scroggs family. They were followers of Tillman. He had heard of them through his mother who knew of Sam Scroggs and the part he had tried to play in South Carolina in 1876. He had been killed,

but his widow and children still lived in the country near Jerusalem. Other parts of the family lived in Atlanta. Abe Scroggs,
now 26, had for a while been active in the Farmers Alliance.
He was now in Cuba as a volunteer in the Spanish-American war.

Abe Scroggs was born in Jerusalem and thus grew up in the
hard pattern of its racial culture. He hated Negroes with a dark,
unreasoning passion. Had he tried to explain his hatred he would
have traced it to an incident of his life when a small child. But
he did not try. He was not conscious of any beginning or reason for
his hate. It was just there.

This one incident, however, young Scroggs always remembered.
He would never forget it although he was at the time only six. It
patterned his life. They were a large family, ten children and many
dead. A scrawny, ugly, half-starved mother; a father, usually drunk,
who died when Abe was five. There was simply nothing to eat one
day, but the Negroes next door were slaughtering a hog—a fat hog,
carefully brought up and nurtured and looked forward to as support, indulgence and well-being.

The black father had had a hard time making ends meet, paying his rent after the piece of land which he had tried to buy had
been taken away from him by open fraud against which he could
do nothing. But now the Fall looked promising to him. They had
this hog, they had plenty of vegetables and garden stuff stored away.
The man had a job as porter and the woman worked most of her
time up at a white folks' mansion on the Square. The children
were in school, when there was a school. And now they were con-
gregated about celebrating the hog-killing. The father had gone
to work; mother and children were cleaning up.

It was dusk when Mrs. Scroggs, distraught with apprehension
and yet trying to keep herself conscious that she was a white woman,
went over into the Negroes' yard. The customary race code was
observed: she was called "Mis' Scroggs," by the hard-eyed black
woman whom in turn she addressed as "Nancy." Mrs. Scroggs wondered if Nancy would sell her a bit of "meat"? She had been late in
getting to the store before it closed. They would, of course, pay
her "soon."

Nancy was sorry, very sorry, but she "reely didn't have a bit of
meat to spare." Her own six children needed every single scrap.
Mrs. Scroggs sidled up to the table where Nancy moved the meat
that was being cut up just beyond her reach. But there were some
of the guts and entrails there, and the tail; and on these Mrs.
Scroggs laid her scrawny hand before Nancy could remove them.

"Just this little bit, what would you charge?" Nancy looked at her with venom in her face. She knew that without a fight she could not keep Mrs. Scroggs from getting this bit of chitterlings. If there was a fight Nancy or her husband would go to jail without any question. She would have no standing in court against Mrs. Scroggs. So Mrs. Scroggs gathered up the tail and a couple of handfuls of manure and guts and started away immediately.

Then from behind the fence exploded a shout of derisive laughter and mocking from the black children: "Crackers stealin' hogguts!" Young Scroggs, who was hidden behind his mother's skirt, was hurt to the heart. From that day he hated Negroes with perfect hatred. He could kill them. He would do anything to hurt them. They had laughed at and derided his poor old mother who was trying to get a bit of food for herself and her half-starved children. With tragedy like this, the sixth year of young Scroggs had begun in Jerusalem.

At 14 Scroggs had stopped school. He had learned to read and write and figure fairly well. He was not interested in the other studies offered. Grammar eluded him. He could not understand what "algebra" was up to, and he did not care about the doings of foreigners, especially in the past. Moreover, he felt that he must have a job in town and help his mother and the family. He worked at first in the fertilizer factory, but the labor was hard and uninteresting and his wage only a little above that of Negroes. He tried to oversee a farm and direct Negro and white tenants, but both the merchants and the tenants cheated him. He tried other jobs and loafed in the Square between times.

He joined the Ku Klux Klan. It was fun to ride masked and gowned on a good horse. Moreover, he could steal from the Negro cabins which were often invaded, and that was helpful support to his family. Then came the mad lust of the man hunt. He had hunted squirrels, rabbits and a few bigger animals, but there was nothing like hunting a man. In his first adventure a Negro had been found lying with a white girl. She was a bitch, as everyone knew. But the cry of rape roused all the wildest passions of the town and countryside. They rode at night, and Scroggs was among the first to grab the terrified boy and split his head open with an axe. Then they dismembered his genitals, burned him, and danced about the body, mad with hard liquor.

When he came home that night Scroggs went to bed trembling. He was frightened at what he had done. He could see the face of that boy and could not forget it. He rushed to the church next night and for a week thereafter. On Sunday he was "saved" by a passing Evangelist. He gradually began to persuade himself that he was doing God's appointed work in helping restrain or exterminate black criminals. His attitude toward black folk now changed. He had disliked them before but now he despised them because they were not really human. He learned something of this in school, more of it in the newspapers, and read one or two frightening books. Manifestly it was his duty to make it impossible for this vermin to live like other men.

But it was to live like other men and the better kind of men that Manuel Mansart was striving. And his beginnings in this town were not favorable. In fact his life was from the first discouraging. He lacked the equipment for the kind of teaching he wished to do. On the other hand, here was a chance to do work at the ground level. He was impressed by Booker Washington's criticism of young Negroes leaving the rural districts where they were needed and rushing to the cities. Perhaps right here in Jerusalem he could start building and laying foundations for a real life. Perhaps the tenuous bond between him and the three Johns—his nexus with the great Northern forces building a New South—might become stronger and more real.

As a physical and spiritual partnership the marriage of Manuel and Susan was perhaps average. It was certainly not made in Heaven, nor was it a failure. It lasted without thought of termination for 37 years and brought four children into the world. Yet the union was not ideal and encountered from the first storms and obstacles. First, neither party had been prepared for marriage either in theory or practice. Both had been raised in an era and in a group of sexual laxity and loose family ties; yet neither was physically tainted nor mentally twisted.

Susan had had a hard-working father who paid her no attention whatever. Her mother worked hard also to help support a large family. They lived in poor surroundings. But the mother was strict. Susan was the youngest and from babyhood had learned that there was something evil about sex and its organs. She must not even think of them, and being obedient she almost never did. What she saw and heard about rape, bastard children, and sordid indulgence she seldom understood. She gathered that what was largely evil and even nasty became in some curious way right, or at least permissible after marriage. Being but moderately sexed herself her curiosity carried her no further.

Manuel saw sex about him and had a certain understanding
but little actual experience. His few experiences were so frustrated
and incomplete that he was never tempted to looseness and promis-
cuity, but rather spurred toward early marriage. Thus the experiences of their marriage at first frightened Susan and then brought
her to shamefaced submission and enjoyment. They thrilled and
uplifted Manuel and then disappointed him in some not easily
understood way, as if they had opened up Heaven and revealed that
there was no Heaven there or at least none yet discoverable.

All this was natural and rested on the fact that the couple had
to earn a hard living under difficult circumstances. They had little
time or space for adjustment. If their path had been easier and
more immediately rewarding the results might have been different.
As it was there came the fact that the tasks before them could not
be shared nor mutually understood.

Manuel had no conception of the difficulties of housework,
especially in the situation of Susan. Susan's own home was primitive
in many respects, but as the youngest child she was always the
helper and never the responsible doer. Four years at school had
familiarized her with running water, hot and cold; indoor toilets
and garbage which disappeared. Even in her last year at home
there were older brothers and sisters to fetch and carry and do the
drudgery. To her, then, a home had long spelled not the luxury
which Dr. Jones had dangled before her, but at least a certain cozy
comfort with a mate to talk to and to whom she could run for
help and advice. But she knew little about marketing or buying,
and her cooking was a blend of custom, with okra, and rice, red
pepper, and what she had tried to learn in the "science" of cooking
at the university.

Manuel had been used to a home where what he wanted appeared forthwith. Of course his wants were few, and as they grew
there grew too his own ingenuity for satisfying them, along with
quick cooperation and understanding. Thus his meals had always
been ready on time and consisted of just what he liked because he
had always been used to it. When he wanted to have a place to
study, the "front" room became his without to-do. The whole
house was regulated with regard to his work and study. Dormitory
life changed this and yet even there, he and his work were first
except as his roommate must share. Eating, bathing and play were
relegated to other places.

Add to this that Manuel had an impossible job before him. The
position of teacher of a Negro public school in the rural South was

not an easy one. The teacher was not welcomed nor encouraged; he was endured. He must get on with four separate entities: the colored parents, the white town, the white school board and superintendent, the colored pupils in the school. The children were wretchedly untrained—most of them in the lowest grades. They had had little or no training in the surrounding country schools on account of forced work and parental helplessness or carelessness. They came irregularly to this school. Even in the upper grades most of them could not really read nor write.

The school was practically unequipped—no desks, planks to sit on, one grey blackboard, no maps, few textbooks. Manuel had to make desperate effort to raise equipment which the town did not furnish; and the town did not furnish equipment because the white people did not want a colored school. They were jealous of everything done for the school. It was not only direct loss but greater indirect loss since it trained colored boys and girls away from house service and labor, made them want more wages, and often made them "impudent." They ran away to the big cities in a steady stream. There were continual incidents on the street and in homes, trivial in themselves but liable to become desperate in result. Manuel found much of his time taken in interracial peacemaking.

The superintendent seldom called upon him and did not want Manuel to come to his office. His answer to everything was practically no. It was not because he did not want a Negro school, it was because his own job depended upon his spending as much on the white schools as possible and as little on the colored school; otherwise in the next election, with no Negroes voting, he would lose his job.

Faced by grim necessity Manuel began at once to learn the etiquette of living and surviving in the rural South. He did not enjoy it but he had no choice. He must conform or go. He had nowhere to go. He became careful of his superiors, particularly of the white superintendent. When the superintendent expressed an idea Mansart tried to agree. Afterward, Mansart might suggest some modification, some difference and improvement. He found, to his surprise, that his suggestions were often received and carried through, especially if they involved little or no expense. Sometimes he was allowed to carry them through himself. He sensed gradually that the Superintendent himself was also in chains which rattled ominously.

With those colored folk who had some authority because of

their long residence and relation to the whites he did not get on so well, because he did not feel the necessity for hypocrisy. He talked out and told the things which he wanted or criticized; and they told him not exactly what they might have said had they themselves been free, but what they knew they must say if they wanted to retain their own jobs and influence.

In the midst of this growing effort at adjustment toward the world and its people there came an earthquake. It was in the shape of a small baby. Of course Mansart had always expected to have a child sometime, but to have it appear within ten short months after his marriage was astonishing; but not nearly so surprising and revolutionary as the difference which it made in his home.

As he looked back he could see that with the birth of Douglass Mansart in 1899, his home never again was the same thing. He ceased to be the center of it. His wife began to lose her health and looks; especially as Douglass was followed in 1901 by Revels.

It did not occur to Manuel that anything could be done about this; in fact he probably wouldn't have done anything if he had known what to do. Children were among the natural phenomena of the world. But their coming did make a tremendous economic problem and almost broke up the home. Of course no one would have said so, least of all the over-worked mother, and not even Manuel. But he did not return now after a hard day's work to a quiet, neat little nook where he could make love to a pretty girl and dream about the future. He came to an over-crowded house with a poor yard, and a squalling baby who seemed to attract every disease of infancy, as was natural with contaminated water, flies and insects. Meals were never on time and Manuel was expected to help in the housework. To the problems of his day at school were added the most startling problems of mother and child, food and fire, clothes and neighbors, and the fearful threat of an unknown future.

This became clearer when Abe Scroggs returned to Jerusalem as a veteran of the Spanish-American War. His racial antipathies had been accentuated, his hatred of Yankees increased, and he was incensed to find the Negro school using money belonging of right only to whites and taught by a well-dressed and college-bred Negro.

Manuel Mansart was made vividly aware of this one November morning in 1898. The work in the cotton fields was finished and nearly all the children were in school. The rickety benches were crowded and there was a subdued hum of little voices with a few deep ones from the overgrown boys.

Suddenly the schoolhouse door flew open and in it stood Abe Scroggs. He had just come from the town Square where he and his buddies had been celebrating his return. Someone told how his black cook that morning had related some information from the colored school. It seemed that in a talk about the Spanish-American War and Teddy Roosevelt the new teacher, Mansart, had told the pupils that black soldiers had saved Roosevelt and his Rough Riders from annihilation at El Caney last July; and that a Southern white officer had testified to this.

"It's a damn lie!" Scroggs roared in anger. In fact he knew nothing of the incident but "niggers" couldn't fight! "Everybody knew that!" He proposed that they all go right down to the Negro school and make Mansart retract.

Scroggs was half drunk and was easily dissuaded from this project for the moment. But as he took another whiskey and started home he caught a glimpse of the Negro schoolhouse and with a fresh burst of anger turned toward it alone. He walked down through the Negro quarter elbowing loitering Negroes aside and entered the schoolhouse through the back door. Standing right beside Mansart Scroggs yelled:

"I hear your 'nigger' teacher here has been telling you lies about black troops in Cuba. No 'niggers' ever rescued Roosevelt there, and you damn well better not say so. Do you hear?"

He swung about and glared at Mansart. Mansart started to his feet and then slowly sat down. He saw the eyes of a hundred black children fastened on him. He knew what they were thinking. He was The Teacher. He knew all things. He could tell colored folk what to do when white people stepped on their faces. Well, now let him talk! Let him do something! He did nothing. He sat motionless and silent. What could he do? He had no weapon. Should he knock Scroggs down? He doubted if he was strong enough or knew how to fight. He had not struck a human being, much less a white man, since he was a child. But suppose he could and did fight? He would be lynched before night, his people homeless, his family helpless and his school in ashes.

To this end he had come! He was hardly earning a living. He saw small prospects of betterment. Who knew of his efforts or would know? What was his future or for that matter the future of his people in America? The world stood shut and fast before him. Any low, dirty, ignorant white hoodlum could publicly insult the most respectable Negro in Jerusalem and go free and exulting. How long could a black man live in a world like this?

Slowly the clock ticked. A wave of unrest fluttered over the silent children. Scroggs wavered. Should he slam his fist into this black ape's face? But if he did, what would this mad mass of black children do to him? He faltered and then a step was heard. Everybody heard it and started. Somebody came crunching up the path. And then the Superintendent of Schools loomed in the doorway in front of Scroggs.

Mansart arose. The Superintendent paused a moment and took in the scene. He knew a crisis was at hand but he ignored it.

"How do you you, Mr. Scroggs," he said. "I have been waiting to welcome you back."

Scroggs straightened up and shook hands. He stuttered, "I've been telling—these little darkies—a thing or two," he muttered awkwardly and lurched out.

The Superintendent turned to Mansart and said, "You may dismiss the pupils. It's a bit early, but I've got news for you."

"Dismissed," said Mansart, mechanically.

The children swarmed out quietly until they reached the border of the school grounds. Then a roar mounted. Scroggs heard it and looked back. That God-damned Superintendent had set this passel of "niggers" on him. He walked fast and then started to run as he approached the corner where he could descry the Square. He was almost too late. A shower of stones overtook him and one knocked off his broad-brimmed service hat and brought blood streaming down his temple. He ran for his life.

The Superintendent took no notice of this: he was staring at Mansart's face and saw how the ashen pallor had killed the rich deep brown. He asked no questions but hastened to say, "Mansart, I've got news for you. The Atlanta city schools want you. I've offered to release you. I reckon you'll be willing. The salary is twice this."

He paused; then waited for no answer but turning, left quickly. He fumbled at his tobacco pouch, but his hands trembled and he could not light a match. He glimpsed Mansart as he turned. Mansart was standing very still and the tears were streaming down his cheeks.

Chapter XIII

COLOR CASTE

A new century dawned, the century which would crown the power and the glory of the great Nineteenth. It was October 1901 and in the capital of the nation an unexpected president was at dinner in the White House. Theodore Roosevelt had been in office a month. He was exuberant. He was strong and healthy and eager for this immense task of governing the United States. His family was at the table—his wife, his daughter, Alice, and one of the boys. Two members of the cabinet were there also, and a special guest. This guest was Booker T. Washington.

The subject of discussion was one which the president would have called minor and time-consuming but it was pressing. He was in a hurry for he had other things to do. This talk had been continued from a morning interview and postponed until dinner. It was the question of appointments to political office in the South. Appointments over the country were difficult enough to face, but more so in the South because there, due to the pressure of Negroes, democratic government was not being allowed to function.

This brought forward many considerations which people outside political life and unconnected with the question of Mr. Washington's philosophy had to consider. Was the United States to be a democracy and if so, how could the democratic process be carried out? It must not be thought that this question arose solely from the Negro problem. It was exacerbated in that case because of long controversy and the Civil War; and because it had become involved with the whole world problem of races.

In centers like New York City where Theodore Roosevelt, at the time Booker T. Washington was making his Atlanta speech, began service as head of the Police Department, there was in practice a method of government which was not democratic and yet which people spoke of as a method of democratic government. It consisted of manipulation and control, particularly of the votes of the foreign-born, so that certain political parties gained and kept their power through bribery by money, jobs and public dole.

Reform in the method of government was beginning in New York. In the South reform probably would have grown and gone forward had it not been for the memory of the disrupting slavery controversy which resulted in Civil War; Civil War resulted in the enfranchisement of the Negro, and then by more or less secret understanding the Negroes were disfranchised. The South and the North agreed upon the Atlanta Compromise proposed by Booker T. Washington; that is, the Negroes were to go out of politics and confine themselves to becoming honest and skilled workers. This would keep white union labor within reasonable demands; it would enable the South to recover and develop; it would help the already developing North, and no harm would be done to anyone because certainly the mass of Negro voters were not yet ready for participation in a Democracy.

Would it be possible to get a Negro leader to agree to this? It had long seemed improbable. Many candidates for the money, publicity and power of this kind of leadership were tried out, but failed to live up to the unalterable conditions. Then Booker Washington came to Hampton and from there went to Alabama, the heart of the Black Belt. As he developed he seemed made to order. So Roosevelt was going to ask his advice.

They had finished the first courses and the President was sharpening the carving knife for the roast. He always insisted on carving himself when the family party was small.

"Now, Mr. Washington," he said, "I want you to tell Mrs. Roosevelt and our friends, as you told me this morning, just what you think of my proposals for Southern appointments."

Up to this point Booker Washington had said almost nothing. He was a shrewd and careful man. He had come from the depths of poverty, hard toil and ignorance. He realized that the whites had the power. He saw no use arguing about that. There was also no use trying to force the whites. There was no chance that the white North would long side with the Negro against the increasing power of the white South. Therefore the case was clear; seek the best terms which the Southern whites would offer and accept them. This was sense.

But back of this in his mind also was Right. Washington believed that the present power of the white race was natural. He believed that work made wealth and wealth was the sign of virtue. The whites were rich because they worked. The Negroes were poor because they did not work hard and did not know how to work. He believed also that Negroes were inferior to whites; not in every case, not by nature, and not forever; but inferior today and for many days to come. They must learn how to work and then get rich by work, and then naturally they would share in the power of wealth. Whites were not angels. They were often ruthless and capable of cruelty and dishonesty to gain their ends. But on the whole their power was rightly based on accomplishment.

This belief was basic and never was for a moment questioned by Washington. He disliked white laborers not because they were white but because they were poor, which proved they were lazy and inefficient. Their fight against Capital was a fight against the foundations of the universe.

Back of this belief lurked a pride in his own aristocratic white blood. He was a Taliaferro, one of the First Families of Virginia. He never referred to this, but he never forgot it. It placed him on the side of the employers, the owners, the "quality." Alongside of all this and contradicting it was his inferiority complex, born of slavery and poverty. Was he wise enough and educated enough to assume leadership? He must watch his step; he must be wary. White folk could not always be trusted; they were jealous of their power and not above fooling "darkies."

In addition to this he believed that Negroes with education were envious of him and only too willing to have him fail. He never forgot and never forgave the reception he received at the colored Wayland Seminary in Washington in the short time he spent there, as a sort of graduate course after Hampton. The careless, jolly sons of Negroes generations free, along with ambitious newcomers from the South, openly sneered at this awkward country bumpkin, silent, brooding, watchful. He thought their fun was indifference and their bravado laziness. His forte as he gradually conceived it was to weld a fast alliance of dependable Negro labor with the rich whites, while watching narrowly for betrayal; for this purpose his white advisers insisted that he must get firm hold of Negroes despite their weaknesses and jealousies.

Thus Washington became an introvert, silent and watchful, until he was sure of his ground and then he could be disarmingly simple and appealing. He was yellow in color, of medium height, and inclined to be stout. His features were heavy and might be considered full; but his grey eyes were watchful and could be keen. His hair was crisp and he was always clean-shaven. He dressed carelessly at first, but later with studied care—never conspicuously, always with a suggestion of quite moderate income.

His forte was listening with deep attention; but he never over-did this. At the right moment he would speak and even take charge of a conversation, speaking simply and to all appearance, frankly; saying at first just the things which he sensed the other speaker believed, and then shrewdly injecting his own suggestions. For instance, once when Andrew Carnegie offered him $10,000 for Tuskegee, Washington answered: "But I could not accept $10,000— not from Mr. Carnegie!"—implying that if the great Carnegie gave so little, most folk would give nothing. In the end he got $600,000 from Carnegie for Tuskegee.

He spoke now clearly and decisively in answer to the President's question: "Mr. President, as I said before, I am convinced that you should put in office in the South, men of the highest ability regardless of their politics. I especially recommend Thomas J. Jones of Alabama for the vacant federal judgeship. He is a fine man and an upright judge. I know him personally. He has often helped Tuskegee. I am certain no one will oppose him. As you suggested, I have asked him if he would accept and he is willing."

"Bully!" said the President, and his wife smiled. "Then that is settled."

"And now, Mr. Washington, let's face the tougher problem— the appointment of Negroes."

Roosevelt was impatient with the Negro Problem. It was already too much talked about. There were also matters about Negroes which bothered the conscience of Theodore Roosevelt. Only three years before, Negro regiments at El Caney had saved his Rough Riders from certain defeat. Later, that 25th United States Negro regiment which he crucified, had held San Juan Hill for his undisciplined troops. Roosevelt knew this; he acknowledged it; but he could not help contradicting himself at other times and hinting cowardice on the part of some Negroes. One doesn't like being rescued by blacks. Especially he claimed that white officers like himself were responsible for the efficiency of Negro troops. Negroes resented this, for in this Spanish War every device was used to keep efficient Negro officers from the front. Even black Colonel Young was kept in Ohio. They insisted that Negroes could fight under Negro officers, and said that in Cuba, Negro troops had fought well when most of their white officers were dead or absent.

But here was a peculiar case. The southern Negroes were pretty thoroughly disfranchised by violence, the "White Primary," and increasingly by actual law. Yet they were residents of the South and on their numbers in the population representation in Congress was based. Not only that, but they were members of the Republican Party and almost the only persons who cast a vote for that party in the South.

Now in appointments to Federal office and in accord with democratic tradition this population could not be absolutely ignored. On the other hand the white people of the South did not want Negroes appointed to office, and they expected now as never before to have this affront to White Supremacy met by the new president of the United States. Here was a quandary which could not be evaded. Ordinarily appointments to federal office in a state were made in pursuance of advice from residents. Republican residents in the South were almost entirely Negroes.

Gradually but firmly the Republican Party had been dropping the Negro from notice in its national conventions and campaigns. Since the Republican National Convention of 1868, Negro delegates attended the Republican nominating conventions. In the convention of 1884 a former Congressman, the black John R. Lynch from Mississippi, was chosen as temporary chairman. Yet from 122 words in the platform of 1888, the Negro sank to no mention at all in the platform in 1916.

Should Negroes continue to hold the balance of power in the Republican organization? No, said some, because they do not vote in the South. Very well, but they live in the South, and work. Nevertheless, they should be disfranchised so far as possible in the Republican National Convention. But they still existed and their political power remained and the South based its representation in Congress on it. This meant that Southern Congressmen needed but a quarter to a tenth the number of votes which a Northern Congressman needed, and by seniority the Southerners got the powerful chairmanships. Then came Booker Washington and his message was interpreted as saying:

"Negroes should not vote; they should not join unions; they should not strike."

This was not just what he said, but this was the interpretation put on his words, and this interpretation he did not deny. It resulted that the better class of Negroes got out of politics; they did not join unions often when they could; and they scabbed on strikers. Yet a fifth of the working class of the nation were Negroes. Where did this leave the labor movement?

Then there were the "Lily Whites," white Southerners who proposed to take over Republican patronage in the South and displace the Negroes as advisers or appointees. They were usually men of neither character nor ability. Roosevelt recoiled from recognition of them, but could he refuse to appoint any Negroes?

Thus Teddy Roosevelt stood at the edge of an era which sought to eliminate the black man from undue power in the Republican Party. But this could not be done suddenly. The Negro vote in the North was growing. The President did not want to affront the white South. He had many Southern friends and sympathized with the problem of the white south. On the other hand, certainly it would be bad politics to affront Negro voters.

Washington also was in a difficult position. Of course he had not meant to advise Negroes to give up political rights entirely. He had meant to advise them to stop insisting on political rights as the first thing needed. He expected that the South in turn would offer the right to vote to deserving, hard-working and thrifty Negroes. He believed this was about to come true. He was overwhelmed with invitations to speak, especially in the North but frequently to whites in the South. When now he found himself called in as consultant on appointments by a President he saw a chance to make a subtle deal. He would recommend a white Southern Democrat on the one hand and a first-class Negro on the other. He would thus appease the white South and satisfy the uneasy Negroes.

He paused and then answered the President's last question: "Mr. President, I don't see how you can avoid appointing some Negroes to office. Former Republican Presidents have always appointed Negroes to office. President Hayes, President Garfield and President Arthur; President McKinley and President Harrison; also Democratic President Cleveland appointed Negroes. Negroes have thus occupied positions as U. S. Marshal, Collectors of Customs and Treasury officials. I venture therefore to suggest that you select a Negro of ability and irreproachable character and appoint him to an important position."

Roosevelt looked thoughtful. He had half-hoped for different advice. But he saw the inevitable logic. "Do you know such a man, and what office do you suggest?"

"Well, Sir, there is J. C. Napier of Nashville; a banker of recognized character and ability."

"And what office?"

"Treasurer of the United States."

Roosevelt scowled and drummed on the table. This was ridiculous. The nation would not stand for it. Moreover his Secretary of the Treasury would never accept a colored subordinate in so high a position. Then another excuse occurred:

"But that would not be a Southern appointment. The capital does not like to be considered South."

Washington sensed that he had bid too high. He assented to the objection and looked thoughtful. At last he said: "I think I have it. South Carolina has a Negro majority. Why not appoint a Negro Collector of the Port of Charleston? There have been Negro Collectors in New Orleans and Galveston and there is one in Atlanta now."

"Do you know a good man?"

"Yes. Dr. William D. Crum is a fine man and well-liked by all. He is a physician and a man of property."

"You vouch for him?"

"Absolutely."

"Good. I'll appoint him."

Washington added: "Dr. Crum is a fine specimen of my race. His appointment will satisfy the Negroes and I cannot think that the whites will be opposed."

There ensued other questions pertaining to appointments of whites and Negroes, of political activity, and of education. It was a most interesting dinner and everybody felt that much had been accomplished.

More had been done, however, than either the astute president or the careful Mr. Washington had anticipated. Roosevelt had quite unwittingly transgressed one of the major racial taboos of the South, and that is, that white gentlemen and ladies did not eat with Negroes. Of course this custom was often violated. White mistresses ate with their cooks; white farmers ate with their hands. But always care was taken about this and either the incident was not mentioned or the eating together was so conducted that the implied equality was not manifest. Something resembling medieval "eating below the salt" was the custom between white and black in the South.

For a week nothing was said of the Washington dinner although as usual it had been noted in the daily press. Meantime, in the office of John Sharp Williams, Democratic majority leader of the House of Representatives, several Southern members of Congress were in conference. They were worried.

"That appointment of Jones is shrewd and dangerous. Jones ought to be horsewhipped for accepting a judgeship on the recommendation of a Negro."

"Sure, but he's a good judge and if this policy continues it will build up a Republican Party in the South. What?"

Williams' secretary had hurried in with a whispered message.

"Very well, send him in. A reporter, whom I trust, has an idea, Gentlemen."

A young man came in and outlined a plan.

"It may work. Try it. And you gentlemen write and wire home."

So it started. So a reporter spread the news throughout the South and the underground Southern white leadership sensed something to offset Roosevelt's two excellent appointments. The South was reminded that Roosevelt had crossed the color line and eaten with a Negro.

The white South erupted. The South quite literally foamed at the mouth. It yelled and shrieked. The secretly fed upheaval, and it could be called nothing less, was astonishing. From the Mason and Dixon line to the Gulf, from the Atlantic to California, the Southern papers were filled with vituperation against Theodore Roosevelt. A Mississippi politician publicly called Roosevelt a dog and apologized to the dog. The South scored Booker Washington harshly. There were threats of personal violence to both Roosevelt and Washington which literally filled baskets. One man who was arrested at Tuskegee confessed (whether with truth or not) that he had been sent from Louisiana to kill Booker Washington. Judge Jones of Alabama was forced to do some elaborate explaining.

This clamor eventually died down but neither Roosevelt nor Booker Washington ever forgot it. Evidently it was a concerted action based upon a determination completely to exclude Negroes from political life in the South, and to establish them as a social caste by law and custom.

Roosevelt now did some fast foot-work along the color line. He elaborately ignored the clamor of the South on the Washington dinner. He appointed the Southern white Democrat as Federal judge in Alabama. On the other hand he intervened in Panama and established in Panama a dependent territory, with all the Southern paraphernalia of "Jim-Crow" from separate schools to separate currency and lower wages for Negroes. Then turning swiftly, that same year he appointed Washington's nominee, Dr. Crum, as Collector of the Port of Charleston, South Carolina, and announced the reappointment of a colored postmistress to a minor Post Office in Mississippi.

Clamor arose again. He ignored it in South Carolina. But in Mississippi a new complication appeared. Vardaman, a Poor White demagogue from the hills, wanted to be governor of Mississippi and then senator in Washington. He chose the Negro as his stalking horse, and having started a vitriolic newspaper in Indianola, the *Commonwealth*, he hit on Minnie Cox, the colored postmistress as his victim, and the Washington dinner as his text. Dressed in white, with long flowing hair, he paraded the state as the "White Chief," drawn by big white oxen and haranguing the people. He out-Tillmanned Tillman, and roared against the infamy of having a "nigger wench" handle white folks' mail.

A valiant white officer, commanding the "First Squadron of Cavalry," of Arkansas, sent a telegram to Vardaman: "Subject to your order, I tender my services with one hundred and fifty cavalry to the good people of Indianola for their protection against Negro domination." After a bitter and nation-wide struggle with the stubborn President, Vardaman won and Minnie Cox lost her post office in 1903.

Booker Washington was shaken and deeply disappointed by the incident of the White House dinner. He saw clearly that the South had not responded to his offered compromise in 1895 nearly as readily as he had assumed or as his popularity seemed to indicate. He witnessed with apprehension the rising influence of Ben Tillman.

Ten years older than Washington, and his bitterest white opponent, was Ben Tillman. Tom Watson, nearly Washington's own age and better known than Tillman at the time of the Washington speech, was rapidly overshadowed by Tillman as spokesman of the New South from the time Tillman became governor of South Carolina in 1890 and United States Senator in 1895 until after the First World War. The *Boston Transcript* described him in a phrase from Virgil—"Monstrum, horrendum, ingens, infandum cui lumen ademptum" — "hideous, profane monster, with one eye!"

Tillman became leader of the movement toward legal and permanent color caste in the United States. He demanded openly and unequivocably the disfranchisement of every Negro no matter what his education or fortune. He demanded the enfranchisement of every white man no matter what his status, education, fortune or work. He declared that Negroes were congenitally so inferior to whites that the races could live together only as master and man. He wanted these differences written into state and national law and enforced by penalties. He would admit Negroes to the body social and politic only as servants or low-wage labor occupying no position which any white man wanted. He wanted no education for Negroes because they could not be educated and never in all history, he said, had a black man proven himself human in the same sense as whites.

Tillman demanded this program in the halls of Congress and from the seats of wealth and power where he was invited and listened to. He offered cooperation on no other terms. How far he really believed all that he preached on the huskings and lecture platforms over the land, it is hard to say. He had Negro friends and liked Negroes "in their place." But there is no shadow of doubt as to his reiterated demands. Under his bulldog impulse, legal disfranchisement of Negroes was made law in the South between 1890 and 1910. Caste legislation providing separate travel, no racial intermarriage, and segregation in school and state, followed from the Washington speech in 1895 to the Atlanta riot in 1906.

The depths to which American civilization sank in race hate is almost unbelievable. Tillman raged openly on the floor of Congress:

"Yes, we have stuffed ballot-boxes, and will stuff them again; we have cheated 'niggers' in elections and will cheat them again; we have disfranchised 'niggers,' and will disfranchise all we want to; we have killed and lynched 'niggers' and will kill and lynch others; we have burned 'niggers' at the stake and will burn others; a 'nigger' has no right to live anyhow, unless a white man wants him to live. If you don't like it you can lump it!"

Vardaman, leader of white Mississippi, shouted: "I am opposed to Negro voting; it matters not what his advertised moral and mental qualifications may be. I am just as much opposed to Booker Washington as a voter, with all his Anglo-Saxon reinforcements, as I am to the coconut-headed chocolate-colored, typical little 'coon,' Andy Dotson, who blacks my shoes every morning."

The presiding officer of the Louisiana Constitutional Convention said in his closing speech: "What care I whether the new Constitution be more or less ridiculous or not! Doesn't it meet the case? Doesn't it let the white man vote and doesn't it stop the Negro from voting?—and isn't that what we came here for?"

Thomas Dixon, Jr., author of "The Klansman," said: "My deliberate opinion of the Negro is that he is not worth hell-room. If I were the devil I would not let him in hell. The Negro is a human donkey. You can train him, but you can't make him a horse. Mate him with the horse, you lose the horse and get a larger donkey called a mule, incapable of preserving his species."

Dixon's play on Negro inferiority and crime swept the nation, and Griffith's motion picture, "The Birth of a Nation," based on it, was long the most popular and lauded picture in theatres north and south.

Another prominent Southern clergyman, Henry Frank, advocated the re-establishment of slavery: "The Negro's native sluggishness, and the evidence of his general extinction since his emancipation, his imperceptible improvement since liberation, his startling lapse into barbarism, all must incline thinking people to conclude that the freeing of the Negro was a disastrous failure."

Lynching, long prevalent, was now openly defended. Tillman said: "There might be no alternative for the Southern people but to kill Negroes to prevent them from holding office. There are still ropes and guns in the South."

No one dared to stop such talk. The North, guided by Big Business, was frantically engaged in appeasing the South; it was closing the "Bloody Chasm" of the "War Between the States" and as one Negro put it, "Closing up the Negro inside!" In the nineties the public killing of untried persons accused of crime rose to 200 a year. They were almost always Negroes who had not been judged by any court or jury. Between 1896 and 1906, 1200 such public murders took place and they now began to turn into public exhibitions of fiendish sadism.

This horror spread in the part of the nation noted for its vociferous religion. The South proclaimed a personal acquaintanceship with God and His Purpose which seemed almost blasphemous to Europeans. The cities swarmed with churches and the countryside was liberally dotted; and no man sought public office unless he was an Evangelical Christian, and preferably a Methodist or Baptist.

Yet the Southern church was strangely silent on lynching of Negroes. Of course, the long defense of slavery formed a solid background of thought; but here many liberal Southerners had balked. They knew all Negroes were not inferior. They knew that all "colored" people were not Negroes, but that many shared the blood of the best families of the South. They knew that these white, yellow and black folk could be educated; that they could and did fight as soldiers against whites and because of this brought the surrender of the South at Appomattox; and that the real nightmare of Reconstruction was not the failure of the Negro voter, but the fact that he did learn and could rule.

Such persons were in cruel quandary. The ignorant simply preached that Negroes were not human and not the "children of God." The mass of educated Southerners took refuge in current racial theory and the European imperialism based on it; and on evolution which promised possible human equality in "a thousand years" or more. They adopted the fatalistic attitude that God would work out the mess in his own time and they were only required to wait on his movements.

Once in a while the stark crime of the South was forced into the face of the Church. This happened in 1904 at the General Conference of the white Methodist church of north Georgia in Atlanta. The sessions were nearly over when a young white preacher asked for the floor. He was small, thin, and pale with long hair falling down at the sides of his chalk-like cheeks, with skin drawn tight over sharp bones. He was painfully shy and trembling but insisted on speaking, despite the kindly advice of the presiding bishop.

"I must talk," he said. "I have been silent too long. It was last Fall up in Doddsville, where I preach. Luther Holbert, a Negro, had quarreled with a white man. They shot at each other and the white man was killed. The Negro and his wife tried to run away, but were caught by a mob of whites. I must tell you what happened. I saw it. I have kept silent too long."

The audience moved uneasily. Two missionary women went out to the toilet rooms. He continued: "The two Negroes were tied to trees while bonfires were prepared. The blacks were forced to hold out their hands while one finger at a time was chopped off. The fingers were distributed as souvenirs. The ears of the murderer were cut off. Holbert was severely beaten, his skull was fractured, and one of his eyes, knocked out with a stick, hung by a shred from the socket. Neither the man nor the woman begged for mercy, nor made a groan or plea. The most horrible form of punishment consisted in the use of a large corkscrew in the hands of one of the mob. The instrument was bored into the flesh of the man and the woman, into the arms, legs and body, and pulled out, the spiral tearing out big pieces of raw, quivering flesh every time it was withdrawn.

"After these tortures the mutilated bodies were burned. Had this Negro outraged a white woman? Oh, no; he had killed a white man who was trying to kill him. His wife had committed no crime, but simply fled with her husband."

The ministers sat stunned; the presiding bishop arose, but the little preacher refused to stop talking.

"Hear me; I am not through yet. Last year I was stationed in Burnside, South Georgia. A white man was killed and his murderer escaped. So the mob started killing other Negroes. They killed Joe Turner who, they said, knew the murderer, but he declared he did not know where he was. Mary Turner, Joe's wife, often worked in our home. She was about to have a baby and when she heard of Joe's lynching she cursed the mob and swore she'd name the murderers of her husband. So the devils seized her and tied her to a tree; they slit her belly—"

"Stop!" cried several ministers and the bishop stepped forward. But the pale young preacher leaped into the pulpit and shouted:

"They slit her belly and the unborn child dropped to the ground. Then they poured gasoline over the woman and burned her—"

Several hands seized him. The bishop raised his hands and shouted for silence.

"Judge not that ye be not judged," he said. "God moves in a mysterious—"

"God wasn't there. God didn't do a thing. Neither did any of you. Shame—"

But the young preacher was silenced and hurried out.

"Mental case," said a minister. "Ought to go to Milledgeville."

"To that place?" asked a layman. "If he ain't crazy already and goes to that hell hole called a lunatic asylum, he'll be a raving lunatic before he leaves."

The Presiding Elder and the Bishop rode to the latter's home together. The Bishop was upset.

"Did you hear what that fanatic said?" he gasped.

"Yes," said the Elder, who was what most folk called a "worldly man."

"It can't be true."
"Yes, it can and is."
"My God! What can we do about it?"
"Dine—and soon."

It was in the North, then, that the real battle was fought, and lost only after sincere struggle. There were a few persons there who pretended to themselves that this disfranchisement in the South was normal and only a consequence of the general democratic movement to protect the ballot from illiterate and lazy folk; and that the caste legislation was a yielding to the timid and would wear away in time. These folk knew they were deceiving themselves; that Negro disfranchisement was not simply a matter of illiteracy, and that caste was deeper than whim. The majority of Northerners knew that they were assenting to a dirty deal which was a flat denial of democracy, a slap in the faces of those who signed the Declaration of Independence, and base ingratitude to the black soldiers and laborers who helped win the Civil War. It affronted a race whose emancipation they had loudly proclaimed to the world was the cause and excuse for civil war—"the glory of the coming of the Lord!" They knew lynching was the crowning disgrace of American civilization.

Such persons excused their souls and their country by reminding themselves that the ruling white race, entrusted by God with the care of this muddled world, was sometimes compelled by the sinful and incompetent mass of the world's peoples to take harsh and unpleasant measures for the good of mankind as a whole. The glory of God and the salvation of the world must be pursued even while a few suffered temporarily. They therefore redoubled their missionary efforts in Africa, China, India and other lands, while cutting down their contributions to Negro schools in the South. They received the assurances of good business men that disfranchisement would restore normal life and wholesome economic conditions and that profitable business was civilization. Moreover, contributions to Hampton and Tuskegee would encourage the right sort of training for American Negroes.

There were other Northerners who took refuge in stubborn silence. They neither talked, wrote nor preached on this subject, pleading that it was either insoluble or at least that they did not understand it and would leave its settlement to those who did. But there were a few who recited the Golden Rule and the Declaration of Independence. They held high the tattered flag of the Abolitionists and accused the nation of betraying freedom and democracy. With these last stood the thinking and independent Negroes. The group formed the only Americans, at the opening of the 20th century, defending real democracy in the United States.

In the South there was a group including John Pierce who were trying a path of compromise between the Abolition-democracy and the liberal South, to settle the Negro Problem. This grew out of John Pierce's interest in Negro education. Pierce had had much to do with that speech of Booker Washington in Atlanta in 1895. Indeed, none knew so well as John Pierce how protracted and delicate were the negotiations which preceded this speech. And even John Pierce knew only the part which he was foremost in manipulating.

The situation was involved. Race segregation had to be preserved in the South or a united labor movement would threaten Capital North and South. Lynching and lawlessness had to be curbed or society was threatened by revolution. The Negro must be legally disfranchised or his political power would be added to white labor; the Negro must not be educated above his necessarily low station or he would become ambitious and a prey of half-educated demagogues. The Negro must work cheerfully and intelligently, with elementary education and hope; but he must be given definitely to understand that social intermingling with the whites or political domination over them was forever impossible.

Now these were contradictory propositions, impossible of entire reconciliation. Yet no part could be neglected without disaster. If all were pushed and successful, what would result? Nobody knew. Yet they must work now and quickly. The rest must be left to chance or the luck of "God's country."

First then, Education—not first in time nor importance but in availability for attack. Conferences on Negro education began to be held by liberal Southerners, in Capon Springs, a Virginia vacation resort. Of course no Negroes could attend; this was a white man's resort. The Negro must be educated, but his education at present must be limited to elementary subjects and industry, and it must be preceded by and predicated upon the earlier and better education of poor white children.

This was the conclusion relayed to John Pierce and his collaborators. He organized trips to Hampton, an avowed Negro and Indian industrial school, where "learning by doing" as at Dotheboys Hall was emphasized, and Negro colleges sneered at. There conferences between Southern whites, Northern business men like Robert Ogden, and a few picked Negroes took place. Propositions were formulated and published. For the development of this program, Booker Washington became the chosen and often perplexed and unhappy leader. Then the Southern Education Board was organized to push education in the South; first white schools, then Negro industrial schools.

There was immediate difficulty. There was not enough money for white schools, much less for black schools. And Negro teachers were needed. They were now being trained in the very Negro colleges which it was proposed to discourage. The Rockefellers were induced to endow a General Education Board for all education. It would eventually encourage Negro colleges, but the white schools must be pushed first and colored colleges last. To this program Negroes must assent even though with it would go, at least at present, legal disfranchisement and caste status.

In 1900, shortly after Manuel left Jerusalem, there had come to Atlanta University a young colored teacher as successor to Miss Freiburg. For Miss Freiburg had given up the struggle of a white woman teaching Negroes History and Politics in a Negro-hating environment. She married a Minnesota farmer—a widower who had worn out two wives in securing his farm, and now wanted a third to help him die in peace. Miss Freiburg found much satisfaction in chickens, cows, flowers and sunsets, and established treaties of peace and friendship with two sets of offspring. Also, she got a will signed and sealed which insured her own comfort for life. She bought books and subscribed to periodical literature.

James Burghardt, her successor, was a Northern Negro. John Pierce, the white financier and trustee of the University, knew of his family. It had often been related in the Pierce family how in the early part of the 19th century a clan of Negroes, not more than three generations removed from Africa, owned a group of small farms near the large Pierce farm. The Negroes in some way had moved from the Hudson Valley, achieved their freedom, and some could read and write. They supported themselves on their farms, doing occasional labor outside.

Stubbornly they refused to sell their land to the Pierce family, to the disgust of Pierce's grandfather. John himself remembered that about the time he was graduating from college he heard that the Black Burghardts had lost nearly all their land and were becoming laborers and servants in the community. Some of their children were in school and at the time of Pierce's marriage one young

Burghardt entered High School. John and his wife, whose Irish ancestors had once worked in this country town, discussed the question as to what a black boy would want with a high school training.

It seemed that this young Negro had finished high school and college and actually earned a Ph. D. in history at Yale. He applied for work at Atlanta University and, with some hesitation, Pierce voted to hire him. He made no effort to get in touch with him but he watched his work.

There were many in the Atlanta college community who were uneasy at Burghardt's coming: white teachers who wondered if a colored man had the scholarship to make a teacher of History and Sociology; or more than that, if he would have manners and culture which for these students were more needed than facts. Also, most of the colored students had more subtle but just as real objections. During all their lives color had denoted inferiority; much as they disliked and even hated most white folk, yet as a matter of fact they granted white superiority, because the white world dominated their values and judgments, while the surrounding dark world was evidently inferior even if that inferiority was not the black man's fault; or (and this was the lurking inner doubt) what if the Negro was in fact lesser in ability than the white? So the student body was at least uneasy if not actually antagonistic to Burghardt.

Mansart had determined on returning to Atlanta to do graduate work in history and social science so as to prepare himself for promotion. He had looked forward to the inspiration of Miss Freiburg and was disappointed when she went. Also, while he would have been the last to admit prejudice, he could not honestly believe that a colored person, with his necessarily limited opportunity, could give him the guidance he wanted. The fact that Burghardt had been trained in the North and spoke New England English was in his favor; but on the other hand no one in the student body liked his stiff, unsympathetic manners, his strict methods and impossibly high standards of work.

Burghardt himself seemed to harbor no doubts. He started out his very first year by failing in his high school course in Medieval History the daughter of a prominent colored undertaker, about to graduate. Of course all knew the girl was spoiled and had neglected her work from sheer self-will. Burghardt stubbornly stuck to his guns and the girl did not graduate. This may have been keeping up a standard of scholarship, but it did not add to the new colored teacher's popularity.

But Mansart was rather intrigued by this show of independence and was ashamed to admit prejudice against a colored man. He signed up for a late afternoon seminar in current politics. The instructor was cold, difficult of approach, but clear and precise, and he knew his subject. He condemned American imperialism in Cuba and British rule in India. He blamed Big Business for current conditions.

When study swung back home, Populism, Tom Watson and the labor movement came in for discussion. The class was strongly anti-labor and resentful of this professor's radicalism and defense of unions. Later, when he began to side with Negro intellectuals against Booker Washington, even the new young white president of the University, successor of Sheldon, now dead, had to take notice. The college was still starving; many Negro schools and colleges were disappearing and millions were being poured into Tuskegee, Hampton and other industrial schools.

The President appreciated Burghardt's ideals, which Burghardt explained clearly: the Negro problem must no longer be regarded emotionally. It must be faced scientifically and solved by long, accurate and intense investigation. Moreover it was not one problem, but a series of problems interrelated with the social problems of the world. He laid down a program of study covering a hundred years. The first study, Health, would begin this year, followed by nine other subjects for nine years. Then the tenth year he would return to the matter of Health and study it again with more data, more money, a better laboratory and assistants. He outlined this quite blandly and earnestly to the rather bewildered young president who was trying to collect alms from missionary societies who wanted to convert the heathen in Africa and the South.

The studies of the Negro Problem which had immediately begun were the only scientific studies of the kind in the world, and were soon widely recognized. But the President had been warned: he could expect no increased aid for Atlanta so long as this man was there. John Pierce had soon sensed the situation and had talked with the President.

But Burghardt went serenely on his way. Being invited to one of the educational conferences at Hampton, he made so spirited a defense of Negro college education that he was never invited back. Mansart liked this and yet it raised a question which all his long life was never satisfactorily answered, was never solved but always solving: What attitude, what action should he take toward that part of the white world which held him and his people in bondage? He was sure of what was right; he knew what he wanted. Should he state this openly and frankly or should he declare it only partially? Or, under certain circumstances, should he not only demand nothing but yielding, ask only what the whites were willing to grant, or perhaps a little less?

Naturally much or nearly all would depend on how strong and determined the white group was—or did it? Or how weak the Negro remained. Was he, while in Jerusalem, a coward to demand so little, when now in class at the University he defended a demand for all that was right or even more? Or in both attitudes was he merely wise, and is wisdom always a matter of compromise? In fact, is Wisdom always a little false?

Burghardt did not talk freely to many persons, but just as Miss Freiburg had taken to Mansart, so Burghardt several times struck up conversations with him. This happened one day in 1903 when Burghardt returned to the campus from a trip North. He looked at Mansart speculatively after the evening class and as they walked toward the street together.

"I've been talking to Booker Washington," he said.

Mansart expressed surprise. "I thought—"

"That I did not agree with him. I don't in many matters. But I respect his effort and just now I'm sorry for him. He's in a tight place."

"How so? He's still very popular."

"He made a generous gesture toward the white South. Probably too generous, as I thought at the time. Their reply was disfranchisement and color caste including almost unrestrained lynching. Washington finds that the students of Hampton and Tuskegee cannot be induced to go on the farms amid mobs and with no political power. Moreover Tuskegee cannot teach industry without machinery and openings for work. Machines cost too much and white trade unions will not admit Negroes except to a few of the old building trades where they used to work; and even there they are being edged out by law and new techniques. Tuskegee can only teach dying skills like cobbling, or caste duties like house service. Therefore, Washington is trying to re-deploy his forces. He is turning toward retail business and, using my studies, has formed a Negro Business League."

"Isn't that a good line?"

"Perhaps, but dangerous. It needs scientific guidance. The whites have strongly advised that Washington acquire my services."

"For what?"

"That's just it. For what? I went to talk to him in order to find out what he wanted me to do."

"What did he say?"

"Nothing. Literally nothing. I talked my head off: about my plans and methods. About my ideals. He just let me talk until I realized that he had made me no real or definite offer. I saw that he did not trust me, that he was probing to learn just what my 'game' was. I had no game. But now I know what his white advisers' game is. They want to place me in a position where they can guide and curb my thought. Well, I don't like it. I am going to refuse his offer of employment at Tuskegee, which he never made definite. I am going to publish this year a criticism of Washington and his philosophy."

"You'll attack him?"

"No, I'll advise him and show him where he is wrong."

Mansart pondered and then ventured to say: "White people won't like it."

This was true. Pierce was back of the effort to remove Burghardt from Atlanta University to Tuskegee. Burghardt had brains and ability and worked hard, but he must be kept under disciplined restraint. It was first proposed to settle him at Hampton to edit a magazine for Negroes, but he immediately told Dr. Frissel, the Bishop of Rhode Island, and John Pierce, who formed the committee to test him out, that he would accept only if he had full charge of the policy of the magazine. In the face of this presumptuousness the plan was quietly but quickly dropped. Then the Tuskegee offer was made, and Burghardt's widely read book was the result of that.

This was too much and this man must leave Atlanta University and be silenced. But there were obstacles, first of which were his undoubtedly scientific and widely acclaimed "Studies of the Negro Problem." Nowhere else in the world was such a set of studies being made. They were not good but they were the best being done and might be the foundation of a new science of sociology.

Then in 1905, as color caste hardened, this firebrand formed the "Niagara Movement." It was a band of only a dozen Negroes, none of whom were rich or famous, but their Manifesto rang over the nation like a scream of defiance. And in 1906, this group, grown to over a hundred, met again at the Harpers Ferry of John Brown and issued what Burghardt had written:

In the past year the work of the Negro hater has flourished in the land. Step by step the defenders of the rights of American citizens have retreated. The work of stealing the black man's ballot has progressed and the fifty and more representatives of stolen votes still sit in the nation's capital. . . . Never before in the modern age has a great and civilized folk threatened to adopt so cowardly a creed in the treatment of its fellow-citizens, born and bred on its soil. Stripped of verbose subterfuge and in its naked nastiness, the new American creed says: fear to let black men even try to rise lest they become the equals of the white. And this in the land that professes to follow Jesus Christ. The blasphemy of such a course is only matched by its cowardice.

Chapter XIV

THE ATLANTA RIOT

Disfranchisement, caste and lynching brought hatred, riot and murder. The year 1906 was in a sense the year of Doom. Japan had just won a war against Russia; India was struggling toward freedom. Blind Tom, a musical prodigy, was dying in poverty after making his white owners rich. Then in April, 1906 came the San Francisco earthquake and fire, just 20 years after Charleston. In June a rich playboy in New York murdered the leading American architect and went unpunished. In July the new Niagara Movement for American Negro freedom met at Harpers Ferry. In August, Theodore Roosevelt punished the Negro 25th Cavalry for resenting color discrimination in Texas. In September came the Atlanta race riot, and in October Manuel Mansart was thirty years old.

Mansart's five years in Atlanta had not been without success. He had made a good principal and had been promoted; but his financial position remained difficult and he came to see that much of his time must go to family problems and not to the Negro Question or even to his public schools. His salary was, to be sure, now more than twice its former size, but it appeared soon that his expenses would be at least three times their former amount. There was the house: it was not new nor really good, but the rent was fantastic and the only remedy seemed to be to buy a home, as all the teachers were trying to do. The white real estate dealers were eager to arrange this, but the results resembled life slavery to mortgages, interest and taxes.

He must remain at present satisfied with a rented house of five rooms, but not fewer because the two-year old baby whom they had brought from Jerusalem was joined by another boy the very year they arrived, and by a third in 1903. The house became pretty crowded, the wife driven by housework, and new furniture, new clothes and shoes and growing quantities of food were in constant demand. With the best effort Manuel found himself running into debt and patronizing the loan sharks who fattened on Negro teachers and artisans.

The organization of the Atlanta Negro schools followed that of Jerusalem in avoiding as much as possible the wasting of the

time of the superintendent on them. He did not want colored
teachers complaining to him or even visiting him. There was little
he could do about their complaints even if he wanted to and he
did not much want to. So the colored schools were put in nominal
charge of a colored "supervisor" who had neither initiative nor
power. John James had served in this position since 1890, and he
was tired and old. Manuel Mansart had deliberately ignored him.
His object was eventually to head the Negro schools of Atlanta.
For this he knew he needed better preparation; also he knew that
he must make friends with the white school authorities. The Washington doctrine had been criticized, but it had taken deep root.
He proposed to "put down his buckets" right in Atlanta.

The general labor conditions in the city were not good. The
very fact that there was an abundance of labor made for trouble.
There was white labor and black labor, and they had to be carefully balanced against each other. The Negroes were stirring, and
the stirring of the Negroes meant jealousy among the poor whites.
In 1899 the white city proletariat began to move forward. They
consolidated the various white unions and formed the Georgia
Federation of Labor. Then they began to fight the attempt of
Negroes further to enter the ranks of skilled labor and the by
no means negligible efforts of Negro capital. Whenever Negroes
were hired in a mill or at any work not recognized as their usual
work, the white unions struck and usually secured the dismissal
of the person. This happened in machine works and in cotton
mills several times. When, however, the white workers struck to
better their own working conditions they usually lost, and always
met the threat of Negroes being hired to replace them. This increased race hate, until at last in 1901, the Federation of Labor
came out flatly in favor of disfranchising Negroes, thus deliberately
cutting the labor vote in two. This was easily accomplished, because it tied white labor to the same race superiority as the owners of property and in a way foreshadowed the day when all whites
would be rich and all blacks their servants.
In 1902, came the Georgia Industrial Association of Millowners, a powerful body of white employers, with propaganda and
political influence. Already millowners had been cooperating; they
had combined in 1896 and defeated the first law against child
labor. It was forty years before child labor was even partially abolished and in 1900 one-fourth of the eighteen thousand mill workers in Georgia were under seventeen. The new organization was

wise in its day and generation. It brought pressure on members of the legislature; it spent money on "welfare" work; it began to move the mills out from the cities toward country towns where the employers owned the homes, school houses and churches and paid for the teachers and preachers. Political power drifted almost entirely into the hands of the employers and the next step was to induce the powerful white Baptist Church in its State Convention to take a stand against trades unions. That same year the legislature made the Age of Consent for girls 10 years; graft and bribery ruled the state; and the leasing of convicts to private employers was still one of the most profitable enterprises in the state.

In this environment John Pierce as the years passed became more and more Southern in his thought and reactions. He did not, like his father, say bluntly "the public be damned!" He said the public must be cajoled, bought and controlled. He had learned much since he had come to live in the South in 1885. Gradually the South had assimilated and molded him. He lived in an environment which talked of the "drivel" about "democracy" and the "popular will." It said: Look at England and the Empire "on which the sun never sets!" It was the greatest government in the world and the most benevolent. Did anybody hear of East or West Indians voting? Did the Fiji cannibals or the Chinese coolies elect members of Parliament to make laws for the British aristocracy to live under? Yet here we were with what would yet be the greatest colonial dominion on earth right in our hands, and we were belly-aching because a lot of lazy Negroes wanted to vote instead of work.

They should be thankful for the chance to live in this great land and work for its wealth instead of yelling bloody murder because they could not go to Congress or marry white women. Business was King. The white race ruled the world and always would. "We ruling whites have made our mistakes and blunders. But we have built the greatest civilization the world ever saw and by God! we are going to keep it pure, and profitable."

Great applause greeted this speech before the New York Chamber of Commerce in 1900. Big sums of money had been contributed to elect McKinley and defeat Bryan. The Free Silver craze and Populism were beaten in America; just as the "Little Englanders" were beaten in England. The impudent Boxers—haters of white people—were overthrown in China. Life insurance in America touched $400 millions. Movies, radios and autos became common; and world commerce reached $20 billions. The triumphant rule of Capital was rising, only marred by the crisis of 1893 which birthed the miserable Coxey's army, shuffling to the capitol with its rags and hunger.

But this crisis in business was ominous and synchronized with world-wide reaction. Its gambling gains raised new millionaires, drove the nation toward imperialism; it induced McKinley to withhold that Spanish telegram which might have avoided the Spanish War, and threw the United States into imperialism over Atlantic and Pacific, with Japanese coolies in Hawaii, Negro peons in Cuba and Puerto Rico, and hordes in the Philippines ready to pour profits into itching hands. Great combinations of capital began to unite and monopolize industry. Teddy Roosevelt came unexpectedly to power against the calculations of Business and the politicians whom Business owned. A fight between capitalists and laborers emerged on levels far higher than before and more dangerous to business because it now included educated and trained leadership.

In 1904 Tom Watson reappeared. He thought he saw new opportunities for his ideas. Teddy Roosevelt, who was up for election to the office he inherited by chance, had antagonized the business interests which once elected McKinley. The Democrats nominated a Southerner, and immediately Watson accepted the nomination of the Populists. Now came his chance to unite farmers and laborers North and South into a new party.

But the New South refused to follow him. The white workers no longer believed in solidarity with Negroes and there was no longer a Doyle to make Watson see the absolute necessity of this union if labor was to carry the South. The Southern white workers had been beguiled by a new ideal: disfranchised Negroes, whites as an aristocracy, with cheap Negro servants and laborers.

Legal disfranchisement was sweeping the South; Georgia hesitated, but it was only to be sure that John Pierce and his Northern friends would keep their word and swing the courts in line behind the new legislation. Meantime the trick of the "White Primary" was tried. The primary election of the Democratic Party was opened to white voters of any party. It gradually came to be recognized as the real election, and the legal election became a meaningless gesture. Even educated and propertied Negroes could thus be stripped of political voice. Slowly but surely the court decisions upheld all this betrayal of democracy in the United States.

Here in the critical year 1905 lay the opportunity for a great American; some man with guts to stand for democracy in politics and industry across lines of race and poverty. Bryan was not the man, for he utterly misunderstood or deliberately ignored the race problem and the labor problem of which it was a part. Teddy Roosevelt began his career of trust-busting; that is, of complaint against understandings between great industrial organizations in 1902 which enabled them to control the markets. He worked against them through anti-trust legislation; reclamation of resources; pure-food laws; and the Interstate Commerce Commission. Wealth fought him through the courts, which practically overthrew his anti-trust legislation and opposed his conservation program.

This illustrated a tendency in the whole nation to surrender Democracy; and the increasing rule of wealth in the government of the country was soon realized by Theodore Roosevelt himself. His affiliations were naturally with the owning and employing class, but he soon saw the danger in the power of wealth in American politics and he spoke out. At the John Brown celebration at Osawatomie in 1910 he said:

"We grudge no man a fortune if it is honorably attained and well used. But it is not enough that it should have been gained without doing damage. We should permit it to be gained only so long as the gaining represents benefits to the community."

Then from the great fight before him to release Democracy from organized wealth Roosevelt was unfortunately drawn into imperialism. He used the Big Stick in Panama; he fought for the "open-door" for Big Business in China.

The political dichotomy in Georgia in 1905 was extraordinary. Capital from the North was plentiful as John Pierce, one of its chief representatives, knew. The pall of the Crisis of 1893 was passing. But Capital wanted security—wanted assurance. Strikes were still raging in the North: the bitter anthracite strike was hardly settled; the typographers had been striking for two years; there had been this very year 2,500 different strikes as compared with 750 twenty years ago. Railroads all over were under fierce attack; trusts were growing and merging; and the popular demand for cheaper money was frightening.

The dominant Democratic Party of Georgia was torn in two. One faction was led by Clark Howell of the powerful *Atlanta Constitution,* representing the Press, Wealth, Capital, the Railroads, banks and factories. Behind him stood, naturally, John Pierce and his Northern interests. On the other side stood Hoke Smith, a member of Cleveland's Cabinet, who saw the radical trend in the North and yielded to it. Like Roosevelt he began to attack the growing power of corporate wealth and especially the railroads. As a result, Smith had lost his place in the state political hierarchy and was headed for the political scrap pile unless he could carry his state, become governor and eventually senator. Smith ran for governor in the Democratic primary and fiercely fought against the trusts, the railroads, against corporations and Northern investors. He took over entirely Tom Watson's Populist platform except in one respect, and that was in regard to the Negro.

Watson was aghast. In 1904 he had emerged from his retirement to become Populist candidate for president. He received little support in the West and less in the South. But the very fact that Smith espoused his labor program showed that that program had a chance to win. This fact, too, made the Howell faction cautious. If they followed South Carolina, Alabama, Mississippi and Louisiana and disfranchised the Negro, on what vote could they depend to keep themselves in power against their own radical whites? If they did not disfranchise the Negro could the Democrats continue their present methods of political domination?

Both factions therefore began to make overtures to Watson as the key man. Howell offered a political career and Smith, through friends, offered money. Neither offer was put in words, but they were clear. If Watson backed Howell he could return to Congress and perhaps go higher. If he joined Smith he need no longer worry over mortgages. He was in a quandary, for the decision was not simple. If he joined Smith and followed his own platform, he must drop one plank—the Negro. If he followed Howell, he would lose his white radical following.

He hesitated. He was a broken man, crushed in body and soul, bankrupt in purse. He had lost his black mentor, Doyle, whose superior education, high character and staunch logic had led Watson along the path of unswerving democracy for all men. Watson's mind began to break; he began to have a persecution complex and see the Negro as a cause of his own continued frustration and failure. His youthful culture-patterns of Negro hate and fear rose again to consciousness.

Then, searching for escape, he caught a gleam of light. He need not choose. He could put the politicians on the griddle. He'd make them choose or reject the Negro. They would not dare. Howell would fear loss of the chance to manipulate the Negro vote. Smith would not dare affront popular democracy, of which he had been champion under President Cleveland.

Watson issued his boastful challenge. He would support any faction in Georgia which would disfranchise the Negro and so change the constitution as to "perpetuate white supremacy in Georgia." Immediately Smith replied, pledging "the elimination of the Negro from politics . . . without disfranchising a single white man!"

The bluff had been called. Watson accepted. He had to accept. But this called for a change in political procedure on the part of both Smith and Watson. The white radical vote must be retained at any cost. The Smith campaign therefore, which had begun as an attack on predatory wealth, now was suddenly switched to the most virulent attack on the Negro race which the South had seen for 30 years.

Hoke Smith ceased to talk about corporations and returned to the platform of Alexander Stevens in 1861. He said in 1906:

"I believe the wise course is to plant ourselves squarely upon the proposition in Georgia that the Negro is in no respect the equal of the white man and cannot in the future in this state occupy the position of equality."

He called meetings of the rural white folk and told them that when they had to choose a Negro teacher, not to choose the best one, but to choose the least qualified. He pointed out, especially to white laborers, how the Negroes were bringing down their wages; he distributed photographs of Negro carpenters building white homes. All the virulence which formerly was thrown against capital and monopoly was now used against black folk. They were the cause of all the trouble in the South. They were lazy, they were shiftless, they were impossible.

Smith realized that he must make the Negro question the center of his campaign. The Negro must as never before be painted as criminal, menace, rapist and devil, else opposed by money influence and power Smith could never win. This must be turned into a mad campaign of race hatred and hysteria, harking back to 1876, without the threat of that period really present.

But Pierce and the Northern corporations realized something else: so long as the electorate was being convinced that the Negro was the cause of the ills of the South, attention could be turned from the alleged errors of corporations and investment. "Free Silver" faded entirely out of the picture; the faults of railroads brought less and less attention; Northern investors began to appear as benefactors of the Negro-ridden South.

In August 1906 Teddy Roosevelt had a chance to show the

white South that he was not unduly favoring Negroes. When a black army regiment was placed in a small Texas city and given treatment reserved for black folk, it stood all it could and then one night it shot up the town. The damage was small. Only one white man was killed. But Roosevelt remembered this black regiment and how it once saved his neck at San Juan hill, Cuba. He reacted savagely to show the South that he, too, was "white." He dismissed a whole battalion in dishonor. The black world protested. In Texas Sebastian Doyle, dying from tuberculosis, wrote to young Foraker, his classmate in Ohio. Foraker aroused his father, the United States Senator, who fought ten years before he secured partial redress.

In September came the Atlanta riot.

The real cause of the disaster was not, however, just the Smith campaign. It lay ten years back in the tirades by Tillman of South Carolina, Vardaman of Mississippi, and Tom Dixon of North Carolina. They painted the Negro as an enemy of the nation and threat to civilization. The North, in newspaper and club, listened sympathetically. Through the long, fetid years the pus of race hate festered and swelled in the putrid boil.

The labor situation in Georgia was in turmoil. Negroes were fleeing the country to escape slavery and congregating in villages and cities. Then came the Crisis of 1903; especially in Atlanta they were arrested wholesale. There was a mass of unhappy resentful people, black and white. 16,000 were arrested in 1903; 6,000 white and 10,000 Negroes and among them 3,000 women. All were jailed for disorderly conduct and drunkenness, idling, loitering and vague suspicion. In 1904, 18,000 were arrested. Atlanta in 1905 had three times as many arrests as cities three times its size, and the overwhelming majority of the prisoners were Negroes, despite the fact that Negroes formed less than forty per-cent of the city population.

The State was aroused as never before. Race bitterness seethed, and white labor took the bit into its teeth. It demanded economic disfranchisement of the Negro to follow political. The Negro must be kept from buying land, his education must be curtailed, his occupations limited.

"The minds of the mob must be turned again and turned from political and economic thought to pure race hatred. Immediately the sex motif arose to leadership. All subconsciously, sex hovers about race in Georgia. Every Negro question at times becomes a matter of sex. Voting? They want social equality. Schools? They are after our daughters. Land? They'll rape our wives. Continually the secrecy, the veiled suggestion, the open warning pivots on sex;

gossip rages and horrible stories are spread. The ignorant, the superstitious, feed on such flame and go mad with anger and hate. There is something horrible in the air that swells at times and bursts. The world goes stark mad."

The entire state of Georgia was fanned to fury. The newspapers of Atlanta, owned by Howell, Smith and John Temple Graves, particularly vied in lurid tales of assault. Denunciation of the Negro race followed; cooked up stories of rape and murder filled the press; Negro schools were denounced. Negro leaders were vilified. And all at once it seemed that not capitalistic exploitation but the presence of the Negro race was the chief cause of Georgia's poverty and ignorance. The campaign of betrayal and lies climaxed three decades of deception. And above the shrill chorus of Negro hate rose the shriller yell of Tom Watson. He shrieked and raved like a maniac. Nothing was too low, too revolting for him to pile on the prostrate Negro, once his friend, ally and guide.

Manuel Mansart was terrified. At first in accord with his Washington philosophy, he had "kept out of politics." The campaign was not mentioned officially in his school. He even refrained from talking about it among his friends. Then he went to hear Watson. He could not believe all the newspapers were saying about his message. As he stood far in the rear listening, he again could not believe his eyes and ears. Was this the man who had defended Doyle from lynchers? Was this the champion of the laborer and small farmer? If so he must be insane. He must have gone mad.

In 1906 Hoke Smith was elected governor of Georgia with the support of Tom Watson and John Pierce, and on an anti-Negro platform. And that year the nation went mad. In San Francisco in April, earthquake, fire and flood engulfed the city, killed thousands of men, women and children. The world wept at a disaster so frightfully beyond human effort, so remindful of man's puny civilization. But few connected in thought this disaster with another, six months later, the riot in Atlanta the same year.

It was Saturday afternoon, September 22, 1906. Atlanta was filled with country people, idle workers, casual loafers. On this hot half-holiday the saloons were wide open; drunkards were reeling and petty politicians yelling loudly, while newsboys screeched "rape" extras. All the Atlanta newspapers threw "extras" on the street—the *News* alone had five of them with headlines five inches high announcing four "assaults" on white women in succession. Then suddenly it broke out: an oath, a scuffle and the mob was

loose. Like most mobs, the core of this rabble was hoodlums, drunkards and half-grown boys. They started to chase and beat lone Negroes, those huddled in the rear of street cars or hurrying along
the crowded streets. They chased black boys and beat old men.
Some they shot dead.

But this lawless core of whites was not the real cause. There
were rich and respectable whites who the day before had warned
their colored servants to avoid the streets this particular afternoon.
There were officials who ignored the repeated plea of quiet Negro
well-to-do communities to send police protection. All night the mob
raged through the city until Negroes were cleared from the streets
or dead in the gutter. But they did not go to Darktown where crime
and degradation festered amid hardworking laborers, churches and
saloons. Here the massed black folk gathered silently. Here were
thousands to be killed while in the main city only stragglers remained. The black mob yelled along Decatur Street: "Come on
down, Crackers, we're waiting for you!" But the white mob rested
until next day.

On Sunday they muttered and drank and went to church. Then
early Monday, behind the police, circling defiant Darktown they
moved on south Atlanta beyond the city limits. Here was a Negro
college where Crogman taught and Sebastian Doyle once studied;
here were well-to-do colored homes of teachers, craftsmen and shop-
keepers. Here were the Negroes who trusted white folk and followed
Booker Washington. The police came "looking for guns," and
behind them surged the white mob looking for loot. The mob
broke open homes, killed the unarmed, and stole everything they
could lay hands on. The police with guns and clubs subdued all
Negroes who tried to resist.

Four days in all this drunken, sadistic orgy of murder, theft
and maiming swept on, in and about the city. Then at last the
city began to come to its senses. Those intelligent reapers of Atlanta's wealth, the merchants, the top politicians, the preachers and
professional men, realized that this lawless surrender to the mob
was getting out of hand. A captain of industry characteristically
wailed: "Saturday evening the credit of Atlanta was good for any
number of millions in New York. Today, Monday, we couldn't
borrow fifty cents."

This thoroughly awakened the city. Wealth, Power and Re-
spectability took firm hold, and Religion preached. They counted
the damage. So far as could be ascertained, a hundred human beings, nearly all black, had been killed and wounded; hundreds had

been scattered, without work; and widows and orphans were home-less, helpless and alone. And property—not of the white rich but the hard savings of the black poor—had been stolen or destroyed. But not a single known criminal nor vagrant, white or black, had been found or arrested.

It is not often today that men see the fabric of civilization loos-en, dissolve and give way. John Pierce saw it from his office window on Marietta Street, and he did not soon forget it. And too, one little black boy saw it and never forgot. He was Douglass, the eldest of Mansart's children. Himself seven years old, he had his five-year-old brother by the hand. They were hurrying home from the city. A man came running toward them. He was black. He ran crazily in zig-zag leaps; the blood was streaming down his face, and in his arms was a baby. Behind him was a crowd of shouting, yelling, cursing white men and boys. They were shooting and throw-ing stones and clods of dirt, and swinging clubs. Their cries rose like a cloud of sound; the fury of their rush swept over the children like a breath of hell.

Wildly Douglass scrambled to his feet only to see the mob strike another crowd like a great crash of soft and hard masses. The on-coming mass was black; they, too, were bloody. They, too, yelled with fury, and then all writhed together until suddenly all were gone; all save the few stark, dirty, reddened forms that never stirred again. Douglass staggered home long, long steps, to find it bare and open. He and his brother crept upstairs. Late that night he heard his parents enter with the other boy and creep upstairs to look for him and his brother. He lay very still with closed eyes. They came and looked, then shut the door and went back downstairs. All night he heard them moving about. All night he heard the far off cries of angry and dying men. This was the Atlanta Riot.

Dr. Carter of Friendship Baptist, who had once advised the boy Manuel Mansart on race relations, sat in his darkened study. The Atlanta Riot had terribly discouraged him, for his belief in God and Ultimate Right was profound. He had preached this Sunday after the riot and ended with that low monotone of the Negro folk song. The audience joined in the solemn voice of the Negro dirge: "God's gonna shake this wicked world!"

He could raise little fervor and did not try, but plodded monot-onously through his conventional phrases. During the following weekdays he attended inter-racial meetings. The whole world seemed reeling.

Later with some hesitation Dr. Carter prepared for the annual "revival" in his church. For some years now the larger Negro churches had farmed out this chore to hired evangelists who were trained to arouse and frighten "sinners" to join the church and help pay its expenses. Dr. Carter had long resisted this because he saw it was artificial and unsound. But now after this awful riot, he simply did not have the heart to summon hard working people to come to a God who had failed them in their helpless distress. He hired a popular colored evangelist and stayed home.

The evangelist was a shrewd and intelligent man and did this sort of thing for a living. His knowledge of the psychology of crowds, and particularly of Negro crowds, was profound, and preachers were willing to pay him a goodly sum to relieve them in this annual recruiting of their congregations. Carter did not think much of his methods, but he knew his power and technique, and he had to acknowledge that in "conversations" he was a finished artist.

This year his opportunity was unusual because the nerves of the people had been set on edge by the riot. They had seen Death in its ugliest form and they were prepared to learn about God and what he had done and what he proposed to do. But the evangelist did not quite strike the right note. These people were not disposed to think about submission and Heaven; they had been through Hell and they wanted to talk about the vengeance of the Lord right here on earth. The stranger who had not lived through the riot did not understand their attitude. His usual vocabulary and stock of antics left his audience curiously cold and he realized it. Into this fervor, which was usually so productive of loud "amens" and even screams of approval, crept a doubt. He confessed to himself that this was the hardest and dumbest crowd that he had met for a long time. While he was shouting and gesticulating he began seriously calculating whether he was going to be as successful in this church as he had expected and if he would be able to raise a large enough sum to pay his expenses and to justify himself before the Reverend Dr. Carter; and be able to get further engagements on Carter's valuable recommendation. He had already been here a week and if things did not pick up, he did not propose to fool away another week.

He raised his voice to a great shout: "Come to Jesus!" pausing dramatically. And then the break came. He was used to it; if he could work his audience up to a certain point the floodgates would give way and a wave of emotion would seize them and toss them up and on. Usually there were premonitions of such an event, increasing centers of excitement here and there, murmurs and sobs; but tonight in an audience cold and still, suddenly a scream rent the air. It startled even the evangelist. For a moment he did not connect it with his preaching. He thought perhaps somebody had been hurt, or vaguely pictured a white mob. Then he gripped himself and realized. A woman had arisen and was standing in the audience. Tears were streaming down her face and she had beside her a little boy fiercely clasped by the hand.

The evangelist paused and then bent forward. He was himself again: he knew the symptoms. Here was the call, the demoniac possession, the frenzy of religious madness. It was typified by a woman who evidently did not easily let herself go; who was struggling even now to keep back the emotion that surged within her. The evangelist stretched his arms; he was a big man and standing high in the pulpit loomed tall over the audience. His vast voice rolled: "Come to Jesus," he said, looking straight at the woman, and she came with a swift rush, dragging the little boy beside her, frightened but unresisting. She came up the aisle and the intensity of her emotion, the trembling of her hands and the swelling of her hard-held sobs gripped the audience because they knew her. She represented all that they had been through; these awful days; the police; the chain gang; murder, rape, mobs and fire; the horror of everything that was called "the race problem." And she represented too the hard hand which had held out against God all these years and now had been miraculously touched.

A great moaning swelled over the audience. It rose to a murmur and broke into a prayer with low obbligato of strophe and antistrophe:

O Lord (Hear her, Jesus—bless His name)
Receive this soul (Bow down our knees—and bow our hearts
     beneath our knees)
That comes a-weeping to your breast.
(Make a way, God—in the Sin Wilderness)
Open your great arms, God (O Crucified One—open your
     arms)
And take her in, give her Peace, God! Give her Peace.
(Wash her sin away—save her soul)
And wash her sins away in your own blood—your own blood,
     O Lord our God and Savior of Men.

Suddenly the bowed and praying woman looked up, dry-eyed and grim. The evangelist, watching her with narrowed eyes and only partial comprehension, stopped the waving of his hands and sudden silence fell. The woman said, low-voiced: "I have seen Him!"

"Now what's coming?" said the evangelist to himself. He was afraid she was a crank or crazy and that he might not be able to keep the spell which he had woven over his audience. But he said aloud: "Speak, sister, testify!"

She spoke in a clear voice and he realized that here was not one of the usual unlettered, emotion-tossed colored women. She was educated and well-bred and had been through some awful and unusual experience. She said in a clear voice, "I saw Jesus!" Then she paused. Finally she continued, speaking more distinctly, "I saw Jesus. I did not know before that people ever really saw Him. I thought they lied when they testified. But I saw Him last night. I saw Him plain, with his poor, crucified body all dust and blood."

A groan of pain shook the mass of folk as they sank to their knees. She went on. "I thought at first it was my husband lying there, in the house which the mob looted and burned after they had killed him. But no, it was not my husband, for this dead body spoke. And he said, 'I forgive you!' And then I knew as I never knew before that I was the sinner. I was the murderer. I alone had killed God." And she beat her breast slowly, and her voice rose louder above the rising tumult.

"And Jesus said, 'Bring me a sacrifice, that I may save you and yours. Bring me your first-born and stretch him on my altar and let his blood and mine wash all the sins of the world away.'

"And I have brought him, O People. I give this boy to you. Take him, preacher, and make him a man of God, a preacher of The Word, that through him Jesus may live again and all my people, my poor black people may be saved."

Falling to her knees she worshipped a second in ecstacy. Rising quickly she lifted the little boy bodily and thrust him toward the evangelist. The scared child, trembling, stared at the sea of faces. But the evangelist took him in his arms and soothed him. The magnificent cadence of his great voice shook the building and voice on voice joined.

The preacher said with staccato bursts of recitative:

"Shall I—be car—ried to—the skies
On flowery beds of ease?
No—I must fight—to win the prize,
And sail—through bloody seas."

Above the jerking explosion of the preacher's voice rose the voice of men in bass and above, the voice of women, an octave higher. The woman herself filled the pauses and spaces of the recitative with pure music. This audience knew singing instinctively. It knew music. But somehow it seemed that never before had Friendship heard a voice like this. It was an immense voice and yet full of glorious harmony. And the roll of the preacher's rhythm struck like a bared fist. The song of this woman swept on and up until it thrilled the rafters. The audience went wild. A thousand voices throbbed and swelled, and finally the evangelist in silence led them only with wild waving of his hands. There had been no such singing for many years in old Friendship.

Thus did the boy Roosevelt Wilson, companion of the young Mansarts, become dedicated to preach the gospel. A sort of sacrifice to the Atlanta riot, made by his mother.

After this sweep of emotional fervor the evangelist sought Dr. Carter in his study, but did not receive as much applause as he expected. The old preacher was depressed. He thought of that April Sunday when he had hailed the San Francisco earthquake as a sign of God's justice. He could not today see in the Atlanta Riot any rebuke of human sin, certainly not of the Negro's fault as the poor, distraught woman had just testified. Nor did the success of the revival in converts or money lead him to think less of this crowning injustice of which God seemed so guilty. He dismissed the disappointed evangelist with short shrift and let his grey head sink into his arms.

On the following Sunday, he took the service himself. His voice rang heavy above the throng. He was no longer the bewildered suppliant. He spoke for a God of vengeance. He roared:

"BE NOT DECEIVED: GOD IS NOT MOCKED: FOR WHATSOEVER A MAN SOWETH, THAT SHALL HE ALSO REAP."

He waited for no greetings, nor handshakes, but groped his way to his study, closed the door and sat long in darkness and silence.

The dark clouds of doubt overwhelmed him; he who had

preached fundamental belief in every word of scripture; who held God as a personal friend as real as the people to whom he preached; who went to him daily in prayer and praise, now wondered how he had ever believed in anyone or anything who could permit or ignore this Atlanta horror. Did He ever exist? Did anything good exist? Why, what, where?

There came after a time a timid knock on his office door. He did not answer. After a pause it came again, low but imperative. He emitted a half impatient, "Come in!"

The door opened gently and in it stood an elderly white woman, gray-haired and dressed in gray. He arose. She hesitated and said in a well-modulated voice:

"Dr. Carter? Please sit. I am so sorry to disturb you. I know how weary you must be, but I will take but a minute of your time. I just had to come."

He could not talk, but silently motioned her to a seat. She sat down, arranging the expensive drapery of her gown and removing her gray gloves. Then she looked at him with an apologetic smile.

"Thank you for your service, dear Dr. Carter. I have two thoughts to add. First, dare I say that you must not blame God too much in these awful days? We know that God would not permit Evil if He could help himself. God did not shake this wicked world; the wicked world shook God."

Dr. Carter murmured, "Men are evil!"

"They are largely incorrigible devils. Therefore we must pity the poor dear God. He is doing his best. And now, one other thing: the earthquake did not cause the riot—it was the other way around. The riot brought the earthquake and fire in San Francisco, just as it did the destruction of Lisbon 150 years before. You see at times the dear God tremble in helpless wrath."

Dr. Carter sat up.

"But the riot was five months later!"

"What difference? Time is but our habit of thought. Reason is more than Time, and Deed embodies Reason. You see, I have just come from San Francisco. I had to go and see for myself. I know now that the riot caused the earthquake. The earthquake was far more disastrous: 500 died and 350 millions of wealth were destroyed. That murder and flame came from the hate and horror of Atlanta."

Dr. Carter protested. "But one was the act of God, the other he evil of Man."

The woman smiled placidly: "Exactly; but first came the evil, then five months before came the punishment."

"Oh, no, no, no! Why punish California for the sin of Georgia?"

The woman said, "We must rely on God's sense of justice. San Francisco suffered not only for Georgia but also for itself. For fifty years it has poisoned the world with Gold. It made this nation greedy and sordid; a mass of thieves and murderers, until finally it burst into shivering flame. But that fire was ignited by the baser instincts of Atlanta. Atlanta financed Slavery, it cajoled gentlemen and made them bandits. How well I remember dear General Gordon, that brave knight, before Huntington made him a thief; and Hoke Smith, the liar, was once a gentle boy; while little Tom Watson was starved and went crazy.

"But no more of that. This last word, dear Dr. Carter: don't blame this on God. Lay the sin on the people. Preach Christ crucified and tell how much more crucifixion is asked of each of us here, and now, or God himself will die. I'm sorry to go on so. Forgive me. Here is a contribution for your good work. And now, may I use your phone? I know my folk will be anxious about me."

Dr. Carter arose a little bewildered to point out the phone, when a peremptory knocking came on his door. He opened it. A group of well-dressed whites and two policemen entered hastily.

"Oh," said his guest. "You're here. I'm so glad. I was expecting you. I was about to call."

She bowed graciously, shook hands with Dr. Carter, and left on the arm of an anxious-looking man.

One of the policemen, who knew Dr. Carter, winked as he left and significantly pointed to his forehead. "Plum crazy," he whispered. "Been giving her family the slip. Where do you think she has been?—San Francisco!"

Dr. Carter sat down and rested in darkness and silence for a long season. Then his hands began to grope among his books and papers until he found it—that copy of the New York *Independent* which came last week and which already he had thumbed to shreds. He held it before him, but did not read; he recited from memory, from bitter memory:

Wherefore do we pray? Is not God of the fathers dead? Have not seers seen in Heaven's halls? Thine hearsed and lifeless form stark amidst the black and rolling smoke of sin, where all along bow bitter forms of endless dead?

Awake, Thou that sleepest!

A city lay in travail, God our Lord, and from her loins sprang twin Murder and Black Hate. Red was the midnight; clang, crack and cry of death and fury filled the air and trembled underneath the stars where church spires pointed silently to Thee. And all this was to sate the greed of greedy men who hide behind the veil of vengeance!

Bend us thine ear, O Lord!

Bewildered we are, and passion-tost, mad with the madness of a mobbed and mocked and murdered people; straining at the armposts of Thy Throne, we raise our shackled hands and charge Thee, God, by the bones of our stolen fathers, by the tears of our dead mothers, by the very blood of Thy crucified Christ: What meaneth this? Tell us the Plan; give us the Sign!

Keep not thou silence, O Silent God!

Chapter XV

ATLANTA REPENTS

On the morning after the riot, white Atlanta rose like a drunkard after a spree, or a careworn sleeper after a nightmare. Those tolerant citizens who had allowed the storm to gather and burst without protest or real action, now suddenly became aware of their civil responsibilities. The natural recoil of men of good will was mightily reinforced by businessmen and capitalists who feared for Atlanta's credit as a safe haven for investment and the financial center of the New South. The nation must be reassured. Especially this race problem must be attacked vigorously and frankly. Interracial committees of prominent whites and Negroes sprang into being, and numberless conferences were held.

The most immediate reaction however was haunting fear; the urge to see if there were any elements in town deliberately stirring up trouble or thinking of revenge. And this meant of course not white folk but Negroes who were dissatisfied and who might be thinking of public agitation or even of reprisal. The editor of a little colored magazine, "The Voice of the Negro," a frank, intelligent young man who had the impudence to write a complaining letter to the New York *World,* was forthwith warned to leave town.

The Atlanta Riot scared John Pierce. There was no other word for it; scared him. He was, in 1906, fifty-six years old. His father had left him not only a millionaire, but with almost uncounted other millions in his control and under his influence.

His wife, Kate, had not been a success in Southern society. Everybody liked her frank manners, but she was a little too frank for a group where sophistication was the ideal and feelings were deliberately disguised and hidden. Atlanta society pretended to live in the vivid memory of a war which was the center of Southern history. To Kate the war had only been hunger and hard work. Bull Run, Manassas and the Merrimac evoked no memories in her, and now and then she made some fatal faux pas, like mentioning Sherman or humming "Marching through Georgia," or professing never to have heard of Stonewall Jackson!

Gradually society leaders like Betty Lou dropped her from her more intimate acquaintances. But of course Kate moved among the best when she moved at all, for her husband was rich. Mostly she stayed at home and made it a most comfortable place for her husband. Her occasional receptions served delicious food and were well-attended, even if return invitations sometimes failed to arrive.

The very excellence of his home arrangements led John Pierce gradually to forget his wife. Of course he was not aware of this and would have denied it. He was fond of Kate, but his business interests grew and did not include her; she knew less and less about them and more and more they did not discuss them. His social life also gradually proceeded without her because of her home duties. Often when she was snubbed Pierce did not realize it, because Kate never complained.

With her son, Kate had never had much contact. He from birth was an institution. After a lovely infancy he had been whisked off to local schools and then north to high school and college. As it appeared to Kate he had never returned to live at home. He only boarded there. He kissed her good morning daily and then disappeared.

A baby girl came in 1892, but after two delirious years of sturdy happiness, it died suddenly of the children's dysentery so common in Atlanta at the time, and closely connected with a partially open sewer system. With this death Kate's interest in life waned. She could not keep from connecting this catastrophe with her religious apostasy. She had not dared even to appear to know anything of Catholicism in Atlanta, much less to attend a Catholic Church. She took the little corpse to New York and buried it in consecrated ground beside her father and mother. After this more and more her life became separate from that of her husband, although characteristically he still did not notice it.

In 1901 the European demand for capital to finance growing colonial imperialism in Africa, Asia and the Balkans made it advisable that John Pierce go abroad. He remembered that his son would be graduating from Princeton that Spring and a trip to Europe would be for his further education. Also, it would cut off his rather too frequent meetings with Henrietta Sheldon; her father was dead and she had spent summers with the Pierces during the last two years. But as Pierce remarked to Kate, such a marriage would be unsuitable—he had other plans for the boy. Also, he remembered to ask Kate to go with them, fulfilling an old dream which they had often discussed.

Kate recalled when her husband had made an unsuitable marriage, but she said nothing and went along. On the voyage another matter of disagreement occurred. Kate had assumed that of course they would visit Ireland. To her a trip abroad had always meant seeing County Cork. But now her son looked at her and said:

"Why Ireland? To get acquainted with the Shanty Irish?"

Kate flared, "Yes!" she said, "My father was one!"

Her husband looked annoyed and the son surprised. "I thought grandfather was a Southerner—a Confederate officer—"

The father hastily intervened: "We've no time for Ireland this trip," he said. "I must hasten to London and Paris."

Nothing more was said on the matter. They spent two weeks in London which Kate hated; and then a month in Paris, which they all loved, particularly the week at Versailles.

When they returned to Atlanta, Kate persuaded Pierce to buy an estate further out than the Peachtree district so as to make her social life less annoying. In a meadow lying rather below the level of the through road they bought fifty acres, and in the center built a mansion fashioned after Versailles in general plan and coloring.

Here Kate occupied her time in decorating, in housekeeping and wandering about field and forest. She saw her husband usually only at the breakfasts which she prepared personally and he enjoyed. Almost invariably he lunched and dined in town, excusing her because of her duties around the new estate. She bought a dog, a Great Dane, for company. They were inseparable on her long walks. Also since the baby's death Kate had secretly re-entered the Catholic church, but with no connections in Atlanta. Continually, the son belonged to the father and not the mother. Even during and after the riot it was with his father that he talked; it never occurred to him to discuss such things with his mother. And Kate was not so forward with her opinions as she formerly had been.

John Pierce had planned to keep his son in the South. He had faith in the South. By 1906, he had spent twenty years here in developing carefully his plans, with studied care regardless of expense. He had not reckoned on race hate as so terrific an impulse; so frightful a motive. Right in Atlanta, the Capital of his new South, he had seen stark murder stalking men like beasts in a jungle.

Pierce was a man of peace and order. He had seen little rioting or lawlessness or blood save as incidents; as a matter for police and instant restoration of order. Once, as a boy in New York in his

father's mills the laborers got wild, but he was quickly hurried
away; he understood these matters were easily settled. Of course the
New South was turbulent and lawless; he had heard of much but
actually seen little. Once he shuddered at the aftermath of a lynching; once he had heard the howl of a mob; several times he had seen
individuals shot. But he avoided disorder and violence as much as
possible, and as law and order became the rule he was unprepared
and startled by this sudden outburst of primitive blood-lust.

After the riot the series of inter-racial meetings of various sorts
continued in Atlanta, where much good-will was expressed and
some remedies proposed. But nothing really radical was attempted.
Young John Pierce III had been awakened by the riot to his first
awareness of the seriousness of life. He had never dreamed of
public murder by a wild, vicious mob in the leading city of the
New South. He was tremendously gratified when Atlanta appeared
to wake up and try to do something about it. But to young Pierce
this meant really going to work immediately to make radical
change and reparation. He had no knowledge of the delicate racial
etiquette of the South which made any approach to race matters
an intricate question of mental fencing, attack, thrust, refusal and
withdrawal, until the net advance was often actual retreat.

In his innocence and enthusiasm young Pierce attended meeting after meeting of inter-racial bodies; listened to speeches of all
sorts and lengths, and gradually came to the conclusion that he and
other earnest persons in these gatherings were being given the
"run-around." Nothing important was being settled or even
frankly faced. Especially the speeches of the Negroes nauseated him.
The speakers were usually preachers and they were oily and placating; they elaborately praised the "good white folk" and apparently
all white folk were "good" except the "riff-raff" which apparently
included all the poor and especially the members of unions. Pierce
inherited no love for unions, but he knew that white labor certainly was not alone to blame for the riot, and that all the whites
and some of the blacks present knew this.

To Pierce's mind there were three sore spots in Atlanta: the
fixed election, the separate churches, and lack of work with decent
pay for Negroes. To his thought, dodging these issues was dodging
the whole problem. He determined to force these issues to the
front at the next meeting of the general committee which had
been appointed. As he made his way abstractedly from today's
gathering, he ran straight into Manuel Mansart who had also been

in attendance. He had not seen him for ten years and shook hands with him cordially. Some whites turned and stared, and Mansart himself seemed a little taken aback.

"Hello, Mansart! How are you? Clean forgot that you were in Atlanta. Good! I want to talk to you." Pierce launched into his complaints and outlined his three points.

Mansart said little at first, and then said, "Look here, come out to my school. It's still in session; I excused myself to attend this meeting. Come and look at us. I think there's a fourth point you've overlooked."

"Good," answered Pierce. "How do we get there?"

Mansart hesitated briefly and then led Pierce to Auburn Avenue at the corner of Peachtree where they boarded a car. They were half-way down the aisle when Mansart said, "You sit here; I'm going back."

Pierce glanced at him in astonishment. "But we could talk—." Then he remembered and blushed. Mansart went to sit with other Negroes in the rear section while Pierce sat in front and silently swore: "This is the God-damnedest country!—"

Mansart showed him his school. Seats for 400, with 1000 in attendance. "But how?—" stammered Pierce.

"Five hundred a half day in the morning, and five hundred in the afternoon, with the same set of teachers for both and very inadequate equipment. I get $1000 a year. The principal of a white school of this size gets $1500 and no double session. You must add Education to your demands."

"I certainly will. And how about the Jim-Crow street cars?"

Mansart smiled crookedly. "That can wait," he answered.

Pierce attended the next meeting of the general committee early and was among the first on his feet. He put his motion briefly and bluntly, suggesting that the underlying causes of race friction were: Negro disfranchisement, poor Negro public schools, lack of Christian unity, and keeping Negroes out of good-paying jobs. He asked for committees to consider these four points and report next week with concrete proposals.

The statement was received in astounded silence. A few of the Negroes quietly left the hall to avoid involvement in difficult arguments. The chairman, the Reverend Dr. Barnswell of the white First Methodist, after clearing his throat, said gravely that he was sure that "all present thanked our young friend for his suggestions and they would certainly receive the attention which their importance and sincere purpose demanded. But might I remind the audience that there were certain matters of regular business before the house which ought temporarily to take precedence over this motion!"

He then proceeded to appoint chairmen of several committees and to listen to many long and vague reports. Finally, when the audience had recovered its breath and poise, the chairman tentatively "suggested" that young Mr. Pierce confer with the several chairmen just appointed, and that in consultation with them a new resolution to which all agreed could be submitted to the next meeting. Rather irregularly but speedily and without objection the suggestion replaced Pierce's motion and the meeting adjourned.

Pierce knew that he had been tactfully out-maneuvered, but he was not licked. The Reverend Dr. Barnswell was rushing away when Pierce, slipping out just as the Doctor was entering his carriage, asked a word. The preacher, looking as near annoyed as he ever permitted himself, graciously made room beside him, telling the colored coachman meantime to "Hurry, please, Ben, I am already late for an important session of our Foreign Missions Board." It was meeting in the very elegant quarters of his Church House. Pierce plunged into his subject:

"The riot was a terrible thing, wasn't it, Doctor?"

"It was horrible! The ways of Providence are past finding out!"

"You don't mean you're blaming God for it, do you?"

"Certainly not. I blame ourselves, poor miserable sinners that we are—."

"Don't you think, then, that we ought to get busy and stop sinning?"

"My dear young man, that is impossible. We were conceived in sin. But we ought to besiege the throne of God for help in bearing this intolerable burden."

"Pardon me, sir, but we don't seem to be getting anywhere. You are not saying, are you, that God is playing a cat and mouse game with us?"

Dr. Barnswell looked outraged but answered quietly, "No, sir, I mean that the ways of God are past finding out."

"That I readily grant, but the ways of men are painfully clear, aren't they?"

"I do not judge my fellow men."

"Wasn't the late Governor Joe Brown a member of your church?"

"He was a staunch doer of good works."

"And a thrifty doer of some mighty evil ones."

The Doctor was annoyed and murmured, "I pray each day—"

"But, sir, we can't have it both ways: either we are guilty or God is. If it is our fault, or so far as it is, we ought to do something besides pray. Now as I see it, one sin is that the churches are so divided; black and white; Protestant and Catholic; Methodist, Baptist and whatnot—don't you think we ought to begin to have common services, joint efforts, interlocking organizations in order to fight evil, to get to know each other better and achieve brotherhood?"

"I do not! The Church of God—"

"Which one?"

"I am sorry, sir, to interrupt this talk, but we have arrived—"

"Then you really think that God likes white Methodists better than black; and Protestants better than Catholics—"

"Good day!" said the Doctor sharply as he left the carriage.

Dr. Barnswell sat down beside the lady chairman of the Missions Board.

"Sometimes," he said as he wiped his brow, "I fear the younger generation has lost all reverence for God!"

Tight-lipped, Pierce took a cab to the Board of Education. The Superintendent of Schools headed the proposed new education program. He was quickly received as his father's son. But the superintendent laughed in his face:

"Mr. Pierce, I haven't the money to make the Negro schools equal to white. And if I had it and used it for this purpose, I'd lose my job as soon as the Board of Education met. And," he added significantly, "some of us have to have jobs."

They looked at each other a long moment and then without another word John walked out, climbed the hill to the City Club and took two stiff drinks. Then he heard the words of his neighbor—"and no God-damned Northern 'nigger'-lover is going to change that!" He turned and looked Colonel Brady, the president, straight in the eye:

"Change what?" he asked.

"The White Primary! No 'nigger' is ever going to vote in Atlanta, Georgia!"

"Even if it costs another riot?"

The Colonel downed another whiskey: "Not if it costs us another riot and the company of every damned 'nigger'-loving carpetbagger in the Pierce office!"

Then John Pierce promptly drove his fist into the Colonel's eye. The Colonel would have killed him then and there but he did not happen to be carrying his customary revolver. The two clinched and were separated, but naturally that ended the short-lived crusade of young John Pierce. He was forced to resign from the City Club and was gradually ostracized socially.

He and his father had a frank talk.

"John, I'm disappointed. I hoped you'd be the third Pierce to head our business enterprises."

"I'm disappointed too. I sort of took it for granted that I'd have to follow you and Granddad, although I didn't like it. But I'm puzzled now. Follow what? Where are we headed? Just what is Business, anyway? You see, I had a vague idea that Business might become a kind of professional service to help the world. I didn't see myself as any knight-errant, but I was willing to do my part. Now I wonder if my part is worth doing.

"Remember the first job you set me to? A clerk in a little drugstore down on Marietta Street had concocted a drink with cocaine in it to relieve headache. The public liked it and drank so much of it that the druggist organized a company. The company began to make real money. Then the United States Collector stepped in. You know that colored Collector, Rucker? He was Collector of Internal Revenue for the State of Georgia for 23 years under McKinley and Roosevelt. Rucker stopped operations because of the cocaine and the new Pure Food Law.

"The company, however, substituted concentrated coffee extract for cocaine and began to expand. Prohibition came and 'soft' drinks increased enormously in demand. There we came in and were asked to furnish capital. I was to look into it. For profit it sure was a gold mine. You could manufacture ten cents' worth of material into ten dollars' worth of drink, while patents stopped all imitation. From the point of view of profits, it was a natural. But for the public,—well, it was taking candy from babies."

His father blushed and retorted: "True, but babies exist and if we don't take their candy someone else will. If we had not grabbed this opportunity a dozen other capitalists would have been ready with the cash."

"So Business is Profit, not Service," said John.

"Business is Life—it has its nasty, cruel side; but much of it— most of it is service; it is grasping at Power which others will get if you do not. So profit first, then service. Without profit, no service."

"No, no!" protested John. "Without service, no profit. Surely that is possible!"

"Perhaps, in Heaven above where all is Love. But here—"

"I see," said John, "I resigned the job. You put a hundred thousand dollars into it so as to substitute bottling machinery for human labor and increase profits still more."

"John," replied his father, "It is plain that you'll never make a business man. Private profit is Life, as sometime you'll discover. But don't take my word for it. Travel and look. Perhaps you'll find what I never found; or perhaps Life will knock some sense into you."

"Thanks, Dad. I'll take you up on that!"

Pierce put his son out of his mind and turned toward business. He had been scared by this riot, but he began to see it as an unimportant interruption—bad and unnecessary but not of real significance. There was something wrong in the South but it wasn't business; it could not be Business.

Some astonishing figures had just been brought to his notice. They were astonishing, and meant that for every dollar in use in 1900 there was $2.50 in 1910. Buying had been doubled and more, and the profits of buying had risen. Today was the day for manufacturing and a wide and shrewd manipulation of labor.

In 1900 the value of manufactured goods in the nation was not only larger than that of agricultural products but twice as large as farm, orchard and dairy products. Before the War one man owned his own business or ran it by partnership; but beginning with the 20th Century, the Corporation, in which the investor was liable only for the amount he invested, was the director of large-scale enterprises.

The Corporation was the Frankenstein of the 20th Century, contrived by the lawyers of the 19th. By 1950 in America it would be the Robot ruler of Man. It had "neither Body to be kicked nor Soul to be damned"; but in the present century, it owned the Earth and enslaved Mankind. It could not be controlled in a world where the greatest force was control of Wealth and the weakest the sense of Right. It directed the kinds of Business and the route of Commerce and set prices, salaries and wages. It decided the careers of men. It was King by the Grace of whatever God remained in the calendar of Saints. And if this was not really true, if individuals in secret still wielded the power and made the decisions, yet legally the Corporation ruled.

With 1900 began the Age of Big Business. The first billion dollar steel corporation was formed in 1901. Mass production began. Nine out of ten of the auto cars were made by three great companies. Four companies sold over 90% of the rubber. Two electric companies were beginning to monopolize electric lamps, and one shoe machinery company took over most of the shoe manufacturing business. The Sherman Anti-Trust Act had been passed, but because of a decision of the Supreme Court some of the biggest industrial combinations were established after it was enacted.

It was as Woodrow Wilson said: "At the beginning of this century men were cheap and machinery was dear. A man might be dismissed for overdriving a delicate machine, but not for overdriving a man."

We had become a colonial power. The West Indies which the slave power could not annex in the '50's was annexed just before the beginning of the century through the Spanish-American War. We owned in colonies a billion dollars in sugar mills, tobacco plantations, mines and railroads. No country except Russia equalled us in natural resources. We became interested, therefore, in Mexico, Central America and South America. We wanted to buy cheap material raised by cheap labor and sell high-priced manufactured goods.

The volume of our manufactures began to increase tremendously. Soon the manufacturers of the world would be able to make more than they could sell. Then they must seek new markets to absorb the surplus goods. American automobiles, typewriters, electric supplies, electric razors, moving pictures, bathtubs and fountain pens, would be shipped to the ends of the earth and help Americanize the world. We not only had surplus goods but we had surplus capital to make goods. There was a time when English and other European capital had come here to build railroads and dig mines and lay out ranches, but after 1900 American capital began to penetrate other parts of the world. Life insurance, that silent index of business faith, nearly doubled in the last decade. Was that not proof of the soundness of American business?

The interests of John Pierce were largely involved in many phases of American development and had furnished millions of capital. But above all, he was watching with calculating eye the expansion of world trade from 17 to 33 billions of dollars in two decades. It was fabulous; he would be willing to bet that by 1930 it would reach a hundred billions. Astronomical!

Then, too, what politicians called "Trusts" were increasing. What of it? Could not men with brains see that this movement was the culmination of government of Business, by Business and for Business? Did it not miracuously decrease expense and by eliminating senseless competition enormously increase profits? The movement was natural, spontaneous, and nothing could stop it. Let crazy men like Teddy Roosevelt fulminate and caper; let the lying Muckrakers fill the magazines with misleading exaggerations. It was useless. It was fighting the stars of industry in their courses.

Of course Pierce knew that the path of Business was not always straight; something disconcerting was always happening, like this flurry of the banks 1903 to 1907. It was a damn-fool crisis. It was not the fault of industry but of the greed of a few gamblers. He knew them; he had warned them, but they pushed on and nearly precipitated a real crisis. Such unfortunate things would occur in free enterprise. Trusts would put a stop to that in time.

But this Negro problem bothered Pierce. Once he regarded it as incidental and relatively unimportant. He became interested in it as an answer to the difficulties of labor supply; as a partial answer to impudent trade unions, especially in the New South.

The political understanding of which the Atlanta speech of Booker Washington was a high point had seemed to be going smoothly until the Atlanta Riot. He had been visited only recently by one of the agents of the Southern Education Board—a semi-philanthropic, semi-social engineering project. The man was optimistic. Legal disfranchisement of Negroes in the South had progressed like clock-work: Mississippi in 1890 had begun the work and although the law aroused much discussion, the opposition was not great nor effective. South Carolina followed in 1895. There was vigorous Negro protest, but under the crude but sledge hammer leadership of Tillman, this was overwhelmed.

In 1898 came Louisiana, which like South Carolina had a Negro majority. This brought some Northern criticism, and even Booker Washington came out with acquiescence in disfranchisement of the ignorant and poor but with a plea against color discrimination. This was not listened to. It contradicted the Southern interpretation of his earlier stand.

In 1901 and 1902, North Carolina, Virginia and Alabama followed with the "Grandfather Clause," giving illiterate whites an hereditary right to vote. Also, local powers of decision were voted which often made any Negro voting difficult. The Supreme Court promptly supported these enactments, and the plan triumphed. The last link would be supplied when Georgia and Oklahoma closed the Solid South, as they soon would do.

On top of this came a caste legislation covering travel, amusement and civil rights which made the American Negro a subordinate citizen in the South and partially so in the North. Negro representation in Congress disappeared. From six congressmen and one senator from 1873 to 1877, there was but one black congressman from 1891 to 1899; and none since 1906. Pierce and his friends agreed. If disfranchisement was the answer to the Negro Problem, it was at last answered. But was it? The Atlanta Riot said No!

This startled Pierce into seeing the Negro Problem still as a menace to the whole business structure of the nation. If the South could go berserk at any moment, where was the stability of a structure based on an expanding Southern industry? It was serious. The situation must be met.

First of all he watched the impact of the riot on his three young men—the "three Johns." Young John Baldwin, son of the President of the University and now a junior partner in the Pierce Bank; John Sheldon, son of the former white president of the Negro Atlanta University; and especially his own son, John III, who was now 25. He was an upstanding fellow, good-natured, but had not yet seemed to find himself. He liked good company and good liquor, and had an eye for women.

For a time while in college John had paid some attention to Henrietta Sheldon, sister of one of the Johns. She had been taken into the Pierce home the summer after the father's death. She was not pretty, but quiet and intelligent. Nothing had come of this attraction, and personally the father preferred a Southerner as a wife for his son; someone vivid, gay, high-born and handsome. But just at this time came Riot and misunderstanding.

Young John Pierce set out for New York. He had hesitated nearly a year after that chat with his father, turning over in his mind various plans for his future. At home he spent most of his time painting, experimenting in water colors and oils; studying drawing and anatomy spasmodically on the side. He began talking with his mother and she mentioned Henrietta Sheldon.

Then suddenly he made up his mind. He was going to talk to Henrietta. He had nearly forgotten her and had not written since he had come to Atlanta. He got her address from her brother who eyed him speculatively when he inquired, but asked nothing and John said nothing. He remembered talks which he and Henrietta used to have about careers. He wanted to talk again.

Nothing was further from Henrietta's mind that night when without warning John presented himself at the milliner's office in New York where she was typing and keeping books. She could conceive nothing less interesting than her work, except perhaps keeping house for her brother in Atlanta. She had liked the Pierces; she had liked the quiet and smooth working of their summer home where she had stayed after her father's sudden death. But she refused their invitation south; first because she did not like Atlanta; but particularly because she found herself getting too interested in young John Pierce, while he only occasionally remembered she was alive. Also his father, as she knew from his talk, had plans which did not include her.

So she went to New York and lived a few months on her brother's bounty, an unpleasant chore. She wandered, moped, thought and read. She was level-headed, clean, punctual and reasonably healthy. Since that childish episode of the little sandy-haired colored boy she had decided "Love" was silly and she had never felt any particular sex urge. She did not ask much of life but it apparently offered nothing. This bit of nothing presented itself finally as a job in a shop where eight hours of absolutely uninteresting drudgery six days a week paid her board and room rent with a slight surplus.

She was wondering just how long life like this could or should last, when she looked up and saw John Pierce. She looked down at her work and then after a pause glanced up again. There was no mistake.

"Hello!" she said carefully.

"Hello," he replied; and then, "What would you like to do tonight, if you're free?"

They went to hear *Carmen* at the Metropolitan.

"And now," he said briskly, "let's go somewhere and talk."

They went to the "parlor" of her boarding house and were undisturbed. Apparently nobody ever occupied it who did not have to.

"I've left Atlanta and Dad," he announced. She listened calmly and after a pause said:

"You don't like Atlanta?"

"No; and since the riot I hate it."

"Are you going to be a businessman?"

"I have always thought I had to be, until recently. But it's stupid. At least what I had to do was—stupid or crooked. It needn't be. I think a man might be happy running a small shop which was doing a good job for the neighborhood. I know I'd like to fence a farm and cultivate a crop of good potatoes, if I could make a living and have some leisure. But figuring costs and chances, cheating fools, stealing people's underwear off their already naked backs—it's not interesting."

Henrietta leaned forward with blank eyes: "Your grandfather made more money than he could spend. Your father is making more than he or you or your son can spend. I wonder why? There must be a way, of living decently on this earth without piling up wealth, cheating, lying and killing. Just living and doing what one likes to do and having it possible that this work would yield food and clothes; not much, but enough for life. I'd be willing to do some drudgery—hard drudgery, if only I'd have the rest of the time really to live. But all work and no life—no—"

John took her hands. She apparently did not notice. "Let's search for such a life," he said.

She looked up at him. "I'd love to," she said.

John now deliberately put his arms about her. "We'll get the license tomorrow; and then?"

"And then," she said, "I've read that there's a little beach in South France called Vanadou, near Cagnes. I'd like to go there and sit awhile and rest and eat and read."

"Is it near Nice and Monte Carlo?"

"It's ten thousand miles from both,—that is, thought-miles. By bus it's 80 miles."

"Good! We'll go and I'll paint."

In Atlanta naturally one of Betty Lou's first tasks now was to get her son John Baldwin suitably married before he did something foolish. She knew just what he needed. Not a "help-mate" messing into his work. So long as she herself lived she would give him all the help he needed. Above all, he must not marry some opinionated, horse-faced Northerner, no matter how rich she might be.

Thus even while he was at college she kept John in sight; bringing him home vacations or spending them with him under watchful care. Betty Lou had of course decided that John should marry a Southern girl of the traditional type, forgetting her own experience in playing that role. She determined to find the suitable mate in Charleston and among the old aristocracy.

She had no sooner laid eyes on Letitia Brett than she was chosen. Her descent was flawless and her beauty startling; tall, with soft, golden hair and blue eyes which were misty and innocent. Her slim height carried her dresses regally, so that all she needed was the materials to suit her perfect taste. That her family was poor was a distinct advantage, so long as they had skimped enough to let this daughter "finish" at the Misses Noble's impeccable school "for Young Ladies."

There was no difficulty on the part of John, either, as indeed Betty Lou had never expected. He had no sooner been introduced to this beauty, after her mother had carefully outfitted her, than he was hopelessly in love. Her poise and fragility; her unsophisticated and trusting ways fascinated him. It did not seem possible that she would ever permit him to hold her in his arms and take liberties of love and deep affection.

And this proved partly true. Letitia did not like to be, as she put it, "squeezed and mauled," and indeed bereft of her protecting garments she did not appear quite so temptingly unearthly. She was a bit angular which helped her costumes hang right. She was so innocent as to approach the stupid side; which was not strange since her education had paid little attention to her mind and more to her hands, legs and complexion. Letitia was in fact almost completely illiterate, and yet her social success was immediate. Their wedding was the social event of the Charleston season, and Atlanta opened its arms. To be invited to her teas and dinners soon came to be social recognition of the highest type.

The real sex life of John Baldwin was arranged in other ways, which at first caused Betty Lou acute distress. It was a mulatto girl, once a maid in the Baldwin home. Betty Lou got rid of her with short shrift, but knew that the connection had been kept up. However it was quiet and kept her son from worse adventures. Betty Lou let the relationship go on. It was quite different with this white Rice girl.

Mary Rice was born in Salina, Kansas in 1887. She had good elementary school training and later took the "business course" in the Topeka High School. She was a strong, well-built and healthy young woman of good parentage. When she began to look about for a career the role of farmer's wife did not appeal to her in the least. So like many other westerners, Mary went to Chicago. Perhaps that winter was no more characteristic of the great city than usual; but the wind and snow and cold proved more than Mary enjoyed. Then quite by accident she got a temporary job representing her Chicago firm in Atlanta.

Again, perhaps by accident, Atlanta climate was at its best in the fall of 1912 while Mary stayed there and made final settlement of a contract with the First National Bank. The details were arranged with Mr. John Baldwin, and frankly, he was surprised to find so much efficiency, accuracy and punctuality in a hired clerk. He asked her finally if she wanted a job and she said "Yes" without hesitation or qualification.

The fact was that October in this city set 1400 feet above the sea, with its floods of cool, bright sunshine had quite captivated Mary. Her Chicago employer resented her sudden desertion and said so. But Mary decided to live and work in Atlanta, at least at present. She made a good bargain in wage and hours with Baldwin, and with his help secured a reasonably priced room in a hotel on West Peachtree where unmarried business women were usually viewed askance. She began what proved to her very interesting work in banking and investment. Before long she was entrusted with wide responsibilities which she bore with complete satisfaction.

Indeed, John Baldwin's only complaint was her apparent indifference to him as a male. She never complained of her load of work. She knew her business and in surprisingly short time knew his too. But apparently she made no distinction between him and the black office boy in awareness of his sex. One incident brought matters to a crisis. He had a commitment with a New York firm to take over certain foreign bonds. Acceptance was due on Saturday morning. The Friday night before the Mesdames Baldwin had an unusually gorgeous dinner. William Howard Taft, President of the United States, with two senators and three southern governors, were present. A caterer had come up from New Orleans, and the dress worn by Mrs. Brett Baldwin ran the *Constitution* reporter into verbal hysterics.

John, after unsatisfying overtures to his wife, spent the night at a poker game in a hunting lodge about 20 miles from Atlanta and did not get to the office until nearly Monday noon. Mary, after exhausting all means of reaching him and after being advised by Betty Lou to mind her own business, calmly forged his signatures to the Bond papers, and wired acceptance to New York. The package arrived by express Monday morning.

John Baldwin entered his office Monday and began fingering his papers as Mary entered and took her usual seat. Suddenly John sat up.

"My God!" he yelled in pale consternation as he saw a million dollars or more go down the drain of his forgetfulness. "That contract—!"

"Signed and sent Friday," answered Mary.

"But—"

"I forged your name and sent it. Here are the bonds," she explained.

John seized her, wrapped his arms about her and kissed her more thoroughly than she remembered ever having been kissed before.

Mary Rice was no wanton. She had never yielded to a man and her last thought was an affair with a married employer. But she was healthy, lusty and lonely and John Baldwin was the most attractive man she had ever met. The loud western men whom she knew, without manners, grammar or tailors, had never tempted her. But Baldwin did as they worked closely together daily in a private office at a fascinating job. Mary was moral but no innocent prude. She entered this relationship with open eyes, knowing Betty Lou would soon take notice.

Betty Lou did take notice, as Mary foresaw; and sooner rather than later. She invited Mary Rice to tea when John and his wife were in Macon at an important social function. Betty Lou had cleared her calendar and was quite alone. But Miss Rice did not turn up. Instead, at the last moment a formal note of declination came, pleading office duties as an excuse. Betty Lou said nothing, but when a month later John Baldwin went to New York, Betty Lou walked into his inner office unannounced in the middle of the afternoon. She did not beat about the bush but said, as Miss Rice arose from her loaded desk and indicated a chair:

"You did not accept my invitation to tea, Miss Rice."

"No. As I wrote, I was sorry, but I had work which Mr. Baldwin left." She sat down. Betty Lou leisurely removed her gloves and settled back in her chair.

"Let us be frank," she said. "Just what are your relations with my son?"

Mary Rice laid aside her papers.

"I am his secretary and private stenographer; I have charge of his mail and files. Also," she paused, "I am his mistress."

Betty Lou rose and approached the desk. Miss Rice never stirred. Then Betty Lou took hold of herself. "When does John return from New York?"

"Tomorrow at midnight."

"Very good. Will you do something for me—and for yourself tomorrow at six?"

Miss Rice hesitated. Betty Lou unbent. "Please," she pleaded. "It is in your interest as well as mine."

Miss Rice assented. The next night Betty Lou picked her up at the office at five-thirty in a hired cab. They drove slowly down Auburn Avenue and through a better-class Negro residential section. They stopped at a shadowy corner and waited. Neither spoke. At last Betty Lou called attention to a cab which hurriedly dropped

a passenger at a neighboring door. A tall, brown woman opened
it and John Baldwin left the cab and stepped inside.

Mary Rice gasped. She had clear ideas about the freedom of
women and the contradictions of marriage, but she had also limits
of decency. Their cab drove on while Betty Lou talked in low
tones.

"This has been going on for years. It began when John was a
boy and this woman worked for us. I knew it, but have not tried
to stop it for in a way it was a protection for John. By law this
woman cannot compel marriage nor by custom can she sue for
bastardy. Before his marriage this liaison kept John from seeking
prostitutes. After his marriage John's home could not be broken up
nor his career ruined. The woman is decent and healthy. There are,
I believe, two children. With you it might be different. Both home
and bank might be in danger. Do you understand now?"

Mary's insides seemed slowly to drop away. She understood.
Next morning she paid her bill and arrived at the bank long before hours. Before nine she had all her work in perfect order and
her own finances straight. She took the nine o'clock train to De-
troit. She never returned.

As for Letitia Brett Baldwin, if she ever knew that Mary Rice
was on earth, or cared, she gave no sign. She was content with her
home and her gowns; her social leadership and her prominence as
the strikingly beautiful wife of the coming mayor of Atlanta. Her
reputation was flawless. In 1911, just before Mary Rice came to
Atlanta, Letitia became the mother of Lee Baldwin. It was a dis-
gusting experience, and her sexual relations with John became
fewer and fewer. Their social relations continued most successfully.

To young John Baldwin the Atlanta Riot looked like opportunity. It forced the retirement of his difficult old father from the
University and out of the public eye. It drove young John Pierce
out of Atlanta and made Baldwin a closer associate of John Pierce,
Sr., in his wide business interests. It broadened the control of business men over the South and discredited the politicians.

The last years of old Dr. Baldwin, the father, were not happy.
His theories on race and progress came to be seriously at odds with
those of his trustees and many of the alumni. He could not be summarily dismissed from his position; he had become an institution
and a legend. It was better to leave him alone, while narrowing his
power and limiting his salary. Meantime, to his family he was an
increasing annoyance. The young mother and son lived in Atlanta,
where their own fortune and his increasing income enabled them

to live in simple elegance. They referred to the father with a shrug;
a difficult person, not quite normal. In fact, the young man had
been brought up always to regard his father as queer and negligible.

Finally Old Dr. Baldwin, at the age of 86, came to such a state
that he had to be "put away" as the euphemism has it. He became
quite impossible in his theories and outspoken comments. On the
occasion of the Atlanta riot, for instance, he said in class that this
"deliberate murder was the direct outcome of the dirty political
deal between Northern industry and Southern race hate."

Word flew over the campus and the trustees hastily were con-
vened. There was, happily, no trouble. Dr. Baldwin quietly and
smilingly resigned, and asked to go up to his summer cottage in
Cherokee county at Tallulah Falls, about 80 miles northeast of
Atlanta, where the waters of the Blue Ridge fall in wild beauty and
rush on to reach Savannah at the Sea. Here, with a housekeeper
and his books he was left to his thoughts and vagaries, far from
harmful influence upon the world.

Young John Baldwin's mother, Betty Lou Breckinridge, had ambitions which gradually he came to share: social prominence, according to the standards of the pre-war regime, wealth, and a
political career. He saw chances in the New South for a planter's
grandson, a Princeton graduate, a partner in the Pierce interests,
and a gentleman of manners to become—who could tell? His mother
whispered: mayor, governor, senator—what not?

To John Baldwin Life was simple. Its work was Business. The
object of Business was Profit. Profit meant Wealth. Wealth meant
Politics, Politics meant Power. Power meant Business. Business
meant Profit, and so on ad infinitum. There were important side
paths—society, golf, drink and women. But in the main life was simple despite riot and murder; despite doubt and bribery. Business
ruled the South. The results were startling. Since John Pierce, his
patron, had come south property values there had increased 122
per-cent. The cotton crop had gone from 6 to 15 million bales
in spite of the boll weevil. Railroads had extended from 25,000 to
75,000 miles, and manufacturing establishments had doubled in
number while their invested capital had quadrupled. It was fantastic. It was the greatest growth of the kind in world history.

John Baldwin watched his step. He became a rising official in
the First National Bank, a popular man-about-town and a shrewd
judge of human character. The riot, he realized, was temporarily
bad for business and northern investment. But it had to his mind
no lasting significance. The Negro must get fair treatment for he

was a valuable laborer and would become more and more valuable. But there was a gulf between black and white which could never be bridged.

As early as 1908 a small and influential committee got together in the Board Room of Baldwin's bank. There were four or five prominent Southern businessmen, a couple of quiet but effective politicians, and John Sheldon. It was in reality one of those secret caucuses through which so much of the government of the South is run, with a few tentative elements which might be useful in the future. The real object was to arrange to nominate Baldwin as "reform" mayor in 1910. He had every recommendation: a well-connected Southerner, young, personable and closely connected with Northern capital. Sheldon would make an excellent off-the-slate manager of the campaign, with plenty of funds.

Chapter XVI

BLACK CAPITAL

To Manuel Mansart, the one personal reaction from the Atlanta Riot and the industrial situation seemed to be escape from the South. Especially after the flight of young John Pierce, he began to consider taking steps toward this end. Principally this decision came from disappointment with his situation in the Atlanta schools. The colored schools here did not greatly differ from those of Jerusalem. There were more of them with a vastly larger enrollment, but just as in Jerusalem, they were given little attention and proportionately less money. Practically all the children were in double sessions. There was no colored high school and no night school. The salaries paid Negro teachers were not only low but half those paid for whites for the same preparation and identical work.

Worst of all, Mansart could not see what he could do about it. Patience, pulling strings, using white influence; all this might accomplish something. But what was needed was a stirring up of the parents; exposition of the facts, and strong demands. Just now, after the riot, any attempt at such a movement might cost him his job. And that was the trouble with the South. The successful black man must cajole and coax; he must conceal his feelings and take insults. He must crawl and beg instead of standing and talking plainly. Mansart decided that he could not accept this as a life work.

His children now became the center of his house and life. His wife began to look old, peevish, sick and worn. The house was never clean and in order. It was never quiet. He could not do any work there, nor thinking; and above all this, he was naturally more upset because he did not have enough income to pay the extraordinary expenses of this family of five people. The money simply could not be stretched. It was astonishing how the children wore out shoes and always needed new clothes. And as for his wife, she became almost a total stranger; they had no time to talk together. There was only one thing they could talk about—the money which was needed and which they did not have.

In her general philosophy of life Susan was simple and naive.

The Good God made a world of Bad Men and had to punish them severely for Sin. At least these men sinned so much and paid God so slight attention that He got a Son (not by ordinary sex methods but miraculously so that the mother remained a Virgin) and sent Him to the sinners who promptly killed Him. But Christ came back to life and would redeem sinners if they repented and got religion.

When the children questioned this tale and expressed some doubt, Manuel sometimes upheld them or at least did not try to stop their doubts. Susan was scandalized.

"Are you an Atheist?" she moaned.

Manuel quickly denied this awful accusation. Finally he let religion alone and turned the matter over to Susan and the Sunday School. The results of this method were not altogether happy. Just what he himself was in religious belief he did not really know.

Then too, the impact of the white world became more threatening. It was one thing to ward off insult and difficulty from yourself; you could ignore it, laugh it off, or forget it. But you couldn't have your children slapped; you couldn't see them disappointed and their dreams turned upside down. It was impossible to sit by and let them suffer, and it was terrible to anticipate the kind of suffering and discrimination that was bound to come upon them later. Manuel found himself almost beside himself at times, thinking of little incidents that had happened and anticipating what might happen.

Because there again Mansart was surprised and puzzled. These children were not just replicas of himself; they did not think as he did, indeed he was never certain just what they thought. They were new individuals come into his life, over whom he had influence but only partial control. He could give orders and they would sometimes be carried out cheerfully but sometimes there was positive, active rebellion.

Douglass was a sturdy, self-reliant boy. Revels, born two years later, was quiet but stubborn. Bruce was a fay, a throw-back, an exception to all rule; athlete and artist, wild and untamed. Instead of Manuel being in position to guide all these singularly different souls, lay down the law and show them what to do, he found himself sometimes almost without any influence at all. They talked back to him, they argued with him and their arguments, being perfectly logical and unimpeded, were very often absolutely unanswerable.

Why shouldn't a man tell another man that he had lied, when

he had? Why should a man get off the sidewalk just because some-body told him, who didn't own the street any more than he did? What right had a boy, just because he had a white face, to assume that he owned the earth, etc., etc. It seemed to Mansart that some-thing had to be done and done quickly before these children grew up.

Mansart now faced for the first time and inexorably the life problem with which he was destined to struggle three-score years and ten and yet never answer to his own satisfaction or that of any-one else: how shall Integrity face Oppression? What shall Honesty do in the face of Deception, Decency in the face of Insult, Self-Defense before Blows? How shall Desert and Accomplishment meet Despising, Detraction and Lies? What shall Virtue do to meet Brute Force? There were so many answers and so contradictory; and such differences for those on the one hand who meet questions similar to this once a year or once a decade, and those who face them hourly and daily.

How noble to "turn the other cheek!" But what effect will this have on the man who can keep slapping with impunity or even with profit? How lofty to be humble before arrogance, but what does this do to your own soul? Who gets the world's praise and oppor-tunities, the Peacemakers or the Conquerors? With such puzzles Manuel Mansart wrestled long nights and longer years.

He had many friends and fellow-students who had gone North to live and often urged him to join them. He hesitated. What could he do in the North to earn a living, particularly the kind of living which he would want to earn? There was limited chance for col-ored teachers; he was too old and had too large a family to study for a profession; he was no businessman, even if business attracted him which it did not. Nevertheless, now he determined to visit Chicago; he had had glimpses of the East, but only during vaca-tions as student singer and largely in contact with rich or well-to-do white folk. He wanted to see just how colored folk fared in the North and more particularly in the West. From reading and listen-ing he had long come to like the West.

Thus, in the summer of 1907, by careful planning, riding in coaches all night and accepting free board from his friends, he spent a month in Chicago while his family visited on a farm near Jerusalem. He was tremendously interested in what he saw. Per-haps it was because he left the Shadow of Fear sitting on the streets of Atlanta that he was so attracted first by the freedom of the Chicago Negroes. They were free; they were impudent; they apparently cared for nothing—neither for God nor man, particularly not for the white man.

Not that the Negroes had by any means the opportunities of the whites; they lived in crowded slums, in reeking tenements, in run-down palaces abandoned by whites and now collapsing in disrepair and dirt. They worked mostly as laborers and servants. And yet they had rights. They could vote. They held office. City officials did not dare insult them as they did in Atlanta. They could protest openly and loudly. The whole world did not gang up against a black man. If a white man struck him he could strike back without fear of lynching. Indeed, on the South Side, the one in most fear of lynching seemed often to be the white man. There was a sort of free expression of manhood in the air, despite poverty and crime, which a Negro just from Atlanta could drink in like a draft of fresh air.

Beyond this, however, Mansart was appalled by Chicago, its size and rush and power. Negroes were an integral part of it, but what were they doing, and what was Chicago doing to them? Some Negroes were prosperous; a few were even rich; many were intelligent and well-trained. In the free-for-all which spelled Chicago this exercise of muscle and brain released among Negroes as among whites large amounts of energy and power; but what for? Where were all these millions of Chicagoans going and why? What was all this about except to make money and then more money?

As a mass, he was sorry for the Chicago Negroes. They were huddled and squeezed, in desperate need of guidance and not only had little but wanted none. They flaunted their freedom lest it disappear by lack of use; they hollered and laughed loud and long. They were crowded both in body and soul.

Naturally Mansart was interested in the school situation. Now of course by law there should have been no colored schools in Illinois, as Mansart knew; but he was not surprised to find schools in Chicago where nearly all the pupils were colored and many of the teachers. This was in part the result of the crowding of the colored population in restricted areas because of income and prejudice; also in part it was a real "Jim-Crow" school system. But the colored school got the same amount of money and sometimes more to keep the Negroes from protesting, and it had the same salary system as other schools. But colored teachers had a hard time securing jobs. In Chicago, Mansart saw little chance for him; the schools were too popular and too well-paid for a stranger to gain easy entrance.

Then by accident Mansart visited Gary in neighboring Indiana. A friend drove him there in his car to visit acquaintances known to both. Here was a new industrial city where separation by race was just being introduced by the Steel Trust. A new high school for Negroes with colored principal and teachers had recently been opened, and colored children from all over the city were practically being forced to enroll here instead of in the city high school. Mansart saw the principle involved, but he also saw the opportunity. Here was a fine schoolhouse, with ample funds and abundant equipment.

Think of anything like this in Atlanta! What a chance for devoted teachers to show the world what Negroes could do. He talked to the principal and that poor man, overwhelmed to find a Negro who did not damn him as a traitor and who saw the vision which he had, urged Mansart to come there as a teacher. He was sure he could find him a place at a salary of $1200. Mansart was amazed and gratified. He promised that if the position were offered he would accept.

He started back to Atlanta, glowing in anticipation of how his wife would greet this chance to escape the South; and of the opportunity to raise the children in freedom. At the same time he felt the South reaching the North, for the "Jim-Crow" coach in which he sat ran boldly in and out of Chicago. Riding through Tennessee on the same "Jim-Crow" coach he winced at the opposition which the Gary school was meeting and would meet from Negro citizens of the town. They wanted to kill the race segregation idea. They were right in principle; but wasn't there a wiser and more fruitful way than opposition to this school and forcing out colored teachers, while Negro children suffered the disdain of white teachers? It was, he admitted, a difficult matter to decide easily; probably because he had been born and raised in a segregated atmosphere he could see his side of this controversy more clearly. He fell into uneasy sleep, sitting in the crowded, dirty coach all the long night.

To Mansart's astonishment on reaching home full of all his thoughts and experience, he found his wife almost in hysterics. She had just learned that she was to have another baby. She wept and moaned, even shrieked. She declared she would no longer live with Manuel; that she would not have another child; that she was not a brood mare; that already she was sick and broken in health; she had not had an undisturbed night's sleep for ten years; that her whole life had been drudgery, with diapers and washing, mending and scolding, cleaning and lugging; she was tired, tired, tired; she wished she were dead; she would kill herself if she only knew how.

Manuel was appalled. He called in the physician and talked earnestly; they all talked together. The physician soothed and reassured them. He told Manuel that such upsets were common; that it probably would be better to have no more children after this. He gave the distracted wife a sedative which put her to sleep and advised Manuel to send her to the country and manage for a few months to keep house with the aid of the three boys. Manuel forgot Gary and sat down to consider whether this thing called Life was worth as much as he had assumed.

Mansart now began to view his future seriously. He was approaching forty and no longer "young." On the contrary he would soon be middle-aged which seemed in many respects worse than old. He was principal of a public school for Negroes, inadequately supported by the city and overcrowded. His dream of escaping to the North with a better-paid job and a better supported school began slowly fading away. In its place began to rise the idea of business venture. Booker Washington had been preaching industry and industrial training for more than fifteen years; but with that gospel had gone the urge for educated Negroes to enter business and get wealth. A Negro business league had been formed by Mr. Washington in 1900 and its membership was growing. Atlanta University in 1905 had made a study of business enterprises among Negroes, and Washington had used its encouraging report to spread his league. Mansart began to consider whether or not he might enter some kind of Negro business enterprise.

Expanding business, growing yearly bigger and more powerful, dominated his era. No one questioned the righteousness and inevitability of the continued rule of that industrial empire which Great Britain and the United States represented and which all nations envied and strove to follow. In a city like Atlanta, Mansart was totally surrounded by a world of Big and growing Business. He watched the rampart of office buildings rise in the city and the beautiful homes of their white owners spread themselves out from the slums of Decatur Street toward the surrounding hills. He saw the raw stuff pouring into Atlanta; lumber and cotton, iron and steel, horses and mules; but he especially was amazed at the legerdemain by which the raw stuff that came into the city was transformed in all sorts of astonishing forms: machines and bricks and garages, furniture and cloth, mattresses and beds, trunks and glass, boxes and soap, paint and bags and bridges. It was all a sort of marvelous fairytale.

Thus by 1912 it would have been hard to convince Negroes that American business was not the normal path to their progress and that, as Booker Washington reiterated, it was only their laziness and ignorance that hindered their rise to riches and consequent equality with whites. Business was the watch-word.

The annual meetings of the Negro Business League became a forum of propaganda. Little grocery stores, cleaning establishments, garages and restaurants were rapidly added to the older barber shops. But they ran into numerous difficulties unless, as with the barber shops and restaurants, they were protected by the psychological protective tariff of prejudice, and catered to such Negro wants as whites were not willing to attend to. Sometimes Greeks and other foreigners competed in the restaurant business, and by alliance with white business and credit, prospered. Negro competing business, in general lines, could not vie with whites. They could not get current wholesale prices or long credit. In case they prospered by reason of unusual factors they were quietly marked for slaughter by the white vampires who were on the lookout.

There was, however, one avenue of endeavor which early attracted Negroes and that was insurance; protection against the sudden impact of accident, sickness and death. Even before Emancipation Northern Negroes and Southern free Negroes formed such small organizations and cooperative efforts, usually in their churches. After Emancipation the secret orders and fraternities tried with indifferent success to enlarge this activity. Out of thousands of small, isolated sick-benefit and burial societies there began to arise mergers. In Virginia the True Reformers and the Order of St. Luke became widespread and successful. There followed efforts in Georgia and Florida; and in Atlanta a large Negro church began a small mutual aid company in 1904, which came to the notice of a prosperous Negro barber, Alonzo Herndon.

The white insurance companies in the South entered into this increasingly lucrative field; their agents swarmed in Negro sections. It was a gold mine; the lapses, the removals; the browbeating and plain cheating made large profits. Negroes began to eye this form of investment as a possible field of new endeavor for themselves. There were several efforts in Augusta and other cities, but the work of Alonzo Herndon in Atlanta was epoch-making. Herndon was a light mulatto who had only primary school training. He owned the finest barber shop for white people in Atlanta. It was almost a patent of social standing to be welcomed at this shop, and especially to be served by the owner in person.

Herndon, nearly white, had been born in a country town about twenty-five miles from Atlanta and had worked as a farm laborer and then as a barber. He was polite, thrifty, and good-hearted. From the first he had saved his money and invested it in tenement houses; very simple, small, cheaply constructed rows of tenements where colored laborers lived and paid him rent weekly. Herndon collected the rents himself, and the total returns from his shop and houses increased. He quietly put his savings in the First National Bank. From time to time he spent considerable sums in making his barber shop beautiful and elaborate until it surpassed any other shop in the city. He shrewdly bought the building where it was housed. There was some hesitation on the part of real estate agencies in selling it to a colored man, but his influential white friends allayed apprehension, bought it for him and turned it over to him at a good commission. He paid cash and asked no mortgage.

Herndon was now well-to-do, but he saw a chance to be rich. He was greatly impressed by the doctrines of Booker Washington and he wanted to invest his money in something that would bring him larger returns than he was getting. First, he multiplied his shops, establishing three or four branch barber shops here and there in the city. They paid, but not as well as his first shop and they met competition and bad feeling from shops controlled by white barbers. Then he built a better grade of tenement houses, but soon saw that they would not pay. The Negroes who could pay rent for such houses were the very Negroes who themselves wanted to buy property and not to rent.

Herndon noticed, however, and with increasing interest, the success of white insurance concerns among Negroes. A large proportion of the colored folk, inspired by agents' sales talks, were now buying insurance against sickness and death; small sums from 5c to 50c a week were paid, insuring members of the family so that when sick, one could receive a small weekly stipend of $2, $3, or $5 a week; if they died the family got funeral expenses of $50, perhaps $100.

On this was built the business of Negro undertakers; tying themselves closely to the white insurance companies on one hand, the Negro churches on the other, they conducted an increasingly profitable business by selling expensive funerals to poor people. The colored people were stirred by death and by the social desire to make a fine showing at the funeral of their relatives; thus a profitable field of exploitation appeared both for insurance companies, the colored undertakers and the white manufacturers of funeral necessities.

The real point of the matter was, as Herndon quickly saw, that numbers of people began to buy insurance, and then after a time stopped, from carelessness or misfortune or unemployment. Huge sums in this way became forfeited, and by law accrued to the insurance societies as pure profit.

This intrigued Herndon. He inquired into it; he joked with some of the white collection agents who drifted into his shop. Ordinarily they got seats in the back of the shop and were attended by the less skilled barbers; but now and then Herndon flattered one of them by putting one in his own front chair and assiduously attending to him. He learned in this way a good deal about insurance business. He had never heard that in some parts of the world the city or state had undertaken this sort of service for the poor, not only for sickness and death but for medicine and other social services. In other parts of the United States this kind of socialism might have been publicly discussed, but not in Atlanta; and nowhere in the South for the benefit of Negroes. Herndon's only problem then was whether Negro or white exploiters should share this profit, and he thought it fair that Negro exploiters share the opportunity.

As competition increased white companies put in colored collectors. They were found to make a better appeal to some of the upper group of colored families who resented the white agents. The white agents felt they must walk into colored homes with their hats on and address the owners by their first names. Colored agents took off their hats and said "Mrs." The number of these naturally began to multiply.

The success of colored collectors had already induced colored business men to try to organize insurance companies themselves. The state had practically no curbs on the business and no deposits were required. But no sooner did successful colored insurance companies appear in Virginia and in some other states and begin to spring up in Atlanta than the state took notice and passed a law which required that beginning with the year 1906 industrial insurance companies must deposit $5,000 with the state as guarantee of their solvency. Herndon bought out a small company and hastened to be the first colored company to deposit $5,000 with the State Commissioner of Insurance. The Commissioner shaved daily in his chair. In 1906 the assets of this company were worth $10,000; ten years later they were worth $71,000. Herndon died a millionaire in 1927.

Thus as political power faded there emerged a new escapism for educated and ambitious Negroes. In the South particularly, the better class not only turned from politics to business, but from industry to exploitation. A class structure began to appear among Negroes, differing from the past. In the past there was a fissure between blacks and colored people which was not simply a color line but a line between the slave and free—the mulattoes claiming, and often legally, freedom from their white fathers. This line, emphasized by ownership of property and better paid employment, became in cities like Charleston and New Orleans a distinct class cleavage.

During the abolition controversy, 1820 to 1860, the class line was naturally between slave and free, with some emphasis on hereditary freedom and increased consideration for wealth. Then with Emancipation the levelling process began to be modified by new efforts to get wealth, which was illustrated by the turning toward business enterprise; and that enterprise began to change from personal service like barbering, restaurants and small shops for trade, to exploitation of labor. The teachers, physicians and writers were thrown with the new exploiters and separated from the workers, the only marked exception being the preachers who became leaders of the working masses without too good an understanding of what modern work meant in the new industrial process.

The physicians and pharmacists inaugurated a new avenue of business enterprise. Negro physicians began to increase slowly because of the difficulty Negroes had in entering white medical schools and because of the few Negro schools available and up to standard. But Negro physicians were in increasing demand and white physicians were eager to be rid of Negro patients. Pharmacy was easily taught and standards low; patent medicine interests encouraged the Negro market. Thus Negro drug stores began to multiply: they became centers of social intermingling for the black world; they sold soft drinks and food and also here and there they concealed gambling in "numbers" and sale of liquor.

Colored people of Atlanta began stirring. They saw the increased prosperity of the city; they began to understand the mystery of investment and the gains from employing labor; they soon realized that a colored business man could hire colored labor and on the whole get better service for less wages than whites paid, particularly if a Negro was in a position to give to his colored employee a certain social standing and a chance to dress well and have pleasant working surroundings. Colored clerks, stenographers and agents began to multiply.

The colored artisans were more than willing to work for colored contractors if the contractors could get the capital and backing. This was difficult, but they did have a chance sometimes to underbid the white contractors by lowering the wages of their workers; and if they could make the necessary connections with influential white forces they could carry on their work. For twenty years or more, up until the riot, a colored builder, by outbidding whites, hiring cheap colored labor, working along with his men, being satisfied with small profits, and doing excellent work, was the biggest builder of wooden bridges in the county around Atlanta.

Meantime, the old Negro fraternities and secret societies began to move in this new economic direction. They had fallen into limited popularity and favor because they had only one appeal to the mass of colored people: their regalia and parades, small death benefits, and the lure of secrecy. But now certain shrewd leaders added the "endowment" or insurance feature. There was, for instance, the Odd Fellows. They represented an ancient triumph of Negro shrewdness over whites. They had flourished in Northern cities and to a less extent in the South.

In Georgia, in the first decade of the twentieth century they got a fearless leader. Ben Davis was a big man of physical power and persuasive manners who had studied at Atlanta University. He and a group of his fellows began to organize new Odd Fellows lodges. They went into the corners and byways and gave the Negroes centers of recreation in Odd Fellows halls; new amusements in the lodge meetings; new places of congregation and cheer; and finally, new methods of saving their pennies and dollars in the endowment insurance plan of the Odd Fellows lodges.

The women were well taken care of in the "household of Ruth," and pretty soon the annual dues rolling into Atlanta became a huge and impressive sum, amounting in 1911 to $80,000. Davis was elated and began to get ideas. In 1912 the order bought an entire block on Auburn Avenue, paying $53,000 for the land and erecting a five story office building at a cost of $250,000. Then they built an auditorium and were so successful that Davis determined to extend his operations to the national field and gain control of the whole colored order which extended throughout the United States but, save in Georgia, had remained relatively unimportant and confined its activity to building a few lodge halls and staging annual parades.

When Davis appeared at the next annual convention where because of his increased membership he was about to control the order, the northern Negroes got jealous of his power and also apprehensive of the soundness of his insurance venture. Morris of Chicago took the leadership of this opposition. He was a rich, brown-skinned lawyer, leader of the criminal bar of Chicago, shrewd and unscrupulous. He simply out-maneuvered Davis and the Southerners on technical points, was himself elected Grand Master and moved to take firm control of the Georgia branch of the order.

Davis went to bed ill from exertion and disappointment, and for months the whole matter was in abeyance. But the beautiful Odd Fellows' hall was finally finished and stood as an inspiration to colored people to save and invest. Other Negro orders, like the Knights of Pythias, were accumulating funds. White men, especially investors and bankers, made friendly gestures toward colored business men.

Davis, who now directed nearly $900,000 worth of Odd Fellows property in Georgia, angrily took a fatal step. He took the matter into the Georgia courts, which promptly made the Georgia branch of the order a state corporation under local law. Davis threw the whole Odd Fellows order into receivership. In this way the efforts of Negro capital came to the attention of John Baldwin, the banker. He called on his patron, Pierce, one day with regard to a mortgage on some land, an office building and other assets. Pierce told him to go ahead if the terms were right. Of course mortgages were risky, but in good times like these and in Atlanta the risk was small.

Baldwin hesitated. "The property," he said, "is on Auburn Avenue and owned by Negroes."

Pierce was astonished. "How much?" he asked.

"Half a million."

"Who owns it?"

"The colored Odd Fellows."

"Colored?" said Pierce in surprise. "You can't touch it. Colored real estate is poison." He scowled and looked thoughtfully out of the window. He was about to say that it was no use for Negroes to own property or try to invest as long as——. He was attacking his own theories.

Baldwin arose. "You are confirming my own judgment," he

said, "but I wanted your advice. Naturally we'll furnish mortgage money eventually, but to the whites who are bound sooner or later to take over. We'll be well-secured."

Pierce nodded, but he sent for John Sheldon. Sheldon came, muttering, "Some more dirty work!" He was commissioned to look into this Negro Odd Fellows business. He did. But he knew it was nothing that would interest Pierce. Pierce was thinking of production and distribution on a grand scale—national, continental, eventually global. His interest in Negroes was incidental and contributory to this.

Sheldon was auxiliary to this and was well-paid. But to him the gambling aspect of business appealed—buying to sell; selling to buy to sell again. His interest and his sole interest was on the margin of gain left in his deals. He was thus the promoter. Using the financiers such as Baldwin, and leaving Big Business and its power to Pierce and his ilk, he himself would become the millionaire which he firmly intended to be.

This Negro Odd Fellows business interested and surprised him. He knew little of secret orders and despised them as the weakness of petty minds, until he realized what the former slaveholders and the capitalists who succeeded them were doing with them among whites in the New South. He joined a number of white orders and sat quietly inside to watch. He learned much of inner politics and "social" movements in this way. He saw a succession of young and enthusiastic Liberals, who began to write in magazines and newspapers and even to speak on the stump, brought to meek conformity and silence in the lodge room.

There he first heard of the Negro Odd Fellows and men laughed and joked over the bizarre fact that the Negro Order was legitimate while the whites were spurious interlopers. Northern free Negroes as early as 1847 had secured a charter from England and set up the Grand United Order. It was not until after that the white American order was started and naturally, without recognition from the parent lodge in England or the black lodge in the United States. A somewhat similar mixup in the 18th century led to black masons which the whites refused to recognize but whose legitimacy they had to admit after a fight of two centuries.

This Odd Fellows matter might have remained a joke but for developments after Booker Washington continued to urge Negroes to go into business. What the Southern whites had always feared and carefully watched for was the development of secret conspiracies in these Negro fraternities. And this might have happened but for the unexpected impact of Negro education. The young, educated leaders were not like the older guild of preachers, grist for the secret underground, but were leaning with Booker Washington toward economic solution of their problem.

The economy of ten million people was no trifle, even if they were in the aggregate poor and ignorant. They earned and spent millions; they had been deliberately encouraged to take a hand in this industrial operation and help run it. In spots, here and there, they were trying with some success. But what of the future? What if they saw themselves continually balked? Again Sheldon viewed this problem as something not outside the nation's main problem but as singularly central.

Sheldon gathered the information about the Odd Fellows and related it to Pierce. Pierce was astonished. This was a development of his interracial program which he had not expected. He wondered how many Negro leaders really understood the game? It was no place for novices. It was dog eat dog and always would be until the Trusts took over and perhaps some Super-Trust—there he reined his thought with a start. Was this Socialism? He was surprised at himself to see the analogy.

He had always pictured Negroes as common laborers, capable with training of becoming semi-skilled, and in a few cases skilled artisans. That would go far to solve the labor problems of the New South. When Booker Washington added to this his talk about the Negro "in business," Pierce smiled tolerantly, thinking this was good propaganda and escapist philosophy for the restless. But of course Pierce was sure that no subordinate race economy could grow up in the all-embracing empire which he was building.

This Negro Odd Fellows business was interesting and perhaps indicative of certain latent capacities in this race which in some dim future might be used. But today no such movement could succeed. Doubtless the actuarial basis of this insurance effort was faulty and certainly if by any chance it succeeded it would only be for eventual swallowing up by white business.

Sheldon put it bluntly. "Negro business without political power is silly. Remember what the city did to those Negro physicians and teachers who bought and built on Boulevard? They stuck so many laundries and factories under their noses that the property isn't worth today half what they paid for it. In Macon,

I'm told, they put a white whore-house in the center of the best
Negro residential district. Davis owns no judges and couldn't buy
any even if he had the cash. They wouldn't dare to sell out to him.
He's bound to lose, and Northern Negroes can't win in Georgia."

Sheldon went out, leaving Pierce bewildered. But Sheldon
himself was getting ideas. It might not be a bad plan to watch
this growth of business among Negroes. There might be pickings.
And if the fools were determined to be fleeced, he might as well
benefit as the next man.

Eventually nearly a million dollars of the hard earned money
of Negro laborers in Georgia were given by the courts into the
hands of a board of white receivers, of which John Sheldon was
one. These receivers borrowed money for expenses from John
Baldwin's bank which John Pierce controlled. When, after years
of litigation these assets were finally "liquidated," there was nothing left for the colored policy holders. So died a dream. But
dreams die hard and other dreams replace them. So it was in this
case.

In 1908, two years after the Riot, Heman Perry came to
Atlanta. He was a little, neat, yellow man with frank, business-
like and persuasive manners. He was altogether different from
the familiar type of Negro preacher, but he was devout and
sober. He did not pretend to eloquence or leadership. He was
born in Texas, had completed only six grades in the public schools
and then went to work as a cotton sampler. Then he became an
insurance solicitor working for white companies who had colored
customers. He went to New York for wider opportunity but
saw no opening there. He said:

"I decided to leave New York and come to Georgia. I went
to a pawn shop and disposed of my cuff-buttons for five dollars.
I went down to a river boat and gave the purser the five dollars
to work my way to Savannah. I made on the journey sixty-five
cents in tips."

He began working in Atlanta for white insurance companies
among colored clients. But he was firm in the idea that Negroes
could start their own old-line legal reserve insurance company.
He asked Mansart's help. Mansart laughed. He was no business
man and never would be; yes, of course he needed more money
than he was earning. He admitted that the Negro problem was
in part a matter of income. He would certainly be glad to introduce Perry to his friends.

The fact was that while Mansart had lately considered a business career for himself, the more he saw of business the more he recoiled. He rode out one day with colored Dr. Gates to look over the new tenements which Gates had built for Negroes. They were cheap, flimsy two-room affairs with no modern conveniences; the city had furnished neither sidewalks nor sewers, and the rents were high.

"Why not put up a little better class of home?" he asked.

The physician grinned. "These are the ones that pay," he said.

Mansart knew from his school children how the insurance agents were cheating the poor, and the new Negro enterprises were doing no better, except that they hired Negro clerks and collectors, and colored business men got the profits.

But Mansart introduced Perry to his friends. After all, an old-line insurance company might do better. Perry got hold of colored men who had some savings or a business and especially of the professional Negroes, and laid before them his scheme for an old-line insurance company. Nearly all these people had trouble getting life insurance. When they applied to the large white insurance companies they were either refused outright as risks, or accepted at largely increased premiums.

Perry had facts and figures; he showed people that it was possible to establish a Negro insurance company and carry it on by business and scientific methods and make money. He was listened to with a good deal of skepticism. Some few were persuaded and invested their money, but not many. But Perry kept working not only in Atlanta but in other Southern cities, and in some Northern centers.

By law Perry had to raise a paid-in capital stock of $100,000 within the year before he could open business. His energy and confidence and the growing confidence of Mansart resulted in the astonishing fact that in 1911 Perry had actually raised $85,000 cash. Then the heartbreaking fact stared him in the face that under the law this sum must be returned to the subscribers with interest if the total sum was not raised within the year.

Perry in after years used to recall this situation: "Reluctantly we voted to return the $85,000 with 4 per cent interest without any strings to it. I sent a letter along with each remittance saying that I had paid the total expenses of raising this money, which amounted to $4,740. I remember the final evening well. It was cold and windy. The fire had gone out. One of the men remarked:

'It's getting dark, boys, let's light the gas.' And another said: 'No, don't light the gas; don't put Perry to any more expense!' And they filed out one by one and left me there alone at the fireless stove, thinking things over."

All the money was returned. But Perry had something in him. He doggedly started again, and by March, 1913, to the astonishment of black and white Atlanta he had actually raised $100,000 and launched the Standard Life Insurance Company.

West, in Mississippi, a similar effort had been started in 1902. It was connected with a colored woman named Minnie Cox. Minnie Cox figured in politics in 1903. She had long been postmistress in a little town called Indianola, whose inhabitants were nearly all colored. She had served acceptably, with no complaints, until the matter of her re-appointment came up to President Theodore Roosevelt. The re-appointment would have been routine had not a new personage appeared in Mississippi in 1901, and that was James K. Vardaman. Vardaman's campaign and Roosevelt's dinner with Booker Washington, lost Minnie Cox her re-appointment in 1903.

She did not care overmuch. The office paid little and it was the principle for which she had fought. Her husband, Wayne Cox, had started an insurance company, inspired by the Booker Washington program and preferring business to politics. His company, chartered in 1909 with a capital of $25,000, became in 1910 the first Negro old-line legal reserve company in the world. Of this effort Perry knew little, but as it afterward happened, both these attempts at business fell into each other's arms for mutual support after the war. But that is a later story.

Perry's success impressed Mansart in several ways. First, he began to see new light for the Negro in the South. Secondly, his son, Douglass, now in college, had become a fervent believer in Perry and during vacations was one of his best solicitors.

The teaching of Booker Washington to black labor was Work and Save. Save and Invest. Invest and become rich. Thus Black Atlanta, in its search for wealth, had its ups and downs. But on the whole it was pressing forward. The insurance business flourished; individual contractors made money; Negro stores and other enterprises multiplied. But the whole development brought fear and jealousy to the poor white laborers.

With Negroes disfranchised, the white voters refused repeatedly adequate money for Negro schools; they refused the Negroes parks and playgrounds, and did not admit them to the city parks. A silent battle between the two laboring classes, and also between white laborers and the Negro capitalists, began to evolve. Segregation in housing and work was persistent. The new Democratic president, Wilson, segregated clerks in the Departments at Washington; and the American Bar Association refused to admit colored members.

Moreover, due to the "white primary" system, the primary election of the Democratic party in which only whites could vote became by threat of mob law the real election. Among the white voters in Atlanta, the political power of the white laborers was emphasized beyond their real strength.

Then came the World War in Europe in 1914. Atlanta paid only casual attention to it until business and commerce were disrupted. The market for cotton began to disappear. Capital became timid and work precarious.

There were other clouds on the horizon, but Mansart tried to ignore them. In 1915 the Ku Klux Klan was revived in a meeting on Stone Mountain, with midnight ceremony and burning crosses. The idea spread not only over Atlanta but over the South and far up into the North. By 1920 the Klan was nationwide and played a considerable part in the elections of that year. The hidden handle to all this was the sale of sheets, pillow cases and paraphernalia at considerable prices, which must have netted the profiteers a tidy sum. A great capitol building for the realm was purchased in Atlanta.

But there were signs of hope. Negroes led by Professor Burghardt of Atlanta formed a radical "Niagara Movement" in the North in 1905 and Negroes and whites held a conference in New York in 1909 to found a new radical organization. This occurred almost simultaneously with the fistic triumphs of Jack Johnson, and the latter was much more influential. Johnson's victory brought national laws, riots in the South, and a bitter increase of racial tension. All this partly because Johnson was strong and sarcastic, but chiefly because he married a white woman who was no better than she should have been.

Little notice was taken of the fact that in 1909 Matthew Henson, a black man, stood with Peary at the North Pole; but a good deal of notice was given to the fact that there were an increased number of strikes against Negro labor in Georgia.

The new National Association for the Advancement of Colored People, formed at the conference in New York, brought Professor

Burghardt from Atlanta as its chief spokesman and adopted a line of concerted action in the courts, which might mean trouble. What would be the refuge of the Supreme Court once it really faced the legality of Caste? The answer was seen in 1915 when for the first time the 15th Amendment was pronounced constitutional. Did the nation realize this epoch-making victory of these new Abolitionists?

Still, in this ointment there was a fly; in the new NAACP was no real representation of the Negro worker. It did not enter the thought of the teachers, professional men and social workers that they did not represent and speak for the black laboring classes. They were, to be sure, nearer the black workers than similar classes of whites were to their workers. The Negro proletariat was not yet quite differentiated from the petty bourgeois. In the same black family might often be servants and laborers, clerks in stores and students studying for professions. This meant a unity and sympathy that few white families showed. Still the workers as such had no representation in the NAACP nor the contemporary Urban League.

Also at Tuskegee, center of the movement for industrial training of the Negroes, most of the graduates became teachers, physicians, dentists and business men. Few became farmers and artisans. Many tried to run farms and enter the building trades, but the white labor movement and growing social forces were against them. It was the Negro Business League that triumphed in Tuskegee and Hampton. Trade unions were frowned on in both of these influential schools. In both, the voice of Northern Big Business was dominant.

The study of Negroes in Business led to the Negro Business League and as Burghardt soon saw, an orientation of the Washington philosophy from primary labor and production with skilled labor as a goal in industry to exploitation of Negro labor for the Negro market. This was because the entrance of the Negro into industry was blocked by the trade unions, especially the new American Federation of Labor. Some effort was made to break through this barrier with the Open Shop campaign of Big Business. But this did not help the Negro worker much, and in the South the political power of white labor prevented the teaching of many industrial skills to Negroes even at Tuskegee. On the other hand, the exploitation of the Negro market in certain fields by Negroes was open to no competition. Beyond this the field of finance among Negroes offered inducements, and soon Negroes entered it.

Tuskegee soon became interested in guiding Negroes toward capitalistic exploitation of the Negro group, and thus turned from promotion of the Negro in industry as its main work. Then Burghardt saw in a few years a new turn in interest: beginning with Washington's dinner with Roosevelt, Tuskegee became gradually the political center of the American Negro. Washington, who under pressure had appeared as advising the Negro to keep out of politics now became, under the same pressure from Northern Big Business, the official referee for appointments to office and for other political advice to both black and white, North and South.

This centering of political power at Tuskegee among Negroes and to some extent among Southern whites, easily led to centering of economic power in the same rapidly growing ganglion, with its great school and with millions of philanthropic funds pouring in from all the world. Around Booker Washington grew a huge machine which suggested appointments and policies all over the South and even in the North. Young Negro men and women who wanted work of any sort, anywhere, applied to Tuskegee or sought Washington's endorsement for work elsewhere. Of course, Washington could not personally attend to all these activities, and a machine grew to vast proportions. Colored newspapers all over the country were subsidized or bought outright. All Negro meetings and organizations were carefully watched. Authors were watched and helped, and every Negro of prominence and all who sought prominence cultivated the acquaintance of Booker Washington, or Washington's agents sought them. No plan of church, state or society was laid without consultation with Tuskegee. No white person of prominence, and no colored person, native or foreign, failed at some time or other to visit, or read about or hear of Tuskegee and be influenced by its propaganda.

Manuel Mansart tried to talk this whole situation out. He was with a group of colored men at the rather poorly equipped YMCA on Auburn Avenue, Atlanta. Of course, it was "colored" and quite separate in organization and work from the elaborate white YMCA uptown. This meeting was the "Monday Club" which once a month dined simply.

"What's happening in the world and in the United States? I'm all at sea," asked Mansart. A history teacher tried to explain:

"There was a labor revolt in this country late in the seventies which came dangerously near to revolution. It was put down by brutal force, but not before the nation was impressed that democratic government was not working so well in America as we thought. The autocratic power of employers and property owners and the distribution of the money stock which they controlled were certainly the cause in part."

Old Dr. Crogman added: "I remember the rise of Populism which swept the South. Some of us hoped it would unite white and black labor. Watson—would you believe it?—then led the movement, and for a while my old pupil, Doyle, led him."

"Then came the elections of '90 and '92," added Dr. Jones, "and there was Hell to pay."

"This part is where I get lost. What happened to Watson?" asked Mansart.

John Hope, a blonde colored teacher at Morehouse who came from Watson's part of Georgia, answered:

"You must realize the split in the Democratic party. The Northern Democrats began to be the party of labor and reform. Southern Democracy was not a party but a group of industrialists determined to run the State for Big Business. Tom Watson the labor party, as Teddy Roosevelt tried to bring Big Business in 1894 captured the Georgia Democratic Party and threatened to capture the South. We were near then to having a national labor party. But Big Business moved rapidly in, bought the election in the North and stole it in the South. Politics for the first decade of the century reeled, and Republicans bade fair to become to heel. The South, by manipulating the Negro vote, began to be the defender of industrial bandits.

"Watson tried in vain to arouse the farmer and labor vote, South and North, in 1904, but failed miserably. Southern Democrats offered to put him back in politics if he would desert the Negro. Tillman and his tribe abetted, and old folkways, suppressed for a time by Doyle, festered and stank. In deserting black labor, Watson had to desert white labor and spend his strength attacking Jews and Catholics. He sold out so completely that lynching, murder and riot in the South scared Big Business all over the nation into hysterics. And here we are."

The Monday Club strolled home in small groups; most of them, including Mansart, passed the new bank building where John Pierce had his office.

"And where do we go from here?" asked Mansart.

Hope replied: "If we can keep out of war and can be led by Woodrow Wilson, the scholar and liberal Southerner, we may unite black and white labor in one movement for the uplift of the working class; we may beat back disfranchisement and restore the ideal of Democracy to the United States. We may restore popular education to evolve a nation, and a people intelligent rather than smart and rich; and integrate into this nation the blood and music of ten million Africans."

Crogman looked at Hope and smiled: "Dear boy, that integration has been made in you, but it has not yet been made in this nation and it will be long before it will." And he put his arm about the shoulders of John Hope, this young white man who was talking black because he had a Negro great-grandfather.

CHAPTER XVII

MANUEL MANSART DECIDES

James Burghardt in July, 1910 was packing his goods when Manuel Mansart called on him to talk over Perry's insurance company. It was just on the point of raising its first $100,000 capital.

"I'm sorry, Mansart, but I can't help," he said. "I've worked here 13 years for $1200 a year, and now I'm leaving. I've saved nothing, but I have no debts."

"Leaving? Have they dismissed you after all your fine work?"

"No. That's the queer thing. I dismissed myself. I have been asked to come North and head a new organization to fight for Negro rights. I feel I should go and yet I hate to give up my life work as a social scientist. At the same time, I know how much pressure is put on young President Ware to dismiss me because of my criticism of Booker Washington and my outspoken demand for Negro equality. What to do was at first not clear. I know that Ware does not want my work to stop. But how much does he dare risk on me? It costs money to run the school and that money must come from rich men like John Pierce who distrusts me and cares little for my work. I determined to test the young President. If he said the word, I'd stay. If not, I'd go. I went to his office with much inward trepidation and said:

" 'President Ware, I have been offered a job in New York to head a new organization for Negro rights. I hate to leave this work, but——'

"The worried face of the President lighted up, and relief outshone regret. I realized this with dismay. 'We're sorry, too, very sorry,' he murmured, and then hastened to add: 'I wonder—do you suppose Thomas Jesse Jones would be willing to come here and take up your work?'

"I hated Thomas Jesse Jones as the dishonest spy for rich philanthropists. This smooth young Welshman had a position at Hampton; but for years he had called on me as a friend and I had talked frankly with him. Then I found that he was peddling my confidential talk to my enemies and traducers. I stopped

295

seeing him. Here now was this man, an enemy of Negro higher education, being proposed as my successor. I felt sick. But that dislike was little beside the realization that the harried president
was more than ready to see me go. So, you see, Mansart, I sort
of dismissed myself."

"I'm sorry, very sorry," Mansart stammered.

"So am I. Sorrier than I dare say. I am giving up a great ideal.
I wanted to be a scholar. I wanted to sit alone aloft and guide
the world to Truth in a field where more than in others, it needs
truth or it will die. I firmly believed that by continued and pro-
longed and increasingly accurate measurement of human action,
a science of sociology might be built as credible as the work of the
physical sciences. I believed too that in the segregated Negro group
in America we had a test group peculiarly adapted to experiment
in examination, measurement and deduction. It was a wild dream
but it was well worth trying out for a century. Here it died after
thirteen years. Instead of this I must go and try to do what least
I'm fitted to do: persuade and cajole men who will hate and despise me for trying."

He looked sadly out of the window across the red hills of
Atlanta to where Kenesaw raised its bulk to hide the sunset.

"There," he said, "my dream lies buried; there my Ivory Tower
falls in ruins. Hence I go to make a people listen to the truth
which will not make them free!"

John Pierce was relieved to see Burghardt leave of his own
decision before he was dismissed. Pierce believed that Negro
leadership under Booker Washington had done pretty well, barring
that luncheon at the White House which was the fault of Roosevelt rather than his. Washington had kept cool after the riot
and given the Negroes good advice. He made a darn good referee for political appointments of white in the South, although
he had blundered or Roosevelt had blundered in the case of that
black postmistress in Mississippi and the Collector of the Port in
Charleston. But Washington was learning; he was basically sound,
thought Pierce.

But Pierce wondered how long could Washington hold the
Negroes in control if his educational program broke down? Already, radical Northern Negroes like Burghardt who had just left
Atlanta University, and certain dark Northern fanatics, were attacking it. And with reason, for no matter how much Hampton
and Tuskegee talked agriculture to Negro students, their gradu-

ates almost unanimously went into teaching or the professions. He had attended conferences at Tuskegee. Good straight advice. But nobody followed it. Negroes kept leaving the country for the city. Something was wrong.

Neither was industry being successfully taught. One colored school he knew built a fine wagon by hand and exhibited it. Trouble was, it cost twice what it would if made in mass by machinery. Negro schools could not afford such machinery or find a market. White trade unions were stopping the teaching of Negroes in industry, even of the building trades in state-supported schools.

Where did this leave the plan to build two mutually checking labor groups? Exactly nowhere. What was building was a white labor group with exaggerated political power in the South, alongside a depressed, uneasy group of black common laborers and servants, underpaid, disfranchised, and enticing food for the mob; and above all, with their political power not nullified but exercised instead by the worst type of reactionary Southern white.

Above the depressed Negro labor group was rising a class of black professional men and women as teachers, preachers, physicians, dentists and a few lawyers. There were also pharmacists who began to dot Southern cities with colored drug stores. To these gradually were being added a new group of business men and there were included the liquor dealers with pool rooms and gambling handed down from earlier days.

Washington's advice for the Negro to go into business was a new idea which Pierce doubted, except it was confined to small shops. He had helped Washington finance his Business League. Its meetings were large and voluble. But something hindered Negro business enterprise. What was it? Pierce did not know. He realized that Negroes were beginning to dream of a new prosperity; a new way in which the Negro problem was going to be solved. Negroes were to become not only professional men for their own people, but capitalists and employers, chiefly exploiting their own group because of the differential advantage which prejudice and discrimination gave them; but also able to exploit white labor to some limited extent, which might increase in the future.

Thus black Atlanta, in its search for wealth, with its ups and downs—on the whole was pressing forward. Some of the insurance business flourished; individual contractors made money; Negro stores and other enterprises multiplied; and the whole development brought fear and jealousy to the poor white world.

Joe Brown, rival of Hoke Smith and now candidate for the Senate, pointed out that in trying to organize labor, white union men were also seeking to raise the wages and shorten the hours of Negro servants and farm laborers. Class lines thus were deftly twisted into racial lines. What poor white family was so poor they did not want a Negro servant? What white farmer could get on without severely exploiting Negro laborers?

Also Southern white skilled labor, even with political power, was getting intractable. They were uniting into unions and staging strikes. First they struck against the intrusion of Negroes into "white" jobs. This was understandable and the employers with some difficulty were induced to yield in several cases. But when in 1910, the white operatives of the Fulton Mills in Atlanta went on strike for higher wages and better conditions of work, the employers took a stand. The workers said that conditions of work had become harder; wages had become lower. They walked out July 1. The mills declared that only eighty-five workers were out; but the strikers from their meager funds were feeding more than nine hundred persons daily.

They brought their grievances to the notice of newspapers and churches. Laborers were discharged because they joined unions. They had to leave a week's wages in possession of the mills which they forfeited if they left without a week's notice. They had to make good from their meager wages damages to machinery; the mills did not pay the laborer for lost time. There was child labor, and despite a long fight, no bill against it could be forced through. The manufacturers would only consent to prohibiting the employment of children under fourteen, and not even then in the case of orphans or children who supported widows. They said: "The incidence where a child learns to read and write after it obtains the age of fourteen years is exceedingly rare." There was no need then, they argued, to keep such children in school, and after all, the strikers were fighting the results of a fall in the price of cotton and an increase in the price of food.

On July 13 a great mass meeting was held. For three hours the meeting lasted. It was in vain that the church, after having opposed unions, turned around and began to plead and protest against the suffering caused by the strike. There were advertisements with wide appeal to Christ. Over 137 columns in the *Constitution,* paid for, declared "God asks results."

Despite everything, the strike gradually petered out and failed. Then the fight went into politics and a Democratic convention in Macon in September became a mob and a riot. "All rules of parliamentary law were ignored; and men resorted to methods which would not be countenanced in well-organized mobs. Chairmen were disregarded; age, office and distinctions were lost sight of; opponents were howled down; the governor of the state was not allowed to speak; the morning session was so disorderly that no business was transacted; howls and pandemonium."

The economic world of the whites faced political domination by a white labor group. This group was obtaining increased and disproportionate power through the "White Primary" election. At the same time it was trying to separate the state into two labor groups and to beat the black group down into helplessness and inferiority. In Atlanta, for instance, the white voters refused repeatedly adequate money for Negro schools; they refused the Negroes parks and playgrounds, and did not admit them to the city parks. A silent battle between the two laboring classes, and gradually between the white laborers and the Negro professional classes and capitalists, began to evolve. Segregation in housing and work increased.

There were thus arising separate and to some extent independent racial groups in the city of Atlanta, just as in other Southern cities. Of course, they knew something of each other. You might think of them as a tree with branches; the roots quite close and indistinguishably together at the bottom in certain common sympathies of life and physical minglings of crime, poverty, and disease. But even here, there was segregation in jails and hospitals. Above that the branches separated, and yet remained close in the relation of householders and servants. Then they tended to separate still more into a more distant relation of employers and masses of employees, who knew each other at a distance and little outside that; save that the white employees had growing political power, which only the threat of black replacement could hold in check.

Finally, above that, the branches curved far apart, making even vision impossible. Negroes began to employ Negroes; and instead of living in the backyards of white people and the side alleys near the front streets, Negroes began to inhabit quarters of their own that were not slums. No white man entered such homes save as landowner or agent and less and less seldom then. No Negro from these homes entered a white home save as servant or friend of such a servant. God was worshipped quite separately, with separate undertakers and different graveyards.

Above all, a new and widening rift within the Southern white organization was manifest. Before the twentieth century no white man would admit that he might not become a rich employer, exploiting Negroes of course, and white workers who would be naturally of the upper laboring class. But now in the twentieth century it was becoming clear that a considerable class of white people were always going to be laborers; that they must look forward to their children earning wages, and that if they did not take care, those children were going to be dragged down to the level of Negro labor. They must therefore organize and fight and use their political power to see that a privileged class of laborers was established, with better wages, better treatment, and above all, political power.

Perhaps in time, although this thought was not clear, but perhaps in time this privileged class of white labor would share more and more largely the wealth of the rich, and become a dominant power in the state. On account of this growing body of thought, white labor easily and eagerly followed Hoke Smith and Tom Watson into the plan of disfranchisement of black labor. Negroes were going to form an underprivileged labor class, paid a smaller wage and working under the least favorable conditions.

The curious racial dichotomy was especially illustrated in the case of the skilled trades, where an aristocracy of labor was emerging with unions and better pay and working conditions; here the employers continually tried to balance the higher pay of the whites by hiring cheap non-union Negro labor, and whites retaliated by trying to drive Negroes out of such jobs. This battle was shown in the case of the Negro locomotive firemen. Negroes had acted as firemen on the few railways running in the South before the Civil War. White union firemen began to replace them in the new railroad building after the war. Then in 1905 the Georgia Railroad began a policy of hiring non-union Negro firemen. There was a strike with much violence. The black firemen offered to join the union but the whites refused. Their leader cried:

"I hope and pray that I may never live to see the grand old brotherhood of locomotive firemen so disgraced as to take into its protecting folds this class of God's creation."

The white firemen, despite the fact that they got higher wages than Negro firemen, blamed Negroes for their low wages and in 1909 the Georgia railroad removed white assistants who were getting $1.75 a day and filled their places with Negroes at $1.25

a day and at the same time gave Negroes equal seniority rights. The Negro firemen sought help but a Negro bourgeoisie was in the making which was thinking not so much of the interests of colored workers as of the new interests of colored investors. They gave Negro firemen only half-hearted support; perhaps more enthusiastic support would not have availed against the growing bitterness of the whites. As it was, whites furiously resented the retention of Negro firemen and began to murder from ambush the Negro firemen whenever and wherever they could be found.

The leader in Atlanta could hark back to the Riot. "White supremacy!" and the city of Atlanta and the towns through which the black firemen ran came to his aid. The Georgia railroad service was crippled. Witnesses were called in an effort at arbitration. They declared Negroes too ignorant to make good firemen; but the railroad defended their efficiency and openly admitted that Negroes were employed because they were cheaper.

"If we can get what we want cheap, is it a crime to take it?"

Finally the arbitration board decided that Negroes must be paid the same rate of wages as white men, and the conclusion was that Negroes would thus lose their jobs. But some Negro firemen remained.

Two years later the white firemen on the Southern Railroad struck, following a strike on the Queen and Crescent line. It was agreed to hire no black firemen north of a certain point on the line, and to make a difference of 30 per cent in the pay. All the southern railroads finally agreed that the percentage of Negroes hired would not be in the future bigger than it was on January 1, 1910. Thus the future entrance of colored firemen and yardmen was blocked.

In this way color caste in social, political and economic relations in the South and to some lesser extent in the North came to firm establishment. Hope of any help from the federal government faded as Teddy Roosevelt turned thought and energy to imperial expansion and when he was succeeded by Taft. Taft kept in touch with Booker Washington for political advice but Washington was very cautious, while Taft, having been reared in the Border city of Cincinnati, had little sympathy with Negroes. He had secured his nomination by purchase of black Southern delegates in the Republican nominating convention and then immediately announced that so far as he was concerned, there was no Negro population in the South that deserved any political recognition; that he would appoint no one to office who did not have the recommendation of the Southern whites. The result of this was an upheaval among Negro voters who were growing more powerful in the North.

When the struggle came, therefore, between Taft, Wilson and Roosevelt, some Negroes appealed to Roosevelt with the idea of having him recognize the plight of the Negro race and promise to restore them to a part in the democratic operation of the government. But Roosevelt had become convinced that this was impracticable. He therefore ignored the advice of liberals like Jane Addams, Joel Spingarn and others, and indirect pressure from the NAACP, and tried to make coalition with that white South which really stood for disfranchisment and monopoly. Roosevelt was beaten and Wilson came to power, partly at least because of the support of black voters.

The election of the first Southern president since the Civil War soon had momentous results. During his campaign in 1912 Wilson had written:

"Should I become President of the United States they [the colored people] may count on me for absolute fair dealing and for everything by which I could assist in advancing the interests of their race in the United States."

But the *Crisis* complained in 1914: "These were Mr. Wilson's words October 16, 1912. Why has the President failed to keep them? The President's party of 341 includes 115 Senators and Representatives from former slave states. If these 115 members withdrew their support Mr. Wilson's party would be a minority of 226 votes against 287. For his policies, therefore, Mr. Wilson must have the solid South, and the solid South has but one political tenet: 'Down with Niggers!' "

The South, and particularly the Negro-hating South, considered that it was now in the saddle. It began therefore to urge upon Congress, to demand from the administration and to advocate in the states, a practically complete program of color caste with disfranchisement and discrimination for the Negro race over the United States. Never in any administration had there been such a demand for anti-Negro and therefore anti-democratic legislation.

Wilson resisted most of these demands, but there was one point where he yielded in what he considered a small matter, and in deference to the insistence of his wife, and that was segregation of the Negro civil employees in the Departments in Washington.

His action here was far more serious than Wilson dreamed. Although Washington was a southern city, yet here the Negro had maintained since emancipation a social status unequalled elsewhere in the nation. Here Douglass had once been chief marshal and presided at official social functions; there had never been discrimination after appointment to political office, and there had grown up a class of well-to-do Negroes, well-educated, who stood on their rights and dignity. There were separate schools but the Negro system was independent of the white, with Negro officials and teachers and an excellently run organization quite as good if not better than the white system. Into the federal civil service, educated Negroes had early begun to enter after the Civil War and having few other openings, they soon formed a large and efficient part of it. In some offices like the War Department and the Land Office, Negroes held high and responsible positions. On the election of the first Southern president of post-war history there poured into Washington a horde of hungry Southern aspirants to office and particularly, many Southern women who were aghast at working beside "niggers." Wilson knew little of the conditions; he had never had a colored student at Princeton and in fact knew Negroes only as servants. He readily yielded to pressure, especially when his wife joined, and permitted segregation of Negro workers in several offices of the federal civil service. Now Negro civil servants were required in many cases to use separate restaurants, separate wash rooms and often entirely separate offices. They felt insulted and appealed to the voting Negroes in the North.

On November 12, 1914 Wilson had to face a delegation of Northern colored voters. They represented the National Equal Rights League, not a very effective organization but active. The delegates were not among the better known and more influential Negroes, save in the case of their leader. One was a congregational preacher who had opposed a "Jim-Crow" school in his town in New York State; another was an outspoken colored Virginian who ran his own printing establishment in Washington; colored social workers were there, and the spokesman, Monroe Trotter.

Most likely Wilson knew little of Trotter, but he was worth knowing. His father had been Registrar of Deeds of the District of Columbia under Grover Cleveland. This office was then paid by fees and the elder Trotter had made considerable money. He lived well in Boston, wrote a book on Negro music, and educated his three children in the best schools. His only son, William Monroe, was graduated from Harvard College with high honors and Phi Betta Kappa the same year that Booker Washington spoke at Atlanta. Also, this fatal year, Ben Tillman went to the Senate; and at Amherst College in central Massachusetts three other men were graduated: a white man, Calvin Coolidge, destined within a decade to succeed President Wilson; and two colored men, George Forbes and Bill Lewis.

This Amherst commencement was a gala occasion for young Negroes. A contingent of them and their friends, including Trotter, journeyed down from Boston with the bewilderingly beautiful octoroon whom Bill Lewis afterwards married. Lewis soon became the great center of the Harvard football team while he was in the Harvard Law School. Taft later appointed Lewis Assistant Attorney General. Trotter and Forbes became close friends.

Trotter, stocky and light yellow of skin, stood high among his classmates. He was by nature and breeding a frank, outspoken leader. His energy was furious, his convictions deep and he counted no sacrifice too great for defense of what he believed right. Forbes, older, darker, and more cynical, was a keen satirical writer. These two agreed on one matter, and that was the danger of the racial philosophy being developed by Booker T. Washington. They united; Trotter used his considerable private funds, Forbes gave all the time he could spare from his job as assistant librarian in a branch of the Boston Public Library. They began publication of the *Guardian,* which from 1901 on fought a fierce battle against Washington and his white friends, and for complete political and social equality despite color and race. These writers changed the attitude of Negroes and led to the launching of the Niagara Movement in 1905, by their friend Burghardt of Atlanta.

Trotter sent a petition to Wilson in 1913 and a year later demanded an interview. Wilson hesitated but it seemed wise to assent. Trotter and his four companions arrived promptly. With scant preliminaries, Trotter plunged straight into his subject:

"Mr. President: One year ago we presented a national petition signed by Afro-Americans in thirty-eight states protesting against segregation in the treasury and post office departments of employees of the national government whose ancestry could be traced to Africa. We then appealed to you to undo this race segregation in accord with your duty as president and with your pre-election pledges. We stated that there could be no freedom, no respect from others and no equality of citizenship under segregation in race especially when applied to but one of the many racial elements in the government employ. For such placement of employees means a charge of physical indecency or infection or of being a lower order of beings.

"At that time you stated you would investigate conditions for yourself. Now after the lapse of a year we have come back, having found that all the forms of segregation of government employees of African extraction are still practiced in the treasury and post office department buildings; and to a certain extent have spread into other government buildings.

"We have come by vote of this League to set before you this definite continuance of race segregation and to renew the protest and to ask you to abolish segregation of Afro-American employees in the executive department."

President Wilson was at the moment a worried and irritated man. World War I had broken out in Europe three months before. He was straining every nerve to keep this nation out of this war. It seemed to him ridiculous to have this eternal Negro question intrude now on his busy day. But he tried to be conciliatory. He said that he had investigated this question and had been assured there had been no discrimination in the comforts and surroundings given to the Afro-American workers. He added he had been informed by officials that the segregation had been started to avoid friction between the races and not with the object of injuring the Afro-American employees. The President said he was deeply interested in the Negro race and greatly admired its progress. He then made the astonishing assertion that the thing to be sought by the Afro-Americans "was complete independence of white people," and that he felt the white race was willing to do everything possible to assist them in this effort.

Trotter was incensed and retorted bitterly that "colored people did not seek charity or assistance but that they took the position that they had equal rights with whites and that these rights should be respected."

"Two years ago," he added, "you were thought to be a second Abraham Lincoln."

The President reddened and interrupted. He was distinctly upset at the comparison. "Leave out personalities," he said. "You are losing your temper."

But Trotter persisted. "Have you a 'new freedom' for white Americans and a new slavery for your Afro-American fellow-citizens?"

The President was now angry. He said that the question involved was not that of intrinsic qualities because all had human souls and were equal in that respect; but for the present it was a question of economic policy; whether the Afro-American race could do the same things that the white race could do with equal efficiency.

Trotter continued to protest and the President told him that if the organization he represented wished to approach him again it must choose another spokesman; that Trotter's tone was "offensive."

Trotter denied this hotly but the President told him he had spoiled the cause for which he had come and said he expected those who professed to be Christians to come to him in a Christian spirit. The President then informed the delegation that never since he had been in office had he been addressed in such an insulting fashion.

The fifteen-minute interview which had lasted an hour was then abruptly terminated.

But Trotter was not alone. The NAACP immediately sent the President a memorial signed by Moorfield Storey and Oswald Garrison Villard and written by the editor of the *Crisis,* saying:

"Never before has the Federal Government discriminated against its civilian employees on the ground of color. Every such act heretofore has been that of an individual State. The very presence of the Capitol and of the Federal flag has drawn colored people to the District of Columbia in the belief that living there under the shadow of the National Government itself they were safe from the persecution and discrimination which follow them elsewhere because of their dark skins.

"Today they learn that, though their ancestors have fought in every war in behalf of the United States, in the fiftieth year after Gettysburg and Emancipation, this Government, founded on the theory of complete equality and freedom for all citizens, has established two classes among its civilian employees. It has set the colored apart as if mere contact with them were contamination. The efficiency of their labor, the principles of scientific management are disregarded, the possibilities of promotion if not now will soon be severely limited. To them is held out only the prospect of mere subordinate routine service without the stimulus of advancement to high office by merit; a right deemed inviolable for all white natives as for the children of the foreign born, for Italians, French and Russians, Jews and Christians who are now entering the Government service. For to such limitation this segregation will invariably lead.

"Who took the trouble to ascertain what our colored clerks

thought about this order, to which their consent was never asked? Behind screens and closed doors they now sit apart as though leprous. Men and women alike have the badge of inferiority pressed upon them by Government decree. How long will it be before the hateful epithets of 'nigger' and 'Jim-Crow' are openly applied to these sections? Let any one experienced in Washington affairs, or any trained newspaper correspondent answer. The colored people themselves will tell you how soon sensitive and high-minded members of their race will refuse to enter the Government service which thus decrees what is to them the most hateful kind of discrimination. Indeed, there is a widespread belief among them that this is the very purpose of these unwarrantable orders. And wherever there are men who rob the Negroes of their votes, who exploit and degrade and insult and lynch those whom they call their inferiors, there this mistaken action of the Federal Government will be cited as the warrant for new racial outrages that cry out to high Heaven for redress.

"Who shall say where discrimination once begun shall cease? Who can deny that every act of discrimination the world over breeds fresh injustice?"

The President took no action and Trotter faced attack which was difficult to repulse. In trying to wreak political vengeance on a white party or leader, a black reformer like Trotter faced serious anomaly. The voting records of Negro legislators and city counsellors in the North showed this. They followed the Machine; they opposed efficiency in government; they helped overload the budgets; they refused to regulate the liquor traffic or places of amusement and gambling; they voted against civil service reform; against efficiency in hauling garbage and government services; and although representing working class constituencies they opposed laws wanted by trade unions.

They defended their votes because unions discriminated against Negroes and because "efficient" government paid them no attention. They went along with corrupt white political bosses because these bosses saw that Negroes got employment even if in anti-social ways, and defended them against attacks on civil rights. The white reform movements almost invariably knew nothing and did nothing to lift the veil of caste from black folk.

From contemplation of this occurrence the attention of Mansart was suddenly drawn home. He received a startling bit of news: the colored supervisor of the Atlanta colored schools was seriously ill. Through the gloomy veil that hung over these sun-drenched hills, burst a gleam of light, still tinged with the blood of the riot.

John James was dark and wrinkled, with something of the hurt dog look in his kindly and dim old eyes. He was alone in his home, lying in a stuffy bedroom with little air and few comforts; without was a living room and kitchen. There was no evidence of extreme poverty, but rather of neglect and lack of plan. The furniture when new had been good but had not been attended to and had been bought at different times and of incongruous patterns. The house stood in a narrow street that was almost an alley, without sidewalks, unpaved, dusty in summer and muddy in winter. It led to wider streets on either side, which being thoroughfares to important parts of Atlanta were paved for wagons and automobiles; but even here the sidewalks had never been properly finished.

John James had been a teacher in the public schools of Atlanta for over forty years, and since 1890 had rejoiced in the somewhat empty designation of "Supervisor of colored schools." In truth he was a sort of errand boy for the white superintendent and the go-between who made known decisions, especially unpleasant ones, to the colored teachers. Yet because of his long service and experience, James had some influence. His voice was listened to in the selection of new teachers, but was not always so influential in the dismissal of the old. He had little or nothing to say with regard to wages or load of work, and despite his rather timid recommendations he had not succeeded in getting a new school or improving facilities for the existing Negro schools in ten years.

As he lay dying he had a full sense of the frustration and disappointment of his life. He was a good man in the common connotation of the term. He had no bad habits. He did not drink nor even smoke. He was afraid of women. He was kindly; he wished everyone well; he gave away much of what he earned, and when he had had a family he had taken care of it. But his wife had died many, many years ago—a negative, hard-working unlettered woman. He had a daughter who married and disappeared in the North; and a grown son who was dead and had left grandchildren whom John James had helped but never seen.

There was no one to see him pass away, and he felt the reasons. He had been cowardly and he knew it; he had been afraid of white people and their power and wealth, because in his boyhood and young manhood he had felt in his flesh the brutal hand of repression. He had seen it flash down many, many times upon the wicked, the impudent, the ambitious, the careless, in all sorts of ways. His plan of life more or less consciously had come to be to avoid trouble with white folks; to ask only what they were willing to grant; to recognize their superiority in ability, wealth and desert.

This latter part was real. He knew they were often unjust to his people but he definitely and sincerely believed in their innate superiority and their ultimate good will. They had power because they deserved power; they had beauty and grace; they had wealth which they had rightfully earned. It was not for the likes of him or his people to dispute this superiority which God had given them; but to live in accordance with it and to keep in his place. Of course all white folk did not measure up to the best or even to the average. There were some who fell below and a few were even below Negroes. But James did not consider these as white folks or even as folks. They were singular misbirths and outsiders; mostly they were "poor whites."

On the other hand, he lately was upset and often bewildered by the attitude of the younger colored people; not of the lowest and outcast, but even of the best; children of good families, well raised in good homes; by the almost blasphemous conduct of the children who seemed younger and younger as they poured into the overcrowded colored schools. They had no reverence for God nor man and they hated white men. They uttered under their breath and sometimes even aloud the most blasphemous threats against the whites. He had seen to his horror a little evil-faced, ragged black boy on the street jump on a beautiful, well-dressed and unoffending white boy and beat him almost to insensibility before the supervisor himself could stagger to the rescue. He hastened to the Superintendent almost incoherent with apologies, and had the little black ruffian in the chain-gang almost before the pitiful white victim reached the hospital.

Even the colored teachers were grumbling and outgrowing their appointed place; he had often taken occasion to tell them so, in spite of their muttered disapproval and open disagreement. But what could be done? What could he do? Negroes formed only one-third of this great, powerful, wealthy city, and not even a third if you took into account income, education, influence. What could Negroes do then, except be better servants, more efficient laborers and stop complaining and keep themselves clean and respectful?

Yet as he lay on his bed with the pain dulled and thought becoming less and less clear, he somehow knew he had failed; that there was something that he could not understand; that perhaps

he could have done more than he had ever tried; and yet he had
wanted to do right, he had so wanted to!

There came rather suddenly to his mind in a moment of illumi-
nation, the figure of Manuel Mansart. Mansart had been now
twelve years in Atlanta, coming from the southern part of the
state. He was principal of the largest and best-equipped colored
school. James did not like him, although perhaps that was a little
too strong to say. He did not understand him. Mansart had come
right in demanding things. He wanted a new schoolhouse. Didn't
he know that white folks were not going to spend fifty thousand
dollars for a Negro school? He wanted more teachers. He wanted
better equipment, lots of new fangled things which they had been
getting on without.

All right, what had his "demands" got him? Nothing. He was
too impatient. White folks would never yield to pressure. You had
to beg and plead. But more than that, James soon saw very clearly
that what Mansart really wanted was to succeed him as supervisor
of schools and make demands that he had never dared to make;
and had not dared because such demands were futile—or were they
futile? Then the door opened and Mansart came in.

Mansart had never taken James seriously. He knew his type and
simply ignored him. Such requests as he had he took directly to
the Superintendent, even when he knew he would meet rebuff or
be in turn ignored. He would have at least the satisfaction of knowing that his complaints and carefully compiled facts would reach
the real source of authority and not be lost in James' halting and
softening phrases.

When he heard that James was ill he had meant to call, for he
knew he must be lonely and neglected. But between his work and
family, his dreams, studies and worries, it was easy to put off this
duty until almost the end. Some teachers this morning mentioned
that they had not seen the Supervisor in days. So hurrying down
the lane, Mansart stopped and knocked. He came just in time to
take the old man's hand and press it and see the light go out of
his eyes and his breath stand still. Mansart was curiously shaken.
He had not liked this man. He was a coward, a white folks'
"nigger," an "Uncle Tom." Yet he pitied him rather than hated
him. He sympathized with him. In a way he understood him, but
he was glad he was dead and as he looked around the curiously
un-homelike resting place of the dead body, tears came to his eyes.

He sat down thoughtfully and stared at the dead man. This
death was going to make a difference; a difference in education in

Atlanta and a difference in Negro education. The reason for this was not merely the passing of John James, but because Atlanta must begin to feel new forces. In fact he was the logical person to start these changes as he knew what he must ask: a high school for Negroes; a night school; at least two new elementary school buildings, and more actual power for the colored supervisor. These were reasonable demands. After all this talk of interracial cooperation, they could not long be denied. He would demand these things. If they were granted, his power and influence would rise; if they were denied, he would demand again and again, until—until—there he paused but he set his jaw in firm lines.

As he entered his house he was too occupied with his own thoughts to notice the subdued excitement. Dinner was ready and his three boys, his wife and the five year old girl were awaiting him. Also Roosevelt Wilson, the child of the riot whose mother had devoted him to God, was visiting the Mansart boys.

Mansart sat down after a preoccupied greeting. He asked an impersonal blessing and ate sparingly, as indeed did the others. Mansart was thinking of his family.

Douglass, his oldest boy, was fifteen. He was brown, crisp-haired and stocky in build, slow in his mental processes but a stubborn worker with distinct ideas as to his education and future life; also as to the place and duty of colored folk in general. He was painfully frank. He despised cowards. He believed in saying what he thought. He believed firmly in the equality of races and repeated this belief frequently. All these things had their encouraging side, but in the hard, cruel world which he faced, how would he and his beliefs fare?

Revels, named after the first colored Senator from Mississippi, was at eleven thin, calm and silent. He had a keen mind, expressed himself with difficulty, but had opinions. His father never was sure that he knew him or that the boy was paying him much attention when he proffered advice, as he did frequently.

Bruce, at nine, was a sport of nature. Darker than his brothers, his skin was like fine brown velvet draped over comely features. He was a beautiful boy with a queer, unearthly streak which seemed a throwback to some uncertain past. His black hair curled in ringlets, his eyes dreamed and flashed. As a child, people on the street stopped to greet him, but he was not friendly and his great black eyes swept the world with a certain proud and withdrawn indifference. He grew slim and lithe, but took little interest in his school work. He was his mother's favorite.

Sojourner, born after the riot and the only girl in the family, was unwanted. She was small, delicate and inordinately shy. Her skin was quite dark and her features decidedly coarse and unpleasant. Her hair was hard and sparse. She was always slipping away to herself and regularly forgotten by family and visitors.

Mansart looked up from his plate and suddenly sensed the silence. The family had finished eating and were all looking at him. His wife reached across the table and handed him a telegram which had evidently been opened and read. It was a night letter from Gary, Indiana, offering him the principalship of the Gary Colored High School. He sat and looked at it. It was the call for which he had waited five years. It had not come in 1907 because the Negroes of Gary were fighting the Negro school and objected to outsiders being brought in. It came today because the principal who had first opened the school was now dead and whites sought to replace him with a Negro whom the dead principal had long recommended as one trained in the subserviency and segregation patterns of the South. They offered Mansart $2000 a year.

He looked at his family and somehow for the first time seemed to see them as individuals and not as his property and retainers; he saw them as independent individuals with whom he wanted to converse and ask advice. Perhaps he now felt his spiritual loneliness since his two teachers had gone and he was faced with a great decision.

He said suddenly:

"What shall I do?"

They all listened in surprise. Always before he had talked to them as master or minor god. Now he asked advice. His wife was the first to respond.

"Go North and be free."

"Colored people are not free in Gary; freer than in Atlanta—but not free."

" 'Niggers' ain't free nowhere," growled Douglass.

Bruce piped up: "Why don't we fight—get guns and kill white folks?"

"They got more people than we," said Revels, "and the people got more guns."

"And more than that," said Mansart, "even if we won, we'd lose. Fellowship and equality don't follow murder."

Revels said thoughtfully, "So we can't fight and we can't give up. What can we do?"

"Just sit and take it," said Douglass.

"No," said Manuel, "never that. But somehow, somewhere there must be a way from Wrong to Right that does not use Wrong as the path to an end. There must be, or Life is Death." And then he added, "John James is dead." They were all startled. "I'm going to apply for his position," Mansart added.

Susan gasped and rising said, "You fool!" She began clearing off the dishes, with tears in her eyes.

Manuel continued as he looked into the hard eyes of the boys: "Have I ever told you of my christening?"

"Only about a dozen times," sneered Douglass.

But Mansart continued: "When my father was lynched and I was born, my old Granny took me to the church. She baptized me in my father's blood and called me 'the Black Flame.' For a long time I did not understand what she meant. Today I think I do. I burn, I almost consume myself. I burn slow and dark but always, always. As I have grown old I have seen souls aflame. There was my mother; the white heat within her could hardly be glimpsed through the crevices of her dark soul; Miss Freiburg burned low, tense and green white; Doyle was clear hot blue; Burghardt was crimson flame disciplined by his thought. I too am a flame and I burn."

Mansart arose and looked at his family. Douglass stared back. Revels and Wilson dropped their eyes and Bruce slowly went out to help his mother in the kitchen. Sojourner had fallen asleep on the couch.

Mansart continued: "Granny christened me 'Black Flame.' I have never altogether forgotten it. Jerusalem blurred it in my memory. The flame within me nearly died. I stooped and crawled. The prison bars bent my soul and pressed it in. Then I was released. I was freed and yet I did not understand until this riot, this horror of hate and death which swept over us. Now I live. Now I stand up. I am that Black Flame in which my grandmother believed and on whose blood-stained body she swore. I am the Black Flame, but I burn for cleaning, not destroying. Therefore I burn slow.

"I say this and I mean it; but always behind my firm decisions lurks doubt; numbing, paralyzing doubt. I am not ever absolutely certain. I always see the other side so clearly. I always fear even when I know I'm right that in some way, in some degree I may be wrong. Here is where I need help and encouragement. I envy the red flame that burns straight through, unwavering. A black flame also burns but perhaps not so completely; perhaps more thoughtfully and with deeper sympathy—but it burns; it must burn, for the world needs burning. Therefore I will burn and right here in Atlanta where I have let my buckets down. I know it sounds silly. So much of what I think seems crazy when I try to put it into words. But don't laugh. Help me. I know how my decision hurts my poor wife and what it will cost you; but I must be the Black Flame."

POSTSCRIPT

The basis of this book is documented and verifiable fact, but the book is not history. On the contrary, I have used fiction to interpret those historical facts which otherwise would not be clear. Beyond this I have in some cases resorted to pure imagination in order to make unknown and unknowable history relate an ordered tale to the reader. In a few cases I have made slight and unimportant changes in the exact sequence of historical events and in names and places. In no case have these changes altered, to my mind, the main historical background.

It may well be asked, and as one who has done some historical research I join in the asking, why should one tamper with history at all in order to write truth? The answer of course is Never, if exact truth can otherwise be ascertained. But every historian is painfully aware how little the scientist today can know accurately of the past; how dependence on documents and memory leaves us all with the tale of the past half told or less. The temptation then comes to pretend we know far more than we do and to set down as accurate history that which is not demonstrably true. To me it seems wiser and fairer to interpret historical truth by the use of creative imagination, provided the method is acknowledged and clear.

When in this world we seek the truth about what men have thought and felt and done, we face insuperable difficulties. We seldom can see enough of human action at first hand to interpret it properly. We can never know current personal thought and emotion with sufficient understanding rightly to weigh its cause and effect. After action and feeling and reflection are long past, then from writing and memory we may secure some picture of the total truth, but it will be sorely imperfect, with much omitted, much forgotten, much distorted.

This is the eternal paradox of history. There is but one way to meet this clouding of facts and that is by the use of imagination where documented material and personal experience are lacking.

In the great tragedy of Negro slavery in the United States and its aftermath, much of documented history is lacking because of the deep feeling involved and the fierce desire of men to defend their fathers and themselves. This I have sought to correct in my study of the slave trade and of Reconstruction. If I had had time and money, I would have continued this pure historical research. But this opportunity failed and Time is running out. Yet I would rescue from my long experience something of what I have learned and conjectured and thus I am trying by the method of historical fiction to complete the cycle of history which has for a half century engaged my thought, research and action.

I have personally lived through much of the history of the American Negro from 1876 to 1956. Yet wide as my experience has been, by travel, seeing, hearing and knowing, I of course actually knew but an infinitesimal fraction of all that happened. The gaps of knowledge I can in part supply by the memory of others, by reading published and unpublished matter. Yet with all this I am far from being able to set down an accurate historical account of those fatal eighty years.

Therefore I have assayed first to gather such verifiable facts as I can. This body of knowledge I have compared with the reports of others. But even with all this, much, indeed most, is missing: just what men thought, the actual words they used, the feelings and motives which impelled them—those I do not know and most of them none will ever know. These facts are gone forever. But it is possible for the creative artist to imagine something of such unknown truth. If he is lucky or inspired, he may write a story which may set down a fair version of the truth of an era, or a group of facts about human history.

This I have attempted to do: adhering as closely as I can to historic fact so far as I can ascertain. I have added the fiction of interpretation so as to make a reasonable story. I may have blundered in places; I may have widely misinterpreted what seemed truth to me. But I have tried and I believe the effort was worth while.

Here lies, then, I hope, more history than fiction, more fact than assumption, much truth and no falsehood.